Statement of Faith

We believe in God, the Eternal Spirit, Father of our Lord Jesus Christ and our Father, and to his deeds we testify:

He calls the worlds into being,
  creates man in his own image
  and sets before him the ways of life and death.

He seeks in holy love to save all people from aimlessness and sin.

He judges men and nations by his righteous will
  declared through prophets and apostles.

In Jesus Christ, the man of Nazareth, our crucified and risen Lord,
  he has come to us
  and shared our common lot,
  conquering sin and death
  and reconciling the world to himself.

He bestows upon us his Holy Spirit,
  creating and renewing the Church of Jesus Christ,
  binding in covenant faithful people of all ages, tongues, and
    races.

He calls us into his Church
  to accept the cost and joy of discipleship,
  to be his servants in the service of men,
  to proclaim the gospel to all the world
  and resist the powers of evil,
  to share in Christ's baptism and eat at his table,
  to join him in his passion and victory.

He promises to all who trust him
  forgiveness of sins and fullness of grace,
  courage in the struggle for justice and peace,
  his presence in trial and rejoicing,
  and eternal life in his kingdom which has no end.

Blessing and honor, glory and power be unto him. Amen.

Approved by the Second General Synod of the United Church of Christ held in Oberlin, Ohio, July 5-9, 1959, and submitted to the Synods, Conferences, Associations and Churches for their approval and use. The General Synod encourages the use of the Statement of Faith in congregational worship, in private devotions and for purposes of study.

EC—1-66—60M

Prayers on Entering the Church

Almighty God, from whom cometh every good and perfect gift, and who pourest out upon all who desire it the spirit of grace and supplication, deliver me, when I draw nigh unto thee, from coldness of heart and wanderings of mind, that with steadfast thoughts and kindled affections I may worship thee in spirit and in truth, through Jesus Christ our Lord. Amen.

O thou eternal God, speak to me the word that I need, and let thy Word abide with me until it has wrought in me thy holy will. Cleanse, quicken, and refresh my heart; direct and increase my faith; and grant that I, by worship at this time, may be enabled to see thee more clearly, to love thee more fully, and to serve thee more perfectly. Amen.

O God, who puttest into our hearts such deep desires that we cannot be at peace until we rest in thee, mercifully grant that the longing of my soul may not go unsatisfied because of any unrighteousness of life that may separate me from thee. Open my mind to the counsels of eternal wisdom; breathe into my soul the peace which passeth understanding. Increase my hunger and thirst for righteousness, and feed me, I beseech thee, with the bread of heaven. Give me grace to seek first thy kingdom, and help me to know that thou wilt add unto me all things needful. Amen.

Statement of Faith

We believe in God, the Eternal Spirit, Father of our Lord Jesus Christ and our Father, and to his deeds we testify:

He calls the worlds into being,
 creates man in his own image
 and sets before him the ways of life and death.

He seeks in holy love to save all people from aimlessness and sin.

He judges men and nations by his righteous will
 declared through prophets and apostles.

In Jesus Christ, the man of Nazareth, our crucified and risen Lord,
 he has come to us
 and shared our common lot,
 conquering sin and death
 and reconciling the world to himself.

He bestows upon us his Holy Spirit,
 creating and renewing the Church of Jesus Christ,
 binding in covenant faithful people of all ages, tongues, and races.

He calls us into his Church
 to accept the cost and joy of discipleship,
 to be his servants in the service of men,
 to proclaim the gospel to all the world
 and resist the powers of evil,
 to share in Christ's baptism and eat at his table,
 to join him in his passion and victory.

He promises to all who trust him
 forgiveness of sins and fullness of grace,
 courage in the struggle for justice and peace,
 his presence in trial and rejoicing,
 and eternal life in his kingdom which has no end.

Blessing and honor, glory and power be unto him. Amen.

Approved by the Second General Synod of the United Church of Christ held in Oberlin, Ohio, July 5-9, 1959, and submitted to the Synods, Conferences, Associations and Churches for their approval and use. The General Synod encourages the use of the Statement of Faith in congregational worship, in private devotions and for purposes of study.

The Hymnal

•

Containing Complete Orders of Worship

Authorized by the General
Synod of the Evangelical
and Reformed Church

PUBLISHED FOR THE CHURCH

by

EDEN PUBLISHING HOUSE

Saint Louis, Missouri

Twenty-second Printing, 1965
Containing complete Orders of Worship

Circulation of THE HYMNAL is
restricted to the United States of America

Printed in U.S.A.

Preface

Christianity is constantly finding better forms of religious expression. Symbolism, architecture, and ritual are leading the way to finer sanctuaries and more impressive worship services. A positive theology is asserting itself anew and is greatly influencing religious thinking, thus paving the way for a revival of spiritual living. Religious realism claims a place in the program of the Church and in the life of believers as a means of interpreting satisfactorily for modern man the social phenomena of an awakened world conscience. Out of all this grows a demand for greater unity and strength, and greater dignity and depth in worship, the influence of which becomes apparent in the hymns we sing. THE HYMNAL takes cognizance of this demand.

Many elements go into the making of a good hymn. We submit for thoughtful consideration the definition by Dr. Carl F. Price, adopted by the Hymn Society of America: "A Christian hymn is a lyric poem, reverently and devotionally conceived, which is designed to be sung and which expresses the worshiper's attitude toward God, or God's purpose in human life. It should be simple and metrical in form, genuinely emotional, poetic and literary in style, spiritual in quality, and in its ideas so direct and so immediately apparent as to unify a congregation while singing it."

A definite effort has been made to procure the best from many different sources. The classics of ancient and medieval times, the chorales of the post-Reformation era, and the best hymns of England, Wales, France, Germany, Hungary, the United States of America, and other nations, together with a large selection provided by modern authors and composers, have been chosen and coordinated in a new compilation, characterized by spiritual unity and artistic appeal. The aim throughout has been to help worshipers find God in a large way through adequate means of worship, to voice faith in Jesus Christ as the source of unlimited redemptive power, and to emphasize the moral values of the Christian Church as the bulwark of a righteous society.

Besides many of the more recent hymns THE HYMNAL contains twenty new texts which have never before appeared in any official hymn-book. In addition, fifteen tunes and two descants were especially composed for THE HYMNAL. Where two tunes are provided for a single hymn, both are deemed worthy of acceptance, and the worshiping congregation may exercise the privilege of choice. The desirability of curtailing the size of the book imposed certain limitations in the choice of hymns selected for inclusion. In the arrangement of the hymns the order of the Church Year has been followed.

The Responsive Readings are altogether new. They represent the work of the Reverend Edward S. Bromer, D.D., former Professor of Practical Theology of the Theological Seminary at Lancaster, Pennsylvania. The Responsive Prayers (Litanies) have been compiled from various sources. All other worship material is taken from the new Book of Worship of the Evangelical and Reformed Church. A conscientious effort has been made to meet adequately the need of all congregations, large and small, liturgical and non-liturgical.

THE HYMNAL is rooted in the Reformation heritage of two branches of American Protestantism: the Evangelical Synod of North America which was founded in 1840, and the Reformed Church in the United States which originated in 1725. It represents a response to the need growing out of the union of these two Churches, namely to preserve that which is precious to the faith and tradition of both groups and simultaneously to provide something new in keeping with the ecumenical movement in the Churches of the world and the emergence of a new social order.

As soon as the merger had proceeded so far as to assure a permanent union, the Executive Committee of the Evangelical and Reformed Church appointed a committee in the late fall of 1935, consisting of the signatories below, and instructed this committee "to prepare a hymnal."

We believe that the book contains an emphasis and diversity not found in any contemporary book and that it is an indispensable part of the equipment of each church and home. The book should be used in the home not less than in church. The full extent of the treasures in the book cannot be explored in any one year of church services. The book is destined to fulfill its purpose best when its contents become the folk songs of the people in their daily life and recreation.

THE HYMNAL has had expert editing by Dr. Clarence Dickinson, Harkness Associate Professor of Sacred Music and Director of the School of Sacred Music, Union Theological Seminary, New York City. Valuable counsel and help were given the editor and the committee by Dr. Helen Dickinson, Lecturer on Liturgics and Sacred Art, in the same school.

We trust that this book may go forth on its mission of service and become the means of uplift and joy to thousands of worshipers, who through its use will be united in a significant spiritual fellowship with one another and with God as revealed in Jesus Christ.

THE COMMITTEE,

Joaquin P. Meyer, Chairman
W. Sherman Kerschner, Secretary
Richard G. Appel
Edward O. Butkofsky
Armin Haeussler
Erwin R. Koch
Mrs. Theodore Mayer
Henry I. Stahr

Acknowledgments

We acknowledge with sincere gratitude and appreciation the courtesy of authors, composers, and owners of hymns, who have granted us permission to include in THE HYMNAL words and music controlled by them.

Special efforts have been made in every instance to trace the ownership of hymns and to procure consent for their use. If we have failed to give proper credit because of inadvertence or because ownership rights appeared obscure, we shall be pleased to make good this omission in future editions, if brought to our attention.

Our research work was lessened by the achievements of present-day hymnologists, made available to us in the newer hymn-books published here and abroad. We feel constrained to express a general debt of gratitude to those whose previous labors so manifestly lessened our own.

In the following list of acknowledgments an asterisk indicates that the right to publish has been acquired by the payment of a fee. A dagger designates that the words or the music of a hymn have been written or composed especially for THE HYMNAL, or that they are hereby published in an official hymn-book for the first time, or both.

THE HYMNAL

vi

ACKNOWLEDGMENTS

NAME	WORDS	MUSIC
Geoffrey Turton Shaw		454 *
Mrs. Ozora S. Davis, hymns by Ozora Stearns Davis	279, 400	
Purd E. Deitz	452	
The Downside Abbey, hymn by Alfred Scott-Gatty		266, 311, 393 *
Z. B. Edworthy	510	
W. Gwenlyn Evans and Sons		399 *
Mrs. Harry Webb Farrington, hymn by Harry Webb Farrington	241	
Harry Emerson Fosdick	287, 409	
Walter Greatorex		27
Edith Grubb, hymn by Edward Grubb	64	
James Gordon Gilkey	134, 454	
The H. W. Gray Co., hymn by T. Tertius Noble		520 *
Theo. C. Haeussler		67 *†
S. Ralph Harlow	391	
Harper and Brothers, hymn by Grace Noll Crowell	259 *	
Basil Harwood		305
John Haynes Holmes	70, 387	
M. Morley Horder, hymn by Clement William Poole		409 *
Houghton Mifflin Co., hymns by Lucy Larcom	206	
John Drinkwater	264	
Mrs. John Hughes, hymn by John Hughes		80 *
Messrs. Hughes and Sons		317
The Hymn Society, hymns by Henry Hallam Tweedy	367	
Rhys Thomas		367
Mrs. Barbara Benson Jefferys, hymns by Louis F. Benson	195, 444, 451	
Shepherd Knapp	266	
Edward B. Laufer, hymns by Calvin W. Laufer	265	130, 252, 265, 486

NAME	WORDS	MUSIC
League of Nations Union, hymn by		
Geoffrey Shaw		401
Howell E. Lewis	268, 333	
Mrs. Peter C. Lutkin, hymn by		
Peter C. Lutkin		450
Mrs. John Howard Masterman, hymn by		
John Howard Masterman	363	
Robert G. McCutchan		407
Ernest F. McGregor	137	
William Pierson Merrill	442	
Methodist Book Concern, hymns by		
Edgar Daniel Kramer	127	
William K. Anderson		419 *
J. Lewis Milligan	94	
National Sunday School Union of		
Great Britain, hymn by		
John Page Hopps	458	
Eric M. North, hymns by		
Frank Mason North	365, 382, 394	
John Oxenham	232, 255	
Mrs. Horatio W. Parker, hymn by		
Laura S. Copenhaver	385	
A. D. Peters, hymn by		
Clifford Bax	410 *	
Presbyterian Board of Christian		
Education, hymn by Jean Sibelius		87, 452
Presbyterian Board of Foreign Missions,		
hymn by J. Glover Eldridge	362	
The Presbyterian Tribune, hymn by		
William Pierson Merrill	389	
Carl F. Price		78 *†, 154 *†
Mrs. Julius Roentgen, hymn by		
Julius Roentgen		89, 297 *†
Margaret E. Sangster	374	
Chas. Scribner's Sons, hymns by		
Henry van Dyke	21 *, 392 *, 414 *	
Maltbie D. Babcock	65 *, 293 *	
Silver, Burdett Co., hymn by		
Stella Marek Cushing	110	

ACKNOWLEDGMENTS

NAME	WORDS	MUSIC
Harry Thomas Stock	449	
Frederick A. Stokes Co., hymn by Mildred Whitney Stillman	311	
Dorothy Tarrant, hymns by William G. Tarrant	390, 455	
Mrs. Ethel Taylor, hymn by Robert Jackson		191, 275
Thomas Tiplady	73, 354	
William Toth	62 †, 306 †	
Mrs. Herbert B. Turner, hymn by Herbert B. Turner		456
Henry Hallam Tweedy	190	
Vassar College, hymn by George C. Gow		511
Laughlan MacLean Watt	251	
George A. Whitmarsh, hymn by Frances Whitmarsh Wile	429	
Healey Willan		523 *
Pietro Yon		215 *†

The following are owned and copyrighted by
Eden Publishing House: hymns by

NAME	WORDS	MUSIC
Edward Shippen Barnes		248 *†
David Bruning		383
Frederick R. Daries	41	41
Clarence Dickinson		62 †, 306 †, 368 Descant †
C. G. Haas	6, 494	
J. C. Hansen	152, 478	
Karl P. Harrington		151 *†
J. H. Horstmann	20, 269, 478	
R. A. John	17, 18, 312	
Ewald Kockritz	52	
Lindsay B. Longacre		208 †
Carl F. Mueller		127 *†, 264 *†
G. J. Neumann	62 †, 140 †, 151 †, 248 †, 306 †	
T. Tertius Noble		73 *†, 140 *†, 366 *†
G. Darlington Richards		85, 139 *†, 293 *†
John M. Versteeg	139	
Pierre Wissmer		70 *†, 241 *†

We also acknowledge our indebtedness to the following publishers, who willingly granted permission to use excerpts from their publications for the Responsive Prayers (Litanies) in this book, as indicated below:

The Oxford University Press

"The Kingdom, the Power, and the Glory"

Acts of Adoration, No. 1, page 1

Litany of the Church, 14A, page 27

Thanksgiving and Litany for the Missionary Work of the Church, No. 11, page 18

The Risen and Ascended Christ, No. 13 c, page 26

Litany of Commemoration, No. 17, page 38

The E. P. Dutton and Company, Inc.

"Devotional Services"—John Hunter

A Litany of Confession, page 115

A Litany of Thanksgiving, page 119

A Litany for the Nation, page 129

"The Book of Common Worship"—1932: Editors, Thirkield and Huckel

A Litany of Labor, page 67

Presentation of Offering, page 10

The Macmillan Company

"Acts of Devotion"

Harvest Collect, page 113

Closing Prayer, page 109

An Act of Sympathy, page 35

On the Source of Cheerfulness, page 43

For source material and suggestions used in the following Responsive Prayers (Litanies) we are indebted as follows: No. 2, Percy Dearmer in "Hymns of the Spirit," Association Press; No. 4, "The World-Wide Prayer," Vernon F. Storr, Church Missionary Society, London; No. 5, "Christian Worship and Praise," A. S. Barnes & Co.; No. 6 and No. 12, "The Call to Worship," D. Tait Patterson, The Carey Press, London; No. 11, "The New Church Hymnal," D. Appleton-Century Co.; No. 17, "Hymns of the Spirit," Beacon Press; No. 21, "Divine Services," W. E. Orchard and "Hymns of the Spirit," Beacon Press.

Contents

Classification of Hymns

CONTENTS

Orders of Worship

Orders of Worship

THE MORNING SERVICE

¶ *After the Prelude, and a Processional Hymn, if one be used, the Congregation standing, the Minister shall say,*

IN the Name of the Father, and of the Son, and of the Holy Spirit. Amen.

¶ *The Introit for the Day may be used; or, the Minister shall read one or more of the following Sentences of Scripture:*

THE Lord is in his holy temple, let all the earth keep silence before him.

O come, let us worship and bow down; let us kneel before the Lord our Maker. For he is our God; and we are the people of his pasture, and the sheep of his hand.

God is a Spirit; and they that worship him must worship in spirit and in truth.

Advent. Prepare ye the way of the Lord, make straight in the desert a highway for our God.

Blessed be the King that cometh in the name of the Lord; peace in heaven and glory in the highest.

Christmas. Behold, I bring you good tidings of great joy, which shall be to all people. For unto you is born this day in the city of David a Saviour, which is Christ the Lord.

Glory to God in the highest, and on earth peace, good will toward men.

Epiphany. Arise, shine; for thy light is come, and the glory of the Lord is risen upon thee.

Lent. The sacrifices of God are a broken spirit: a broken and a contrite heart, O God, thou wilt not despise.

Easter. He is risen. The Lord is risen indeed!

If ye then be risen with Christ, seek those things which are above, where Christ sitteth on the right hand of God.

Ascension. Seeing that we have a great High Priest, that is passed into the heavens, Jesus the Son of God, let us come boldly unto the throne of grace, that we may obtain mercy, and find grace to help in time of need.

Pentecost. Ye shall receive power, after that the Holy Spirit is come upon you; and ye shall be witnesses unto me both in Jerusalem, and in all Judæa, and in Samaria, and unto the uttermost part of the earth.

Trinity. Holy, holy, holy, Lord God Almighty, which was, and is, and is to come.

CONFESSION OF SIN

BELOVED in the Lord, let us draw near with a true heart, and confess our sins unto God our Father, beseeching him, in the Name of our Lord Jesus Christ, to grant us forgiveness.

¶*The Minister and Congregation shall say,*

ALMIGHTY and most merciful God our heavenly Father, we humble ourselves before thee, under a deep sense of our unworthiness and guilt. We have grievously sinned against thee, in thought, in word, and in deed. We have come short of thy glory, we have broken thy commandments, and turned aside every one of us from the way of life. Yet now, O most merciful Father, hear us when we call upon thee with penitent hearts, and for the sake of thy Son, Jesus Christ, have mercy upon us. Pardon our sins; take away our guilt; and grant us thy peace. Purify us, by the inspiration of thy Holy Spirit, from all inward uncleanness, and make us able and willing to serve thee in newness of life, to the glory of thy holy Name; through Jesus Christ our Lord. Amen.

or

ALMIGHTY and most merciful Father, we have erred and strayed from thy ways like lost sheep. We have followed too much the devices and desires of our own hearts. We have offended against thy holy laws. We have left undone those things which we ought to have done, and we have done those things which we ought not to have done. But thou, O Lord, have mercy upon us. Spare thou those, O God, who confess their sins. Restore thou those who are penitent, according to thy promises declared unto mankind in Christ Jesus our Lord. And grant, O most merciful Father, for his sake, that we may

4

hereafter live a godly, righteous, and sober life, to the glory of thy holy Name. Amen.

¶ *Then shall be sung or said the* Kyrie. *(No. 518)*

Lord, have mercy upon us.
Lord, have mercy upon us.
Christ, have mercy upon us.
Christ, have mercy upon us.
Lord, have mercy upon us.
Lord, have mercy upon us.

ASSURANCE OF PARDON

¶ *The Minister shall say,*

HEARKEN now unto the comforting assurance of the grace of God, promised in the Gospel to all that repent and believe: As I live, saith the Lord God, I have no pleasure in the death of the wicked, but that the wicked turn from his way and live. God so loved the world, that he gave his only begotten Son, that whosoever believeth in him should not perish, but have everlasting life.

Unto as many of you, therefore, beloved brethren, as truly repent of your sins, and believe in the Lord Jesus Christ, with full purpose of new obedience, I announce and declare, by the authority and in the Name of Christ, that your sins are forgiven, according to his promise in the Gospel; through Jesus Christ our Lord. *Amen.*

PRAISE

Minister. Praise ye the Lord.
Congregation. The Lord's Name be praised.

¶ *Then shall be sung the* Gloria in Excelsis *(No. 489) or a Hymn of Praise.*

GLORY be to God on high, and on earth peace, good will toward men. We praise thee, we bless thee, we worship thee, we glorify thee, we give thanks to thee for thy great glory, O Lord God, heavenly King, God the Father Almighty.

O Lord, the only begotten Son, Jesus Christ; O Lord God, Lamb of God, Son of the Father, that takest away the sin of the world, have mercy upon us. Thou that takest away the sin of the world, receive our prayer. Thou that sittest at the right hand of God the Father, have mercy upon us.

For thou only art holy; thou only art the Lord; thou only, O Christ, with the Holy Ghost, art most high in the glory of God the Father. Amen.

COLLECT

> Minister. Let us pray.

¶ *The Minister shall say the Collect for the Day.*

THE HOLY SCRIPTURES

¶ *Portions of the Psalter or other Scriptures may now be read responsively, and the Gloria Patri may be sung.*

¶ *The Minister shall read the Epistle and the Gospel for the Day.*

¶ *Then the Minister may say,*

B LESSED are they that hear the Word of God and keep it.

or

S ANCTIFY us through thy truth: thy Word is truth.

¶ *The Congregation may sing a Canticle, a Hymn, or a Response.*

THE APOSTLES' CREED

I BELIEVE in God the Father Almighty, Maker of heaven and earth:

And in Jesus Christ, his only begotten Son, our Lord; who was conceived by the Holy Ghost, born of the Virgin Mary, suffered under Pontius Pilate, was crucified, dead, and buried; he descended into hell*; the third day he rose again from the dead; he ascended into heaven, and sitteth on the right hand of God the Father Almighty; from thence he shall come to judge the quick and the dead.

I believe in the Holy Ghost; the Holy Catholic Church†; the communion of saints; the forgiveness of sins; the resurrection of the body; and the life everlasting. Amen.

GENERAL PRAYER

¶ *The Prayer shall consist of the following, or other prayers.*

> Minister.   The Lord be with you.
> Congregation. And with thy spirit.
> Minister.   Let us pray.

---

* Hades *may be used.*
† One Holy Universal Christian Church *may be used.*

6

A General Thanksgiving

ALMIGHTY God, Father of all mercies, we, thine unworthy servants, do give thee most humble and hearty thanks for all thy goodness and lovingkindness to us and to all men. We praise thee for our creation, preservation, and all the blessings of this life; but above all, for thine inestimable love in the redemption of the world by our Lord Jesus Christ; for the means of grace, and for the hope of glory. And we beseech thee, give us that due sense of all thy mercies, that our hearts may be unfeignedly thankful; and that we show forth thy praise, not only with our lips, but in our lives, by giving up ourselves to thy service, and by walking before thee in holiness and righteousness all our days; through Jesus Christ, our Lord, to whom, with thee and the Holy Spirit, be all honor and glory, world without end. *Amen.*

A Prayer for Spiritual Victory

GOD of all power and glory, who hast not appointed us unto wrath, but to obtain salvation by our Lord Jesus Christ, perfect and fulfill in us, we beseech thee, the work of thy redeeming mercy, that, being delivered more and more from our sins, we may be able to serve thee in newness of life. Sanctify us in body, soul, and spirit, and guide us evermore in the way of peace. Help us to overcome the world. Give us courage to confess Christ always, and patience to endure in his service unto the end; that, having finished our course with joy, we may rest in hope, and attain finally to the resurrection of the just, through the infinite merits of our Saviour, Jesus Christ. *Amen.*

A Prayer for the Church Universal

O THOU God and Father of our Lord Jesus Christ, of whom the whole family in heaven and earth is named, cause thy blessing, we beseech thee, to rest upon the Church, which he has redeemed with his most precious blood. Enlighten her ministers with true knowledge and understanding of thy Word. Send down the healthful dew of thy grace upon all her congregations. Deliver her from false doctrine, heresy, and schism; enable her to keep the unity of the spirit in the bond of peace, and clothe her with the beauty of holiness. Establish and reveal thy glory among all nations. By the working of thy providence confound and destroy all wicked devices against thy holy Word, and bring in speedily the full victory of thine everlasting kingdom; through Jesus Christ our Lord. *Amen.*

7

A Prayer for the President of the United States and All Others in Authority

A LMIGHTY God, whose kingdom is an everlasting kingdom, and whose dominion endureth throughout all generations, we pray thee to look with favor upon thy servants, the President of the United States, the Governor of this Commonwealth, and all others in authority. Fill them with the spirit of wisdom, goodness, and truth, and so rule their hearts and bless their endeavors that law and order, justice and peace, may everywhere prevail. Preserve us from national sins and corruption. Make us strong and great in the fear of God and in the love of righteousness, reverent in the use of freedom, just in the exercise of power, generous in the protection of the helpless, so that we may become a blessing to all nations; through Jesus Christ our Lord. *Amen.*

A Prayer for All Conditions of Men

O GOD, the Creator and Preserver of all mankind, we implore thy mercy in behalf of all classes and conditions of men, that it may please thee to visit them with thy most compassionate help, according to their manifold necessities and wants. Especially do we beseech thee to have pity upon all widows and orphans; upon all prisoners and captives; upon all sick and dying persons; upon all such as are persecuted for righteousness' sake. Enable them to look unto thee, O most merciful Father, and to call upon thy Name, that they may find thee a present Saviour in their affliction and distress. And let it please thee to deliver them, and raise them up in due time, giving them patience under all their sufferings, the rich comfort of thy grace here below, and eternal rest with thee in heaven; through our Lord Jesus Christ. *Amen.*

❧ *Here may be offered Special Prayer or Prayers.*

A Prayer of St. Chrysostom

A LMIGHTY God, who hast given us grace at this time with one accord to make our common supplications unto thee, and dost promise that where two or three are gathered together in thy Name, thou wilt grant their requests, fulfill now, O Lord, the desires and petitions of thy servants, as may be most expedient for them, granting us in this world knowledge of thy truth, and in the world to come life everlasting. *Amen.*

ANTHEM

[ANNOUNCEMENTS]

8

OFFERING

¶ *The Offering shall be received and placed upon the Lord's Table with words of praise and dedication.*

HYMN

SERMON

¶ *When the Alternate Order for Holy Communion is used, the Service shall now proceed as continued on page 32.*

¶ *After the Sermon the Minister may offer one or both of the following prayers; and shall offer the Lord's Prayer, in which the Congregation shall join.*

A LMIGHTY God, Fountain of all goodness and truth, receive our thanks for the revelation of thy grace, which is able to make us wise unto everlasting life; and mercifully grant, we beseech thee, that the words which we have heard this day may through thy blessing be so grafted in our hearts that they may bring forth in us the fruit of good living, to the honor and praise of thy Name; through Jesus Christ our Lord. *Amen.*

O God, who art the author of peace and lover of concord, in knowledge of whom standeth our eternal life, whose service is perfect freedom, defend us, thy humble servants, in all assaults of our enemies, that we, surely trusting in thy defense, may not fear the power of any adversaries, through the might of Jesus Christ our Lord. *Amen.*

O UR Father, who art in heaven, Hallowed be thy Name. Thy kingdom come. Thy will be done, on earth as it is in heaven. Give us this day our daily bread. And forgive us our debts, as we forgive our debtors. And lead us not into temptation, but deliver us from evil. For thine is the kingdom, and the power, and the glory, for ever. Amen.

DOXOLOGY OR HYMN

BENEDICTION

T HE grace of the Lord Jesus Christ, and the love of God, and the communion of the Holy Spirit, be with you all. *Amen.*

or

T HE Lord bless thee, and keep thee; the Lord make his face shine upon thee, and be gracious unto thee; the Lord lift up his countenance upon thee, and give thee peace. *Amen.*

¶ *At the close of the Service a Recessional Hymn may be sung, followed by the Postlude.*

THE EVENING SERVICE

❡ *The Congregation standing, the Minister shall say,*

IN the Name of the Father, and of the Son, and of the Holy Spirit. *Amen.*

Let us pray.

ALMIGHTY God, unto whom all hearts are open, all desires known, and from whom no secrets are hid, cleanse the thoughts of our hearts by the inspiration of thy Holy Spirit, that we may perfectly love thee and worthily magnify thy Holy Name; through Jesus Christ our Lord. *Amen.*

ALMIGHTY and everlasting God, who art always more ready to hear than we to pray, and art wont to give more than either we desire or deserve, pour down upon us the abundance of thy mercy, forgiving us those things whereof our conscience is afraid, and giving us those good things which we are not worthy to ask, but through the merits and mediation of Jesus Christ, thy Son, our Lord. *Amen.*

HYMN

THE HOLY SCRIPTURES

❡ *The Congregation may sing a Canticle, a Hymn, or a Response.*

EVENING PRAYER

❡ *The Minister shall offer the Evening Prayer, consisting of the following, or other prayers.*

Minister. The Lord be with you.

Congregation. And with thy spirit.

Minister. Let us pray.
Create in us a clean heart, O God.

Congregation. And renew a right spirit within us.

Minister. Cast us not away from thy presence.

Congregation. And take not thy Holy Spirit from us.

A Prayer for Inner Peace

O GOD, from whom all holy desires, all good counsels, and all just works do proceed, give unto thy servants that peace which the world cannot give, that our hearts may be set to obey thy commandments, and also that we, being defended from the fear of our enemies, may by thy protection pass our time in peace and quietness; through Jesus Christ our Lord. *Amen.*

A Prayer for Deliverance

O LORD, our heavenly Father, by whose almighty power we have been preserved this day, and to whom the darkness and the light are both alike, by thy great mercy defend us from all perils and dangers of this night, and so refresh our weary nature with the help which our weakness needs, that we may behold the dawn and the day with joyfulness, and be devoted to thee both in body and soul; for the love of thine only Son, our Saviour Jesus Christ. *Amen.*

Thanksgiving for God's Bountiful Providence

IN goodness art thou exalted, O Lord, our Father, for ever and ever. We magnify thee, we praise thee, we worship thee, we give thanks unto thee for thy bountiful providence, for all the blessings of the present life and all the hopes of a better life to come. Let the memory of thy goodness, we beseech thee, fill our hearts with joy and thankfulness unto our life's end; and let no unworthiness of ours provoke thee to withhold from us any needed good, seeing that all thy blessings come not by our desert, but only through the mediation of Jesus Christ our Lord. *Amen.*

A Prayer for the Church Universal

ALMIGHTY and everlasting God, who hast promised to reveal thy glory by Jesus Christ among all nations, remember, we beseech thee, thy holy Church throughout all the world; unite all who profess and call themselves Christians in the bond of a holy faith as one body, and so replenish them and us with the grace of thy Holy Spirit, that we may bring forth abundantly the fruits of peace and good works; and that, having persevered in the way of godliness to the end, we may, with prophets, apostles, martyrs, confessors, and saints, of all ages, come into full communion with thee and with one another in thine eternal and glorious kingdom; through Jesus Christ our Lord. *Amen.*

A Prayer for the Whole World

A LMIGHTY God, who hast made of one every nation of men to dwell on the earth and hast appointed the bounds of their habitation, grant them thy guidance and help, that they may seek prosperity in promoting the welfare of their people and of all mankind. Enable all races to realize their kinship with one another as children of the same eternal Father. Restrain them from pride, jealousy, hatred, and selfish ambition. Awaken in them the spirit of justice, brotherhood, and concord. Unite them by the bonds of international friendship, that they may work together for the betterment of the whole world. Make wars to cease, and hasten the day when there shall be peace on earth and good will among men; through him who is the Prince of Peace, Jesus Christ our Lord. *Amen.*

A Prayer for Those in Extremity

M OST merciful God, who art a seasonable refuge in time of trouble, let the prayers of those who, in tribulation or any sort of extremity, cry unto thee, reach thy merciful ears, and grant them relief according to their several necessities, giving them patience under their sufferings, and a happy issue out of all their afflictions; for the sake of the suffering and sorrow of thy dear Son, our Saviour, Jesus Christ. *Amen.*

A Prayer of St. Chrysostom

A LMIGHTY God, who hast given us grace at this time with one accord to make our common supplications unto thee, and dost promise that, where two or three are gathered together in thy Name, thou wilt grant their requests, fulfill now, O Lord, the desires and petitions of thy servants, as may be most expedient for them, granting us in this world knowledge of thy truth, and in the world to come, life everlasting. *Amen.*

HYMN

SERMON

¶ *After the Sermon, the Congregation shall stand, and the Minister shall say,*

Let us pray.

O GOD, who didst teach the hearts of thy faithful people by sending unto them the light of thy Holy Spirit, grant unto us by the same Spirit to have a right understanding of thy saving truth. Visit, we pray thee, this congregation with thy love and favor. Enlighten our minds more and more with the light of the everlasting Gospel; fill our hearts with a love of the truth; increase in us true religion; nourish us with all goodness; and of thy great mercy keep us in the same; through Jesus Christ our Lord. *Amen.*

❡ *Then all shall say,*

O UR Father, who art in heaven, Hallowed be thy Name. Thy kingdom come. Thy will be done, on earth as it is in heaven. Give us this day our daily bread. And forgive us our debts, as we forgive our debtors. And lead us not into temptation, but deliver us from evil. For thine is the kingdom, and the power, and the glory, for ever. Amen.

OFFERING

❡ *The Offering shall be received and placed upon the Lord's Table with words of praise and dedication.*

HYMN

BENEDICTION

T HE grace of the Lord Jesus Christ, and the love of God, and the communion of the Holy Spirit, be with you all. *Amen.*

THE PREPARATORY SERVICE

¶ *The Congregation standing, the Minister shall say,*

THE Lord is in his holy temple, let all the earth keep silence before him. *Amen.*

GOD spake all these words, saying, I am the Lord thy God, who brought thee out of the land of Egypt, out of the house of bondage.

Thou shalt have no other gods before me.

Thou shalt not make unto thee any graven image, or any likeness of anything that is in heaven above, or that is in the earth beneath, or that is in the water under the earth; thou shalt not bow down thyself to them, nor serve them; for I the Lord thy God am a jealous God, visiting the iniquity of the fathers upon the children unto the third and fourth generation of them that hate me; and showing mercy unto thousands of them that love me, and keep my commandments.

Thou shalt not take the Name of the Lord thy God in vain, for the Lord will not hold him guiltless that taketh his Name in vain.

Remember the sabbath day to keep it holy. Six days shalt thou labor and do all thy work, but the seventh day is the sabbath of the Lord thy God: in it thou shalt not do any work, thou, nor thy son, nor thy daughter, thy manservant, nor thy maidservant, nor thy cattle, nor thy stranger that is within thy gates; for in six days the Lord made heaven and earth, the sea, and all that in them is, and rested the seventh day; wherefore the Lord blessed the sabbath day, and hallowed it.

Honor thy father and thy mother, that thy days may be long upon the land which the Lord thy God giveth thee.

Thou shalt not kill.

Thou shalt not commit adultery.

Thou shalt not steal.

Thou shalt not bear false witness against thy neighbor.

Thou shalt not covet thy neighbor's house, thou shalt not covet thy neighbor's wife, nor his manservant, nor his maidservant, nor his ox, nor his ass, nor anything that is thy neighbor's.

> *Congregation.* Lord, have mercy upon us, and incline our hearts to keep all these laws.

Minister. Hear also what our Lord Jesus Christ saith:

Thou shalt love the Lord thy God with all thy heart, and with all thy soul, and with all thy mind. This is the first and great commandment. And the second is like unto it: Thou shalt love thy neighbor as thyself. On these two commandments hang all the law and the prophets.

Let us pray.

O LORD God, who didst at the first deliver thy commandments from the mount which burned with fire, amid blackness and darkness and tempest, we thank thee that this same law is now published unto us from Mount Zion, through the Mediator of a new and better covenant; and we humbly beseech thee to put these words into our minds, and write them in our hearts, that we may delight in thy law after the inward man, and serve thee in newness of spirit; through Jesus Christ our Lord. *Amen.*

THE LITANY

¶ *Here the Litany may be used, the Congregation kneeling.*

O GOD, the Father in heaven,
HAVE MERCY UPON US.

O God, the Son, Redeemer of the world,
HAVE MERCY UPON US.

O God, the Holy Spirit, Sanctifier of the faithful,
HAVE MERCY UPON US.

O holy, blessed, and glorious Trinity, ever one God,
HAVE MERCY UPON US.

REMEMBER not, Lord, our offenses, nor the offenses of our forefathers; spare us, good Lord, spare thy people, whom thou hast redeemed with thy most precious blood.
SPARE US, GOOD LORD.

FROM all blindness of heart; from pride, vainglory and hypocrisy; from envy, hatred, and malice, and all uncharitableness,
GOOD LORD, DELIVER US.

From all impure lusts and desires; and from all the deceits of the world, the flesh, and the devil,
GOOD LORD, DELIVER US.

From lightning and tempest; from fire and flood; from plague, pestilence, and famine; from all disasters by land, by air, and by water; from battle and murder, and from violent death,

GOOD LORD, DELIVER US.

From sedition and rebellion; from heresy and schism; from hardness of heart, and contempt of thy Word and authority,

GOOD LORD, DELIVER US.

By the mystery of thy holy incarnation; by thy holy nativity; by thy baptism, temptation and ministry,

GOOD LORD, DELIVER US.

By thine agony and bloody sweat; by thy cross and passion; by thy precious death and burial; by thy glorious resurrection and ascension; and by the coming of the Holy Spirit,

GOOD LORD, DELIVER US.

In all time of our tribulation; in all time of our wealth; in the hour of death, and in the day of judgment,

GOOD LORD, DELIVER US.

WE sinners do beseech thee to hear us, O Lord God, and that it may please thee to govern and direct thy holy Church Universal,

WE BESEECH THEE TO HEAR US, GOOD LORD.

That it may please thee so to rule the hearts of thy servants, the President of the United States, the Governor of this Commonwealth, and all others in authority, that law and order may everywhere prevail,

WE BESEECH THEE TO HEAR US, GOOD LORD.

That it may please thee to bless the rulers of all lands, giving them grace to execute justice, and to maintain truth,

WE BESEECH THEE TO HEAR US, GOOD LORD.

That it may please thee to bless and protect all who serve mankind by labor, industry, and learning,

WE BESEECH THEE TO HEAR US, GOOD LORD.

That it may please thee to give to all nations unity, peace, and concord,

WE BESEECH THEE TO HEAR US, GOOD LORD.

That it may please thee to keep us in all time of temptation and heaviness, to comfort and help all the weakhearted, to raise up them that fall, and finally to beat down Satan under our feet,

WE BESEECH THEE TO HEAR US, GOOD LORD.

That it may please thee to succor, help, and comfort all who are in danger, necessity, and tribulation; to preserve all women in the perils of childbirth, all sick persons and young children; and to show thy pity upon all prisoners and captives,

WE BESEECH THEE TO HEAR US, GOOD LORD.

That it may please thee to defend and provide for the fatherless children, the widows, and all that are desolate and oppressed,

WE BESEECH THEE TO HEAR US, GOOD LORD.

That it may please thee to have mercy upon all men,

WE BESEECH THEE TO HEAR US, GOOD LORD.

O Son of God, Redeemer of the world,

HAVE MERCY UPON US.

O Lamb of God, that takest away the sin of the world,

HAVE MERCY UPON US.

O Lamb of God, that takest away the sin of the world,

GRANT US THY PEACE.

¶ *The Minister shall say,*

O GOD, merciful Father, who despisest not the sighing of the contrite, nor rejectest the desire of the sorrowful, be favorable to our prayers, which in our afflictions that continually oppress us we pour out before thee; and graciously hear them, that those things which the craft of the devil or man worketh against us, may be brought to nought and by the counsel of thy goodness be dispersed, so that being hurt by no persecutions we may evermore give thanks to thee in thy holy Church; through Jesus Christ our Lord. *Amen.*

O GOD, from whom all holy desires, all good counsels, and all just works do proceed, give unto thy servants that peace which the world cannot give, that our hearts may be set to obey thy commandments, and also that we, being defended from the fear of our enemies, may by thy protection pass our time in peace and quietness; through Jesus Christ our Lord. *Amen.*

¶ *Here special prayers may be offered, followed by the Lord's Prayer, in which the Congregation shall join.*

OUR Father, who art in heaven, Hallowed be thy Name. Thy kingdom come. Thy will be done, on earth as it is in heaven. Give us this day our daily bread. And forgive us our debts, as we forgive our debtors. And lead us not into temptation, but deliver us from evil. For thine is the kingdom, and the power, and the glory, for ever. Amen.

HYMN—OFFERING—SERMON

¶ *The Hymn, Offering, and Sermon may take place according to the accustomed order. An Anthem or Chant may be sung.*

EXHORTATION

¶ *The Minister, addressing the Communicants, shall say,*

BELOVED in the Lord: Our blessed Saviour, Jesus Christ, when he was about to finish the work of our redemption, by making himself a sacrifice for our sins upon the cross, solemnly instituted the Holy Communion of his own Body and Blood, that it might be the abiding memorial of his precious death; the seal of his perpetual presence in the Church by the Holy Spirit; the mystical sign of his one offering of himself made once, but of force always, to put away sin; the pledge of his undying love for his people; and the bond of his living union and fellowship with them to the end of time.

It has not been without reason, therefore, that the celebration of the Lord's Supper has ever been regarded by the Church as the innermost sanctuary of the whole Christian worship. We have to do here, not with signs merely, but with the realities themselves which these signs represent. Our Lord himself calls the bread his Body, and the cup his Blood, or the New Testament in his Blood.

Being of such a sacred nature it is plain that the Table of the Lord can be rightly approached only by those who are of a truly devout, repentant, and believing mind. These holy mysteries are not for the worldly, the irreverent, or the indifferent. All who are impenitent and unbelieving, and who refuse to obey the Gospel of our Lord Jesus Christ, have no right to partake of this Table.

If any of you, then, are conscious that you are the willing servants of sin, being without repentance and faith, and yielding yourselves to the power of worldly affections and lusts, we solemnly warn and admonish you, that ye presume not, so long as this is your character, to come to the Table of the Lord; for those doing so eat and drink judgment to themselves, not because they are sinners, but because they are impenitent sinners; not because they are unworthy, but because they eat and drink unworthily, not discerning the Lord's Body.

On the other hand, we cordially invite to this Table all who are truly grieved and penitent for their sins, who look to the Lord Jesus

Christ for righteousness and salvation, who abide in the fellowship of his Church, and who earnestly desire to possess his Spirit and to walk in his steps. To all such the infinitely compassionate Redeemer himself says: Come unto me, all ye that labor, and are heavy laden, and I will give you rest.

Ye then, beloved brethren, who have looked earnestly into your own hearts and who find in yourselves these good dispositions of penitence and faith, with the sincere desire and purpose of forsaking all sin and following after all Christian holiness, approach with me now to the throne of grace, and make your humble confession to Almighty God.

CONFESSION OF SIN

¶ *Here all shall kneel and say,*

A LMIGHTY God, Father of our Lord Jesus Christ, Maker of all things, Judge of all men, we cast ourselves down at thy feet with deep humiliation and heartfelt penitent grief, in view of our manifold sins. We have sinned against thee in thought, word, and deed; we have broken thy holy laws; we have come short of thy righteousness and glory in all our ways. Righteousness belongeth unto thee, O Lord, but unto us only confusion of face. Unto thee, O Lord our God, belong also mercies and forgivenesses, though we have rebelled against thee; for thou, Lord, art good, and ready to forgive, and plenteous in mercy unto all them that call upon thee. Look upon us, therefore, O righteous and holy Father, with an eye of pity and compassion, as we now humble ourselves with sincere confession, before the throne of thy heavenly grace; and for the sake of thy Son, Jesus Christ, speak pardon and peace to our souls. Let thy mercy be upon us, O Lord, according as we hope in thee. And with the full pardon of our past sins, be pleased also to quicken us, we beseech thee, in the way of righteousness, and uphold us with thy Spirit, that we may walk worthy henceforth of the vocation wherewith we are called, and ever hereafter serve and please thee in newness of life, to the honor and glory of thy holy Name; through Jesus Christ our Lord. Amen.

¶ *The Confessional Questions may be asked.*

Minister. I now ask you in the presence of God, and upon the evidence of your own conscience:

Do you acknowledge and deplore your many sins with contrite heart?

Do you believe that our heavenly Father is willing, for Jesus' sake, to forgive all your sins?

Do you resolve to submit yourself in the future to the gracious direction of the Holy Spirit, so that you may no more purposely sin, but be enabled to follow after holiness?

Answer. I do.

ASSURANCE OF PARDON

¶ *Then the Minister shall say,*

HEARKEN now unto the comforting assurance of the grace of God, promised in the Gospel to all that repent and believe: As I live, saith the Lord God, I have no pleasure in the death of the wicked, but that the wicked turn from his way and live. God so loved the world that he gave his only begotten Son, that whosoever believeth in him should not perish, but have everlasting life. Wherefore, beloved brethren, those of you who have truly turned to God with hearty repentance and sincere faith, may assuredly believe that your sins are forgiven; through Jesus Christ our Lord. *Amen.*

¶ *The Congregation shall now stand and sing a Doxology or a Hymn.*

BENEDICTION

THE God of peace, that brought again from the dead our Lord Jesus, that great Shepherd of the sheep, through the blood of the everlasting covenant, make you perfect in every good work to do his will, working in you that which is well-pleasing in his sight, through Jesus Christ, to whom be glory for ever and ever. *Amen.*

THE ORDER FOR HOLY COMMUNION

¶ *The Sacrament of the Lord's Supper shall be administered in every Congregation at least twice a year, and preferably more often.*

¶ *Having taken his place at the Lord's Table, the Congregation standing, the Minister shall say,*

IN the Name of the Father, and of the Son, and of the Holy Spirit. Amen.

¶ *Then the Introit for the Day (Page 501) may be used.*

EXHORTATION

DEARLY beloved in the Lord: Our blessed Saviour Jesus Christ instituted the Holy Communion of his Body and Blood, that it might be the abiding memorial of his atoning death; the seal of his perpetual presence in the Church through the Holy Spirit; the mystical representation of the sacrifice of himself on the cross; the pledge of his undying love for his people; and the bond of his living union and fellowship with them to the end of time.

The celebration of the Lord's Supper has ever been regarded by the Church as the innermost sanctuary of the whole Christian worship. We have to do here not with signs merely, but with the realities which these signs represent. The Lord's Table, therefore, can be rightly approached only by those who are of a devout, repentant, and believing mind.

We cordially invite to partake of this Sacrament all who are truly grieved and penitent for their sins, who look to the Lord Jesus Christ for righteousness and salvation, who abide in the fellowship of his Church, and who desire to possess his Spirit and walk in his ways. To all such the compassionate Redeemer himself says: Come unto me, all ye that labor and are heavy laden, and I will give you rest.

Ye, then, who have earnestly searched your own hearts and desire to forsake all sin and follow after Christian holiness, approach with me now to the throne of grace, and make your humble confession to Almighty God.

CONFESSION OF SIN

¶ *The Minister and Congregation shall say,*

ALMIGHTY God, Father of our Lord Jesus Christ, Maker of all things, Judge of all men, we acknowledge and confess our manifold sins, which we from time to time have committed, by thought,

21

word, and deed, against thy Divine Majesty. We do earnestly repent, and are heartily sorry for these our misdoings. The remembrance of them is grievous unto us. Have mercy upon us, have mercy upon us, most merciful Father; for the sake of thy Son, our Lord Jesus Christ, forgive us all our sins; and grant that we may ever hereafter serve and please thee in newness of life, to the honor and glory of thy Name; through Jesus Christ our Lord. Amen.

or

ALMIGHTY God, merciful Father: I, a poor sinner, acknowledge and confess my manifold sins, which I from time to time have committed, by thought, word, and deed, against thy Divine Majesty. I do earnestly repent, and am heartily sorry for these my misdoings; the remembrance of them is grievous unto me. I have no other comfort or hope than thy grace, which aboundeth above my guilt, and the precious merits of my Lord Jesus Christ. Longing after this grace, I say: Father, I have sinned against heaven and in thy sight, and am no more worthy to be called thy child. Grant unto me pardon and peace, and strength to lead a new and righteous life, by the power of thy Holy Spirit, through the same Lord and Saviour, Jesus Christ. Amen.

¶ *Then shall be sung or said the* KYRIE. *(No. 518)*

Lord, have mercy upon us.
Lord, have mercy upon us.
Christ, have mercy upon us.
Christ, have mercy upon us.
Lord, have mercy upon us.
Lord, have mercy upon us.

ASSURANCE OF PARDON

¶ *The Minister shall say,*

UPON this humble confession which you have made, and by the authority of the Word of God, as a minister of the Lord Jesus Christ, I do declare unto you, who do truly repent and heartily believe in Jesus Christ, and are sincerely determined to amend your sinful life, the forgiveness of all your sins; in the Name of the Father, and of the Son, and of the Holy Spirit. *Amen.*

or

HEARKEN now unto the comforting assurance of the grace of God, promised in the Gospel to all that repent and believe: If we confess our sins, he is faithful and just to forgive us our sins, and to cleanse us from all unrighteousness. *Amen.*

ORDER FOR HOLY COMMUNION

Minister.   O Lord, open thou my lips.

Congregation. And my mouth shall show forth thy praise.

⁋ *Then shall be sung the* GLORIA IN EXCELSIS *(No. 489) or a Hymn of Praise.*

GLORY be to God on high, and on earth peace, good will toward men. We praise thee, we bless thee, we worship thee, we glorify thee, we give thanks to thee for thy great glory, O Lord God, heavenly King, God the Father Almighty.

O Lord, the only begotten Son, Jesus Christ; O Lord God, Lamb of God, Son of the Father, that takest away the sin of the world, have mercy upon us. Thou that takest away the sin of the world, receive our prayer. Thou that sittest at the right hand of God the Father, have mercy upon us.

For thou only art holy, thou only art the Lord, thou only, O Christ, with the Holy Ghost, art most high in the glory of God the Father. Amen.

COLLECT

Minister.   Let us pray.

⁋ *The Minister shall say the Collect for the Day.*

THE HOLY SCRIPTURES

⁋ *The Minister shall read the Epistle and the Gospel for the Day.*

⁋ *The Congregation may sing a Canticle, a Hymn, or a Response.*

CONFESSION OF FAITH

⁋ *The Congregation standing, the Apostles' Creed or the Nicene Creed shall be said.*

I BELIEVE in God the Father Almighty, Maker of heaven and earth:

And in Jesus Christ his only begotten Son, our Lord; who was conceived by the Holy Ghost, born of the Virgin Mary, suffered under Pontius Pilate, was crucified, dead and buried; He descended into hell*; the third day he rose again from the dead; he ascended into heaven, and sitteth on the right hand of God the Father Almighty; from thence he shall come to judge the quick and the dead.

---

* Hades *may be used.*

I believe in the Holy Ghost; the Holy Catholic Church†; the communion of saints; the forgiveness of sins; the resurrection of the body; and the life everlasting. Amen.

or

WE BELIEVE in one God the Father Almighty, Maker of heaven and earth, and of all things visible and invisible.

And in one Lord Jesus Christ, the only begotten Son of God; begotten of his Father before all worlds, God of God, Light of Light, very God of very God; begotten, not made, being of one substance with the Father, by whom all things were made; who for us men and for our salvation came down from heaven, and was incarnate by the Holy Ghost of the Virgin Mary, and was made man; and was crucified also for us under Pontius Pilate. He suffered and was buried; and the third day he rose again according to the Scriptures; and ascended into heaven, and sitteth on the right hand of the Father. And he shall come again, with glory, to judge both the quick and the dead; whose kingdom shall have no end.

And we believe in the Holy Ghost, the Lord and Giver of Life, who proceedeth from the Father and the Son; who with the Father and the Son together is worshipped and glorified; who spake by the prophets. And we believe in one Holy Catholic and Apostolic Church. We acknowledge one baptism for the remission of sins; and we look for the resurrection of the dead, and the life of the world to come. Amen.

SERMON—HYMN—OFFERING

¶ *The Sermon, Hymn, and Offering may take place according to the accustomed order. An Anthem may be sung.*

¶ *The vessels containing bread and wine having been made ready, and the Congregation standing, the Service shall then proceed as follows:*

THE EUCHARISTIC PRAYER

Minister. The Lord be with you.

Congregation. And with thy spirit.

Minister. Lift up your hearts.

Congregation. We lift them up unto the Lord.

Minister. Let us give thanks unto the Lord our God.

Congregation. It is meet and right so to do.

---

† One Holy Universal Christian Church *may be used.*

❡ *The Minister, proceeding, shall say,*

IT is very meet, right, and our bounden duty, that we should at all times and in all places give thanks unto thee, O Holy Lord, Father Almighty, Everlasting God, who didst create the heavens and the earth and all that in them is, who didst make man in thine own image, and whose tender mercies are over all thy works.

For all thy mercies and favors, known to us and unknown, we give thee thanks. But most of all we praise thee, the Father everlasting, for the gift of thine adorable, true, and only Son, our Saviour Jesus Christ, who by his appearing hath abolished death and brought life and immortality to light through the Gospel. We bless thee for his holy incarnation, for his life on earth, for his precious sufferings and death upon the cross, for his resurrection from the dead, and for his glorious ascension to thy right hand. We bless thee for the giving of the Holy Spirit, for the institution of the Church, for the means of grace, for the hope of everlasting life, and for the glory which shall be brought unto us at the coming, and in the kingdom, of thy dear Son.

Thee, mighty God, heavenly King, we magnify and praise. With patriarchs and prophets, apostles and martyrs, with the holy Church throughout all the world; with the heavenly Jerusalem, the joyful assembly and congregation of the firstborn on high; with the innumerable company of angels round about thy throne, the heaven of heavens, and all the powers therein, we worship and adore thy glorious Name, joining in the song of the Cherubim and Seraphim:

❡ *Here the Minister and Congregation shall say or sing the Seraphic Hymn or the* SANCTUS.

Seraphic Hymn (No. 522)
Holy, Holy, Holy, Lord God of Sabaoth;
Heaven and earth are full of the majesty of thy glory;
Hosanna in the highest!
Blessed is he that cometh in the Name of the Lord;
Hosanna in the highest!

Sanctus (No. 521)
Holy, Holy, Holy, Lord God of hosts,
Heaven and earth are full of thy glory;
Glory be to thee, O Lord Most High.

❡ *The Minister shall continue,*

THE Lord Jesus, the same night in which he was betrayed, took bread, *(Here the Minister shall take the bread into his hands)* and when he had given thanks, he brake it, *(Here the Minister shall break the bread)* and said: Take, eat; this is my Body which is broken for you; this do in remembrance of me. After the same manner also, he took the cup, *(Here the Minister shall take the cup into his hands)* when he had supped, saying: This cup is the New Testament in my Blood; this do ye, as oft as ye drink it, in remembrance of me.

Wherefore, we beseech thee, O merciful Father, to send thy Holy Spirit upon us, and upon these elements of bread and wine, that the bread which we break may be to us the Communion of the Body of Christ, and the cup of blessing which we bless, the Communion of the Blood of Christ. And be pleased now, O most merciful Father, graciously to receive this memorial of the blessed sacrifice of thy Son which we here offer unto thee, in union with the sacrifice of our thanksgiving and praise, consecrating ourselves in soul and body, property and life, to thy most blessed service and praise. Look upon us through the mediation of our great High Priest. Make us accepted in the Beloved, and let his Name be as a pure and holy incense, through which all our worship may come up before thee, a sacrifice acceptable and well pleasing in thy sight; through Jesus Christ our Lord, to whom, with thee, and the Holy Spirit, be all honor and glory, world without end. *Amen.*

¶ *Then may be said any or all of the following prayers:*

THE INTERCESSION

O GOD, the Creator and Preserver of all mankind, we humbly beseech thee for all sorts and conditions of men, that thou wouldest be pleased to make thy ways known unto them, and to grant them life everlasting; through Jesus Christ our Lord. *Amen.*

REMEMBER in mercy thy Church militant throughout the whole earth. Let her ministers be clothed with righteousness, and her priests with salvation. Build up her desolations, restore her disorders, heal her divisions, and grant unto her prosperity, safety, unity, and peace. *Amen.*

WE commend unto thee this particular church and congregation, pastor and people, beseeching thee to accept their piety and faith, and to increase toward them thy heavenly grace, so that they abound more and more in knowledge and love, unto the coming of our Lord Jesus Christ. *Amen.*

WE pray for the rulers in all lands, and for the people committed to their charge. Look with favor upon thy servants, the President of the United States, the Governor of this Commonwealth, and all others in authority, and so enrich them with wisdom and grace, that under their government we may lead quiet and peaceable lives, in all godliness and honesty; through Jesus Christ our Lord. *Amen.*

S END forth thy light and thy truth unto the ends of the earth, cause the glorious Gospel of thy grace to be proclaimed among all nations, and powerfully incline the hearts of men everywhere, that they may hear and obey the joyful sound. *Amen.*

R EGARD in tender compassion those among thy people who are called to suffer heavy affliction, or sore temptation and trial of any kind, and be thou graciously nigh unto them with thy divine help, according to all their need. *Amen.*

E SPECIALLY do we commend unto thee those departing this life. Let the arms of thy love be round about them in their last hour, enable them joyfully to commit their spirits into thy hands, and so receive them to thy rest. *Amen.*

O GOD, the Father of our Lord Jesus Christ, of whom the whole family in heaven and earth is named, we rejoice before thee in the blessed communion of all thy saints, wherein thou givest us also to have part. We praise thee for the holy fellowship of patriarchs and prophets, apostles and martyrs, and the whole glorious company of the redeemed of all ages, who have died in the Lord, and now live with him forevermore. We give thanks unto thee for thy great grace and many gifts bestowed on those who have thus gone before us in the way of salvation, and by whom we are now compassed about in our Christian course, as a cloud of witnesses looking down upon us from the heavenly world. Enable us to follow their faith, that we may enter at death into their joy, and so abide with them in rest and peace, till both they and we shall reach our common consummation of redemption and bliss in the glorious resurrection of the last day. *Amen.*

¶ *Minister and Congregation.*

O UR Father, who art in heaven, Hallowed be thy Name. Thy kingdom come. Thy will be done, on earth as it is in heaven. Give us this day our daily bread. And forgive us our debts, as we forgive our debtors. And lead us not into temptation, but deliver us from evil. For thine is the kingdom, and the power, and the glory, for ever. Amen.

❡ *The* Agnus Dei *may be sung or said. (No. 525)*

> Minister.   O Christ, thou Lamb of God, that takest away the sin of the world,
>
> Congregation. Have mercy upon us.
>
> Minister.   O Christ, thou Lamb of God, that takest away the sin of the world,
>
> Congregation. Have mercy upon us.
>
> Minister.   O Christ, thou Lamb of God, that takest away the sin of the world,
>
> Congregation. Grant us thy peace. Amen.

❡ *Then the Minister may say,*

THE peace of our Lord Jesus Christ be with you all. *Amen.*

COME unto me, all ye that labor and are heavy laden, and I will give you rest.

THE COMMUNION

❡ *Here the Holy Communion shall take place. The Communicants shall present themselves before the Lord's Table. The officiating Minister shall first receive the Communion in both kinds, and administer the same to his Assistants, and he shall then proceed with their help to administer it to the Communicants. But if the Communicants remain in the pews, the following order shall be observed: The Minister shall first receive the Communion in both kinds, and administer the same to his Assistants. Then he shall give the Bread to his Assistants, who shall administer it to the people. When all have received the Bread, the Assistants shall return to the Table, and the Minister shall in like manner deliver the Cup to them. When all have communicated, the Minister shall pronounce the Blessing, and the Assistants shall return to the Table, after which the Service shall proceed according to the prescribed order.*

❡ *The Minister, giving the Bread, shall say,*

TAKE and eat; this is the Body of our Lord Jesus Christ, which was broken for you. Do this in remembrance of him.

or

THE Bread which we break, is it not the Communion of the Body of Christ?

❡ *The Minister, giving the Cup, shall say,*

TAKE and drink; this Cup is the New Testament in the Blood of our Lord Jesus Christ, which was shed for you for the remission of sins. Do this in remembrance of him.

or

THE Cup of Blessing which we bless, is it not the Communion of the Blood of Christ?

❡ *After the People have communicated, the Minister shall say,*

MAY the Holy Communion of the Body and Blood of our Lord and Saviour Jesus Christ keep and preserve you, each one, in body, soul, and spirit, unto everlasting life. *Amen.* Depart in peace.

or

MAY the Holy Communion strengthen and preserve you unto everlasting life. Be it unto you according to your faith. *Amen.* Depart in peace.

❡ *When all have communicated, the Elements shall be placed upon the Lord's Table, and covered with a fair linen cloth. Then, the Congregation standing, the Minister shall say,*

Let us give thanks.

ALMIGHTY and everlasting God, we give thee most hearty thanks for the great goodness thou hast shown toward us at this time in vouchsafing to feed us, through these holy mysteries, with the spiritual food of the most precious Body and Blood of thy Son, our Saviour Jesus Christ, assuring us thereby, that we are very members incorporate in the mystical Body of thy Son, and heirs through hope of thine everlasting kingdom. And we most humbly beseech thee, O heavenly Father, so to assist us with thy grace, that we may continue in that holy fellowship, and do all such good works as shall please thee; through Jesus Christ our Lord, to whom, with thee and the Holy Spirit, be all honor and glory, world without end. *Amen.*

❡ *A Doxology or the* NUNC DIMITTIS *or the* TE DEUM *shall be sung, or said by Minister and Congregation alternating.*

NUNC DIMITTIS *(No. 536)*

L ORD, now lettest thou thy servant depart in peace, ‖ according to thy Word.

For mine eyes have seen ‖ thy salvation,

Which thou hast prepared ‖ before the face of all people;

To be a light to lighten the Gentiles, ‖and to be the glory of thy people Israel.

Glory be to the Father, and to the Son, ‖ and to the Holy Ghost; as it was in the beginning, is now, and ever shall be, ‖ world without end. Amen.

TE DEUM LAUDAMUS *(No. 527)*

W E praise thee, O God;

We acknowledge thee to be the Lord.

All the earth doth worship thee, the Father everlasting.

To thee all angels cry aloud; the heavens and all the powers therein.

To thee cherubim and seraphim continually do cry,

Holy, Holy, Holy, Lord God of Sabaoth;

Heaven and earth are full of the majesty of thy glory.

The glorious company of the apostles praise thee;

The goodly fellowship of the prophets praise thee;

The noble army of martyrs praise thee;

The holy Church, throughout all the world, doth acknowledge thee,

The Father, of an infinite majesty;

Thine adorable, true, and only Son;

Also the Holy Ghost, the Comforter.

T HOU art the King of Glory, O Christ,

Thou art the everlasting Son of the Father.

When thou tookest upon thee to deliver man, thou didst humble thyself to be born of a Virgin.

When thou hadst overcome the sharpness of death, thou didst open the kingdom of heaven to all believers.

Thou sittest at the right hand of God, in the glory of the Father.

We believe that thou shalt come to be our judge;

We therefore pray thee, help thy servants, whom thou hast redeemed with thy precious blood;
Make them to be numbered with thy saints in glory everlasting.

O Lord, save thy people, and bless thine heritage;
Govern them, and lift them up forever,
Day by day we magnify thee;
And we worship thy Name ever, world without end.
Vouchsafe, O Lord, to keep us this day without sin.
O Lord, have mercy upon us, have mercy upon us.
O Lord, let thy mercy be upon us, as our trust is in thee;
O Lord, in thee have I trusted, let me never be confounded.

BENEDICTION

THE grace of the Lord Jesus Christ, and the love of God, and the communion of the Holy Spirit, be with you all. *Amen.*

or

THE peace of God, which passeth all understanding, keep your hearts and minds in the knowledge and love of God, and of his Son Jesus Christ our Lord: and the blessing of God Almighty, the Father, the Son, and the Holy Spirit, be amongst you and remain with you always. *Amen.*

AN ALTERNATE ORDER FOR HOLY COMMUNION

❡ *The Order of Worship shall be followed until the conclusion of the Sermon.*

❡ *The Congregation shall join in the singing of a Communion Hymn.*

❡ *Then the Minister shall address the Congregation, saying,*

OUR blessed Saviour Jesus Christ instituted the Holy Communion of his Body and Blood, that it might be the abiding memorial of his atoning death; the seal of his perpetual presence in the Church through the Holy Spirit; the mystical representation of the sacrifice of himself on the cross; the pledge of his undying love for his people; and the bond of his living union and fellowship with them to the end of time.

The celebration of the Lord's Supper has ever been regarded by the Church as the innermost sanctuary of the whole Christian worship. We enter here into living communion with our Lord and Saviour, Jesus Christ, and do show forth our fellowship with one another as members of his Church. Gathering about his table we profess our desire to be numbered among his people and to walk in his ways.

❡ *If the Confession of Sin has not been said in the preceding service, the Minister shall say,*

YE then, who have earnestly searched your own hearts, and desire to forsake all sin, and follow after Christian holiness, approach with me now to the throne of grace, and let us make our humble confession to Almighty God.

CONFESSION OF SIN

❡ *The Minister and Congregation shall say,*

ALMIGHTY God, our heavenly Father, we acknowledge and confess our manifold sins, which we have committed against thee by thought and word and deed, and by which we have offended against thy holy laws, and have merited thy condemnation in this world and in the world to come. We do earnestly repent, and are heartily sorry for these our transgressions. Trusting in thy grace and goodness, manifested in Christ Jesus our Lord, we ask of thee pardon and peace, and strength to lead a new and righteous life, by the power of thy Holy Spirit; through the same Jesus Christ our Lord. Amen.

ASSURANCE OF PARDON

❡ *Then the Minister shall say,*

ALMIGHTY God, our heavenly Father, who of thy great mercy hast promised forgiveness of sins to all them that with hearty repentance and true faith turn unto thee, have mercy upon us, pardon and deliver us from all our sins, confirm and strengthen us in all goodness, and bring us to everlasting life; through Jesus Christ our Lord. *Amen.*

or

HEARKEN now unto the comforting assurance of the grace of God, promised in the Gospel to all that repent and believe: If we confess our sins, he is faithful and just to forgive us our sins, and to cleanse us from all unrighteousness. *Amen.*

❡ *The vessels containing bread and wine having been made ready, and the Congregation standing, the Service shall then proceed as follows:*

    Minister.   The Lord be with you.
    Congregation. And with thy spirit.
    Minister.   Lift up your hearts.
    Congregation. We lift them up unto the Lord.
    Minister.   Let us give thanks unto the Lord our God.
    Congregation. It is meet and right so to do.

❡ *The Minister, proceeding, shall say,*

IT is very meet, right, and our bounden duty, that we should at all times and in all places give thanks unto thee, O Holy Lord, Father Almighty, Everlasting God. Therefore with the whole company of thy people we laud and magnify thy glorious Name, evermore praising thee, and saying,

        Holy, Holy, Holy, Lord God of hosts,
        Heaven and earth are full of thy glory;
        Glory be to thee, O Lord Most High.

or

Holy, Holy, Holy, Lord God of Sabaoth,
Heaven and earth are full of the majesty of thy glory;
Hosanna in the highest!
Blessed is he that cometh in the Name of the Lord;
Hosanna in the highest!

THE Lord Jesus, the same night in which he was betrayed, took bread, *(Here the Minister shall take the bread into his hands)* and when he had given thanks, he brake it, *(Here the Minister shall break the bread)* and said: Take, eat; this is my Body which is broken for you; this do in remembrance of me. After the same manner, also, he took the cup, *(Here the Minister shall take the cup into his hands)* when he had supped, saying: This cup is the New Testament in my Blood; this do ye, as oft as ye drink it, in remembrance of me.

ALL glory be to thee, Almighty God, our heavenly Father, for that thou of thy great goodness didst give thine only Son, Jesus Christ, to suffer death for our redemption. Wherefore, having in remembrance his holy life, his suffering and death, we thy servants do set forth this memorial which he has commanded us to make; and we beseech thee, O merciful Father, to send thy Holy Spirit upon us, and upon these elements of bread and wine, that the bread which we break may be to us the Communion of the Body of Christ, and the cup of blessing which we bless, the Communion of the Blood of Christ. We beseech thee to accept this our sacrifice of praise and thanksgiving, together with the sacrifice of ourselves unto thee and to thy holy service; through Jesus Christ our Lord. *Amen.*

¶ *The Minister may say also,*

LORD Jesus, for thee we live, for thee we suffer, for thee we die. Thine will we be in life and in death. *Amen.*

¶ *The* AGNUS DEI *(No. 525) may be sung or said in its traditional form or as a chorale.*

Minister.	O Christ, thou Lamb of God, that takest away the sin of the world,
Congregation.	Have mercy upon us.
Minister.	O Christ, thou Lamb of God, that takest away the sin of the world,
Congregation.	Have mercy upon us.
Minister.	O Christ, thou Lamb of God, that takest away the sin of the world,
Congregation.	Grant us thy peace. Amen.

or (No. 526)

O Lamb of God who, bleeding,
Upon the cross didst languish,
Nor scorn nor malice heeding,
So patient in thine anguish,

34

On thee our guilt was lying;
Thou savedst us by dying:
Have mercy on us, Lord Jesus.

¶ *Then the Minister may say,*

COME unto me, all ye that labor and are heavy laden, and I will give you rest.

¶ *Here the Holy Communion shall take place. The Communicants shall present themselves before the Lord's Table. The officiating Minister shall first receive the Communion in both kinds, and administer the same to his Assistants, and he shall then proceed with their help to administer it to the Communicants. But if the Communicants remain in the pews, the following order shall be observed: The Minister shall first receive the Communion in both kinds, and administer the same to his Assistants. Then he shall give the Bread to his Assistants, who shall administer it to the People. When all have received the Bread, the Assistants shall return to the Table, and the Minister shall in like manner deliver the Cup to them. When all have communicated, the Minister shall pronounce the Blessing, and the Assistants shall return to the Table, after which the Service shall proceed according to the prescribed order.*

¶ *The Minister, giving the Bread, shall say,*

TAKE and eat; this is the Body of our Lord Jesus Christ which was broken for you. Do this in remembrance of him.

or

THE Bread which we break, is it not the Communion of the Body of Christ?

¶ *The Minister, giving the Cup, shall say,*

TAKE and drink; this Cup is the New Testament in the Blood of our Lord Jesus Christ, which was shed for you for the remission of sins. Do this in remembrance of him.

or

THE Cup of Blessing which we bless, is it not the Communion of the Blood of Christ?

¶ *After the People have communicated the Minister shall say,*

MAY the Holy Communion of the Body and Blood of our Lord and Saviour Jesus Christ keep and preserve you, each one, in body, soul, and spirit, unto everlasting life. *Amen.* Depart in peace.

or

35

M<small>AY</small> the Holy Communion strengthen and preserve you unto everlasting life. Be it unto you according to your faith. *Amen.* Depart in peace.

❡ *When all have communicated, the Elements shall be placed upon the Lord's Table and covered with a fair linen cloth. Then, the Congregation standing, the Minister shall say,*

Let us give thanks.

A<small>LMIGHTY</small> God, we thank thee for thy great mercy given to us in this sacrament, whereby we are made partakers of Christ and all his benefits. So enrich us by the Holy Spirit that the life of Jesus may be made manifest in our mortal body, and all our days may be spent in thy love and service; through Jesus Christ our Lord. *Amen.*

❡ *A Doxology or the* N<small>UNC</small> D<small>IMITTIS</small> *(No. 536) or the* T<small>E</small> D<small>EUM</small> *(No. 527) shall be sung or said.*

BENEDICTION

T<small>HE</small> grace of the Lord Jesus Christ, and the love of God, and the communion of the Holy Spirit, be with you all. *Amen.*

The Ten Commandments

God spake all these words, saying, I am the Lord thy God, who have brought thee out of the land of Egypt, out of the house of bondage.

1. Thou shalt have no other gods before me.

2. Thou shalt not make unto thee any graven image, or any likeness of any thing that is in heaven above, or that is in the earth beneath, or that is in the water under the earth; thou shalt not bow down thyself to them, nor serve them: for I the Lord thy God am a jealous God, visiting the iniquity of the fathers upon the children unto the third and fourth generation of them that hate me; and showing mercy unto thousands of them that love me, and keep my commandments.

3. Thou shalt not take the name of the Lord thy God in vain; for the Lord will not hold him guiltless that taketh his name in vain.

4. Remember the sabbath day to keep it holy. Six days shalt thou labor, and do all thy work, but the seventh day is the sabbath of the Lord thy God: in it thou shalt not do any work, thou, nor thy son, nor thy daughter, thy manservant, nor thy maidservant, nor thy cattle, nor thy stranger that is within thy gates; for in six days the Lord made heaven and earth, the sea, and all that in them is, and rested the seventh day; wherefore the Lord blessed the sabbath day, and hallowed it.

5. Honor thy father and thy mother, that thy days may be long upon the land which the Lord thy God giveth thee.

6. Thou shalt not kill.

7. Thou shalt not commit adultery.

8. Thou shalt not steal.

9. Thou shalt not bear false witness against thy neighbor.

10. Thou shalt not covet thy neighbor's house, thou shalt not covet thy neighbor's wife, nor his manservant, nor his maidservant, nor his ox, nor his ass, nor any thing that is thy neighbor's.

The Lord's Prayer

Our Father, who art in heaven, Hallowed be thy Name. Thy kingdom come. Thy will be done, on earth as it is in heaven. Give us this day our daily bread. And forgive us our debts, as we forgive our debtors. And lead us not into temptation, but deliver us from evil. For thine is the kingdom, and the power, and the glory, for ever. Amen.

The Apostles' Creed

I believe in God the Father Almighty, Maker of heaven and earth: And in Jesus Christ his only begotten Son, our Lord; who was conceived by the Holy Ghost, born of the Virgin Mary, suffered under Pontius Pilate, was crucified, dead, and buried; he descended into hell*; the third day he rose again from the dead; he ascended into heaven, and sitteth on the right hand of God the Father Almighty; from thence he shall come to judge the quick and the dead.

I believe in the Holy Ghost; the holy Catholic Church†; the communion of saints; the forgiveness of sins; the resurrection of the body; and the life everlasting. Amen.

The Beatitudes

Blessed are the poor in spirit; for theirs is the kingdom of heaven.

Blessed are they that mourn; for they shall be comforted.

Blessed are the meek; for they shall inherit the earth.

Blessed are they which do hunger and thirst after righteousness; for they shall be filled.

Blessed are the merciful; for they shall obtain mercy.

Blessed are the pure in heart; for they shall see God.

Blessed are the peacemakers; for they shall be called the children of God.

Blessed are they which are persecuted for righteousness' sake; for theirs is the kingdom of heaven.

Blessed are ye, when men shall revile you, and persecute you, and shall say all manner of evil against you falsely, for my sake.

Rejoice, and be exceeding glad; for great is your reward in heaven; for so persecuted they the prophets which were before you.

---

* Hades *may be used.*
† One Holy Universal Christian Church *may be used.*

The Hymns

Serve the Lord with gladness;
come before his presence with singing.

Psalm 100: 2

Adoration and Praise

1

REGINALD HEBER, 1826   11. 12. 12. 10.   NICÆA

JOHN B. DYKES, 1861

With exaltation

1. Ho - ly, Ho - ly, Ho - ly! Lord God Al - might - y!
2. Ho - ly, Ho - ly, Ho - ly! all the saints a - dore Thee,
3. Ho - ly, Ho - ly, Ho - ly! though the dark - ness hide Thee,
4. Ho - ly, Ho - ly, Ho - ly! Lord God Al - might - y!

Ear - ly in the morn - ing our song shall rise to Thee:
Cast - ing down their gold - en crowns a - round the glass - y sea;
Though the eye of sin - ful man Thy glo - ry may not see,
All Thy works shall praise Thy name in earth and sky and sea;

Ho - ly, Ho - ly, Ho - ly! Mer - ci - ful and might - y!
Cher - u - bim and ser - a - phim fall - ing down be - fore Thee,
On - ly Thou art ho - ly; there is none be - side Thee,
Ho - ly, Ho - ly, Ho - ly! Mer - ci - ful and might - y!

God in Three Per - sons, bless - ed Trin - i - ty!
Who wert, and art, and ev - er - more shalt be.
Per - fect in power, in love, and pu - ri - ty.
God in Three Per - sons, bless - ed Trin - i - ty! A-MEN.

Adoration and Praise

2

NICOLAUS DECIUS, 1526
Tr. CATHERINE WINKWORTH, 1862, alt.   8.7.8.7.8.8.7.

ALLEIN GOTT IN DER HÖH' SEI EHR'
Adapted from plain song
Deutsch Evangelisch Messze, 1539

Joyously, but with dignity

1. All glo-ry be to God on high, Who hath our race be-friend-ed!
2. We praise, we wor-ship Thee, we trust And give Thee thanks for-ev - er,
3. O Je-sus Christ, our God and Lord, Be-got-ten of the Fa - ther,
4. O Ho-ly Spir-it, pre-cious Gift, Thou Com-fort-er un-fail - ing,

To us no harm shall now come nigh, The strife at last is end - ed;
O Fa-ther, that Thy rule is just And wise, and chan-ges nev - er;
O Thou who hast our peace re-stored, And the lost sheep dost gath - er,
Do Thou our trou-bled souls up-lift, A-gainst the foe pre-vail - ing;

God show-eth His good-will to men, And peace shall reign on
Thy bound-less power o'er all things reigns, Thou dost what-e'er Thy
Thou Lamb of God, en-throned on high, Be-hold our need and
A-vert our woes and calm our dread: For us the Sav-iour's

earth a-gain; O thank Him for His good - ness!
will or-dains; 'Tis well Thou art our Rul - er!
hear our cry; Have mer-cy on us, Je - sus!
blood was shed; Do Thou in faith sus-tain us!   A-MEN.

Adoration and Praise

3

HENRY FRANCIS LYTE, 1834

8. 7. 8. 7. 8. 7.

ALLELUIA DULCE CARMEN
Essay on the Church Plain Chant, 1782
Arr. SAMUEL WEBBE

In march rhythm

1. Praise, my soul, the King of heav - en, To His feet thy
2. Praise Him for His grace and fa - vor To our fa - thers
3. Fa - ther - like He tends and spares us, Well our fee - ble
4. An - gels in the height, a - dore Him, Ye be - hold Him

trib - ute bring; Ran - somed, healed, re - stored, for - giv - en,
in dis - tress; Praise Him, still the same as ev - er,
frame He knows; In His hands He gen - tly bears us,
face to face; Saints tri - um - phant, bow be - fore Him,

Ev - er - more His prais - es sing; Al - le - lu - ia!
Slow to chide, and swift to bless; Al - le - lu - ia!
Res - cues us from all our foes; Al - le - lu - ia!
Gath - ered in from ev - ery race; Al - le - lu - ia!

Al - le - lu - ia! Praise the ev - er - last - ing King.
Al - le - lu - ia! Glo - rious in His faith - ful - ness.
Al - le - lu - ia! Wide - ly yet His mer - cy flows.
Al - le - lu - ia! Praise with us the God of grace. A-MEN.

Adoration and Praise

4

Anon., c. 1757

6. 6. 4. 6. 6. 6. 4.

TRINITY (ITALIAN HYMN)
FELICE DE GIARDINI, 1769

Joyously, but with dignity   *First Tune*

1. Come, Thou Al - might - y King, Help us Thy Name to sing, Help us to praise: Fa - ther, all - glo - ri - ous, O'er all vic - to - ri - ous, Come, and reign o - ver us, An - cient of Days.

2. Come, Thou In - car - nate Word, Gird on Thy might - y sword, Our prayer at - tend: Come, and Thy peo - ple bless, And give Thy word suc - cess; Spir - it of ho - li - ness, On us de - scend.

3. Come, Ho - ly Com - fort - er, Thy sa - cred wit - ness bear In this glad hour: Thou who al - might - y art, Now rule in ev - ery heart, And ne'er from us de - part, Spir - it of power.

4. To the great One in Three The high - est prais - es be, Hence ev - er - more! His sov - ereign maj - es - ty May we in glo - ry see, And to e - ter - ni - ty Love and a - dore. A - MEN.

Adoration and Praise

5

SERUG
From SAMUEL SEBASTIAN WESLEY'S
European Psalmist, 1872

Anon., c. **1757**

6. 6. 4. 6. 6. 6. 4.

Second Tune

Joyously, but with dignity

1. Come, Thou Al - might - y King, Help us Thy
2. Come, Thou In - car - nate Word, Gird on Thy
3. Come, Ho - ly Com - fort - er, Thy sa - cred
4. To the great One in Three The high - est

Name to sing, Help us to praise: Fa - ther, all -
might - y sword, Our prayer at - tend: Come, and Thy
wit - ness bear In this glad hour: Thou who al -
prais - es be, Hence ev - er - more! His sov - ereign

glo - ri - ous, O'er all vic - to - ri - ous, Come, and reign
peo - ple bless, And give Thy word suc - cess; Spir - it of
might - y art, Now rule in ev - ery heart, And ne'er from
maj - es - ty May we in glo - ry see, And to e -

o - ver us, An - cient of Days.
ho - li - ness, On us de - scend.
us de - part, Spir - it of power.
ter - ni - ty Love and a - dore. A - MEN.

Adoration and Praise

6

J. Daniel Herrnschmidt, 1675–1723
Tr. C. G. Haas, 1897, alt.

LOBE DEN HERREN, O MEINE SEELE (HALLE)
Freylinghausen's *Geistreiches Gesangbuch*, 1704
10. 8. 10. 8. 8. 8. 4. 4.

With exaltation

1. Praise thou the Lord, O my soul, now praise Him, His praise con-
tin - ue un - til death; While I the path - ways of
earth am tread - ing God shall be praised with ev - ery breath.
My soul and bod - y He did give, And waits my praise from

2. Hap - py, yea, hap - py are they for - ev - er Whose help the
God of Ja - cob is, Who hath cre - at - ed the
earth and heav - en, The sea and all that there - in is.
Let all the world His prais - es sing, Who life and health to

3. If there are an - y who are op - press - ed, He work - eth
jus - tice in the tide; Food for the hun - gry, for -
lorn, dis - tress - ed, The Lord in sea - son doth pro - vide;
Those bound in chains He mak - eth free, His lov - ing - kind - ness

4. Praise, O ye peo - ple, the Name most glo - rious Of Him who
reigns Al - might - y King: Let all u - nite in one
ho - ly cho - rus To God our hymns of joy to bring.
O Zi - on, with the heaven - ly host, Praise Fa - ther, Son, and

Adoration and Praise

morn till eve, O praise the Lord, O praise the Lord!
all doth bring, O praise the Lord, O praise the Lord!
they shall see, O praise the Lord, O praise the Lord!
Ho - ly Ghost, O praise the Lord, O praise the Lord! A - MEN.

7

S. M. with Refrain

MARION

EDWARD H. PLUMPTRE, 1865

ARTHUR H. MESSITER, 1883

Joyfully

1. Re - joice, ye pure in heart, Re - joice, give thanks and sing;
2. Bright youth and snow-crowned age, Strong men and maid - ens meek,
3. With all the an - gel choirs, With all the saints on earth,
4. Yes, on through life's long path, Still chant - ing as ye go;
5. Still lift your stand - ard high, Still march in firm ar - ray,
6. Then on, ye pure in heart, Re - joice, give thanks, and sing;

Your fes - tal ban - ner wave on high, The cross of Christ your King!
Raise high your free, ex - ult - ing song, God's won-drous prais - es speak!
Pour out the strains of joy and bliss, True rap - ture, no - blest mirth!
From youth to age, by night and day, In glad - ness and in woe,
As war - riors through the dark - ness toil Till dawns the gold - en day!
Your glo - rious ban - ner wave on high, The cross of Christ your King!

REFRAIN

Re - joice, re - joice, Re - joice, give thanks and sing. A - MEN.

Re - joice, re - joice,

Adoration and Praise

JOACHIM NEANDER, 1680
Tr. CATHERINE WINKWORTH, 1863

14. 14. 4. 7. 8.

LOBE DEN HERREN
Stralsund Gesangbuch, 1665
Arr. in *Praxis Pietatis Melica*, 1668

8

Majestically

1. Praise ye the Lord, the Al-might-y, the King of cre-a-tion!
2. Praise ye the Lord, who o'er all things so won-drous-ly reign-eth,
3. Praise ye the Lord, O let all that is in me a-dore Him!

O my soul, praise Him, for He is thy health and sal-va-tion!
Shel-ters thee un-der His wings, yea, so gen-tly sus-tain-eth!
All that hath life and breath, come now with prais-es be-fore Him!

All ye who hear, Now to His tem-ple draw near;
Hast thou not seen How thy de-sires e'er have been
Let the A-men Sound from His peo-ple a-gain:

Join me in glad ad-o-ra-tion!
Grant-ed in what He or-dain-eth?
Glad-ly for aye we a-dore.... Him. A-MEN.

Adoration and Praise

ATHELSTAN RILEY, 1909   8.8.4, 4.8.8. with Alleluias   LASST UNS ERFREUEN
Geistliche Kirchengesäng, 1623

To be sung jubilantly

UNISON

1. Ye watch-ers and ye ho - ly ones, Bright ser-aphs, cher - u - bim and thrones,
2. O high - er than the cher - u - bim, More glo-rious than the ser - a - phim,
3. O friends, in glad-ness let us sing, Su - per - nal an-thems ech - o - ing,

I.   II.   UNISON

HARMONY

Raise the glad strain, Al - le - lu - ia! Cry out, do-min-ions, prince-doms, powers,
Lead their prais - es, Al - le - lu - ia! Thou bear-er of the e - ter - nal Word,
Al - le - lu - ia, Al - le - lu - ia! To God the Fa - ther, God the Son,

HARMONY
I.   II.

Vir - tues, arch - an - gels, an - gels' choirs, Al - le - lu - ia, Al - le -
Most gra - cious, mag - ni - fy the Lord, Al - le - lu - ia, Al - le -
And God the Spir - it, Three in One. Al - le - lu - ia, Al - le -

I.   UNISON II.

ALL   HARMONY

lu - ia, Al - le - lu - ia, Al - le - lu - ia, Al - le - lu - ia!
lu - ia, Al - le - lu - ia, Al - le - lu - ia, Al - le - lu - ia!
lu - ia, Al - le - lu - ia, Al - le - lu - ia, Al - le - lu - ia!   A-MEN.

Descant version, No. 15.

I. II. These may be sung antiphonally by choir and congregation or by men and women in the choir.

Adoration and Praise

10

ROBERT GRANT, 1833   10. 10. 11. 11.   HANOVER   WILLIAM CROFT, 1678–1727

Joyously, with dignified rhythm

1. O wor - ship the King, all glo - rious a - bove,
2. O tell of His might, O sing of His grace,
3. Thy boun - ti - ful care, what tongue can re - cite?
4. Frail chil - dren of dust, and fee - ble as frail,

O grate - ful - ly sing His power and His love;
Whose robe is the light, whose can - o - py space;
It breathes in the air, it shines in the light;
In Thee do we trust, nor find Thee to fail;

Our Shield and De - fend - er, the An - cient of Days,
His char - iots of wrath the deep thun - der-clouds form,
It streams from the hills, it de - scends to the plain,
Thy mer - cies how ten - der, how firm to the end,

Pa - vil - ioned in splen - dor, and gird - ed with praise.
And dark is His path on the wings of the storm.
And sweet - ly dis - tils in the dew and the rain.
Our Ma - ker, De - fend - er, Re - deem - er, and Friend! A - MEN.

Alternative Tune, *Lyons*

Adoration and Praise

LYONS

CHARLES WESLEY, 1744, alt.   10. 10. 11. 11.   Arr. from MICHAEL HAYDN, 1737–1806

With joy and dignity

1. Ye serv-ants of God, your Mas-ter pro-claim,
2. God rul-eth on high, al-might-y to save;
3. "Sal-va-tion to God, who sits on the throne!"
4. Then let us a-dore, and give Him His right,

And pub-lish a-broad His won-der-ful Name;
And still He is nigh, His pres-ence we have:
Let all cry a-loud, and hon-or the Son!
All glo-ry and power, and wis-dom and might;

The Name all-vic-to-rious of Je-sus ex-tol;
The great con-gre-ga-tion His tri-umph shall sing,
The prais-es of Je-sus the an-gels pro-claim,
All hon-or and bless-ing, with an-gels a-bove,

His King-dom is glo-rious, and rules o-ver all.
A-scrib-ing sal-va-tion to Je-sus, our King.
Fall down on their fa-ces and wor-ship the Lamb.
And thanks nev-er ceas-ing, and in-fi-nite love.   A-MEN.

Alternative tune, *Hanover*

Adoration and Praise

DIX
Abridged from Chorale, *Treuer Heiland*

FOLLIOTT S. PIERPOINT, 1864   7. 7. 7. 7. 7. 7.   CONRAD KOCHER, 1838

Joyously

1. For the beau-ty of the earth, For the glo-ry of the skies,
2. For the won-der of each hour, Of the day and of the night,
3. For the joy of hu-man love, Broth-er, sis-ter, par-ent, child,
4. For Thy church that ev-er-more Lift-eth ho-ly hands a-bove,

For the love which from our birth O-ver and a-round us lies,
Hill and vale, and tree and flower, Sun and moon, and stars of light,
Friends on earth, and friends a-bove, For all gen-tle thoughts and mild,
Of-fering up on ev-ery shore Her pure sac-ri-fice of love,

REFRAIN

Lord of all, to Thee we raise This our hymn of grate-ful praise. A-MEN.

DIVINUM MYSTERIUM

AURELIUS CLEMENS PRUDENTIUS, 348–413
Tr. JOHN MASON NEALE, 1854
and HENRY W. BAKER, 1859

Twelfth century plain song (Mode V)
Arr. CHARLES WINFRED DOUGLAS

To be sung in unison with graceful rhythm

1. Of the Fa-ther's love be-got-ten Ere the worlds be-gan to be,
2. O ye heights of heaven a-dore Him, An-gel hosts, His prais-es sing;
3. Christ, to Thee with God the Fa-ther, And, O Ho-ly Ghost, to Thee,

Adoration and Praise

He is Al - pha and O - me - ga, He the Source, the End - ing He
Powers, do - min - ions, bow be - fore Him, And ex - tol our God and King;
Hymn and chant and high thanks - giv - ing And un - wea - ried prais - es be:

Of the things that are, that have . . . been, And that fu - ture
Let no tongue on earth be si - - lent, Ev - er - y voice in
Hon - or, glo - ry, and do - min - - ion, And e - ter - nal

years shall see, Ev - er - more and ev - er - more!
con - cert ring, Ev - er - more and ev - er - more!
vic - to - ry, Ev - er - more and ev - er - more! A - MEN.

Music used by permission of Rev. Charles Winfred Douglas.

Adoration and Praise

14

ELIZABETH CHARLES
11. 11. 11. 5.
INTEGER VITÆ (FLEMMING)
FRIEDRICH F. FLEMMING, 1810

Not too fast; with feeling

1. Praise ye the Father for His loving kindness; Tenderly
2. Praise ye the Saviour, great is His compassion; Graciously
3. Praise ye the Spirit, Comforter of Israel, Sent of the

cares He for His erring children; Praise Him, ye angels,
cares He for His chosen people; Young men and maidens,
Father and the Son to bless us; Praise ye the Father,

praise Him in the heavens, Praise ye Jehovah.
ye old men and children, Praise ye the Saviour.
Son, and Holy Spirit, Praise ye the Triune God. A-MEN.

15

ST. FRANCIS OF ASSISI, 1225
Tr. WILLIAM H. DRAPER, 1855–1933
LASST UNS ERFREUEN
Geistliche Kirchengesäng, 1623
Descant by DAVID McK. WILLIAMS, 1937
8. 8. 4. 4. 8. 8. with Alleluias

DESCANT with stanzas 3 and 5

Al - le - lu - ia, Al - le -

UNISON

1. All creatures of our God and King, Lift up your voice and with us sing
2. Thou rushing wind that art so strong, Ye clouds that sail in heaven along,
3. Thou flowing water, pure and clear, Make music for thy Lord to hear,
4. Dear mother earth, who day by day Unfoldest blessings on our way,
5. And all ye men of tender heart, Forgiving others, take your part,

Adoration and Praise

lu - ia, Al - le - lu - ia! Al - - -

HARMONY | UNISON |

Al - le - lu - ia, Al - le - lu - ia! Thou burn-ing sun with gold - en beam,
O praise Him, Al - le - lu - ia! Thou ris - ing morn, in praise re - joice,
Al - le - lu - ia, Al - le - lu - ia! Thou fire so mas - ter - ful and bright,
O praise Him, Al - le - lu - ia! The flowers and fruits that in thee grow,
O sing ye, Al - le - lu - ia! Praise, praise the Fa - ther, praise the Son,

- - - - - - - - le - lu - ia, Al - le - lu - ia,

HARMONY

Thou sil - ver moon with sil - ver gleam, O praise Him, O
Ye lights of eve - ning, find a voice, O praise Him, O
That giv - est man both warmth and light, O praise Him, O
Let them His glo - ry al - so show, O praise Him, O
And praise the Spir - it, Three in One, O praise Him, O

Al - le - lu - ia, Al - le - lu - ia, Al - le - lu - ia, Al - le - lu - ia! A - MEN.

UNISON

praise Him, Al - le - lu - ia, Al - le - lu - ia, Al - le - lu - ia! A - MEN.

Adoration and Praise

16

Paul Gerhardt, 1606-1676
Tr. O. E. Wieland, 1898, alt.

SOLLT ICH MEINEM GOTT NICHT SINGEN
(CANTATE DOMINO)
8.7.8.7.8.7.7.8.7.7.
Johann Schop, 1641

With confidence and joy

1. Sing, my soul, to God who made thee, Raise to heaven thy grate-ful voice,
2. E'en the Son He loved so dear-ly Died that we through Him might live,
3. When I sleep His care sur-rounds me, With new strength and youth im-bues;

All His crea-tures, sing-ing, bid thee In His good-ness now re-joice.
Was e'er love like His, who mere-ly Lived His life in love to give?
His un-bound-ed grace con-founds me, Each new morn His love re-news.

Pure and ho-ly love un-bound-ed Fills His ten-der heart and kind;
Ho-ly Spir-it, teach and guide me, Fill my heart with lov-ing faith!
In sore tri-al and temp-ta-tion He, my Sav-iour, still is near,

All who tru-ly serve Him find Rest, by God's strong arm sur-round-ed;
Faith can break the power of death, Naught I fear with Thee be-side me;
Bids me, "Child, do thou not fear, Thou shalt yet see my sal-va-tion."

Heaven and earth may not en-dure, But God's love is ev-er sure. A-MEN.

Adoration and Praise

17

GERHARD TERSTEEGEN, 1757
Tr. R. A. JOHN, 1912

9. 8. 9. 8. 9. 9.

ST. PETERSBURG

DIMITRI BORTNIANSKY, 1825

In moderate time

1. I sing the praise of love un-bound-ed, Which God in Christ has
2. The love of God planned my sal-va-tion Be-fore I saw the
3. While life shall last, I'll sing the glo-ry Of Christ the Sav-iour

shown to man; I sing of love that hath been found-ed
light of day, And took a-way the law's dam-na-tion
and His love; With an-gel hosts I'll tell the sto-ry

Ere yet the stars their cours-es ran; The love that of-fers
Of him whose feet had gone a-stray; God's love is mine, O
Of Christ, in Zi-on's home a-bove; God's love is mine, death

free sal-va-tion To sin-ful man of ev-ery na-tion.
bless-ed mor-tal! It o-pens wide the heaven-ly por-tal.
can-not sev-er Me from that heart that loves for-ev-er. A-MEN.

Adoration and Praise

18

L. A. GOTTER, 1697
Tr. R. A. JOHN, 1912

WOMIT SOLL ICH DICH WOHL LOBEN
(GOTHA)

8. 7. 8. 7. 8. 8. 7. 7.

J. H. KNECHT, 1797

Joyously

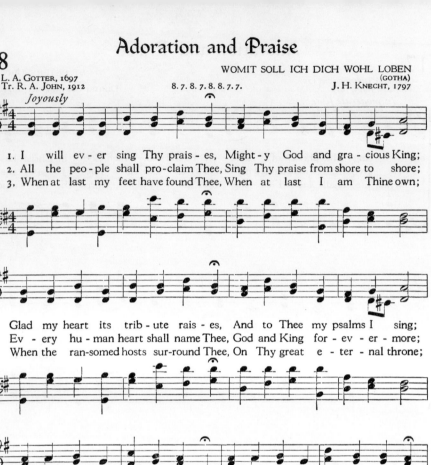

1. I will ev - er sing Thy prais - es, Might - y God and gra - cious King;
2. All the peo - ple shall pro-claim Thee, Sing Thy praise from shore to shore;
3. When at last my feet have found Thee, When at last I am Thine own;

Glad my heart its trib - ute rais - es, And to Thee my psalms I sing;
Ev - ery hu - man heart shall name Thee, God and King for - ev - er - more;
When the ran-somed hosts sur-round Thee, On Thy great e - ter - nal throne;

Thou art King of all cre - a - tion, Ev - ery land and ev - ery na - tion;
On Thy throne in heav - en vault - ed, In Thy maj - es - ty ex - alt - ed,
When in yon - der land of glo - ry An - gels tell re-demp-tion's sto - ry,

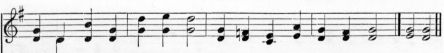

"Thou-sand, thou-sand thanks to Thee, Might - y God," my song shall be!
"Thou-sand, thou-sand thanks to Thee, Might - y God," my song shall be!
"Thou-sand, thou-sand thanks to Thee, Might - y God," my song shall be! A-MEN.

Adoration and Praise

19

JULIA BULKLEY CADY CORY, 1902

KREMSER
Old Netherlands melody in
The Collection, by ADRIANUS VALERIUS, 1625

12. 11. 12. 11.

May be sung in unison. Majestically

1. We praise Thee, O God, our Re - deem - er, Cre - a - tor,
2. We wor - ship Thee, God of our fa - thers, we bless Thee;
3. With voi - ces u - nit - ed our prais - es we of - fer,

In grate - ful de - vo - tion our trib - ute we bring.
Through life's storm and tem - pest our Guide hast Thou been.
And glad - ly our an - thems of wor - ship we raise.

We lay it be - fore Thee, we kneel and a - dore Thee,
When per - ils o'er - take us, es - cape Thou wilt make us,
Thy strong arm will guide us, our God is be - side us,

We bless Thy ho - ly Name, glad prais - es we sing.
And with Thy help, O Lord, life's bat - tles we win.
To Thee, our great Re - deem-er, for - ev - er be praise. A - MEN.

Adoration and Praise

IGNAZ FRANZ, 1771
Tr. J. H. HORSTMANN, 1908   7.8.7.8.7.7.

GROSSER GOTT WIR LOBEN DICH
Katholisches Gesangbuch, Vienna, c. 1774

Not too slowly

1. God of might, we praise Thy name For Thy deeds of strength and glo - ry, Heaven and earth ex - tol Thy fame, And pro - claim the bless - ed sto - ry: As Thou art, Thou e'er wilt be Un - to all e - ter - ni - ty.

2. Cher - u - bim and ser - a - phim Praise Thy name with joy un - ceas - ing; Proph - ets and a - pos - tles are Ev - er - more Thy praise in - creas - ing, And the mar - tyrs, brave and true, Wor - ship Thee with prais - es new.

3. All Thy Church in ev - ery land Lifts its voice in ad - o - ra - tion Un - to Thee, O God of Love, For Thy work of man's sal - va - tion; Thou art King of Life and Love In Thy heaven - ly realms a - bove.

4. Look up - on Thy chil - dren here Who, their love for Thee pro - fess - ing, And in Je - sus' name a - lone, Ask of Thee a Fa - ther's bless - ing; When the course of life is o'er, Bring us home for ev - er - more. A - MEN.

Adoration and Praise

HENRY VAN DYKE, 1907   8.7.8.7.D.   HYMN TO JOY
LUDWIG VAN BEETHOVEN, 1824

With exultation

1. Joy - ful, joy - ful, we a - dore Thee, God of glo - ry, Lord of love;
2. All Thy works with joy sur-round Thee, Earth and heaven re - flect Thy rays,
3. Thou art giv - ing and for - giv - ing, Ev - er bless - ing, ev - er blest,
4. Mor - tals, join the hap - py cho - rus Which the morn - ing stars be - gan;

Hearts un - fold like flowers be - fore Thee, Open - ing to the sun a - bove.
Stars and an - gels sing a - round Thee, Cen - ter of un - bro - ken praise.
Well-spring of the joy of liv - ing, O - cean depth of hap - py rest!
Fa - ther love is reign - ing o'er us, Broth - er love binds man to man.

Melt the clouds of sin and sad - ness, Drive the dark of doubt a - way;
Field and for - est, vale and moun-tain, Flow - ery mead-ow, flash - ing sea,
Thou our Fa - ther, Christ our Broth-er, All who live in love are Thine;
Ev - er sing - ing, march we on - ward, Vic - tors in the midst of strife,

Giv - er of im - mor-tal glad-ness, Fill us with the light of day.
Chant-ing bird and flow-ing foun-tain, Call us to re - joice in Thee.
Teach us how to love each oth - er, Lift us to the Joy di - vine.
Joy - ful mu - sic leads us Sun-ward In the tri-umph song of life. A-MEN.

Psalm xcv
Scottish Psalter, 1650

C. M.

IRISH (THE VENITE)
Melody from *A Collection of Hymns and Sacred Poems*, Dublin, 1749

Moderately fast

1. O come, let us sing to the Lord,
2. Let us be - fore His pres - ence come
3. For God's a great God, and great King;
4. To Him the spa - cious sea be - longs,
5. O come, and let us wor - ship Him;

To Him our voi - ces raise; With joy - ful noise let
With praise, and thank - ful voice; Let us sing psalms to
A - bove all gods He is. The depths of earth are
For He the same did make; The dry land al - so
Let us bow down with - al, And on our knees be -

us the Rock Of our sal - va - tion praise.
Him with grace, And make a joy - ful noise.
in His hand; The heights of hills are His.
from His hands Its form at first did take.
fore the Lord, Our Mak - er, let us fall.   A - MEN.

Beginning of Worship

23

BENJAMIN SCHMOLCK, 1732
Tr. CATHERINE WINKWORTH, 1863. alt.   8. 7. 8. 7. 7. 7.

UNSER HERRSCHER (NEANDER)
JOACHIM NEANDER, 1680
Descant by GEOFFREY SHAW

In moderate time and graceful rhythm

DESCANT with stanza 3

1. O - pen now thy gates of beau - ty, Zi - on, let me en - ter there,
2. Gra - cious God I come be - fore Thee, Come Thou al - so down to me;
3. Speak, O Lord, and I will hear Thee, Let Thy will be done in - deed;

Where my soul in joy - ful du - ty Waits for Him who an - swers prayer:
Where we find Thee and a - dore Thee, There a heaven on earth must be:
May I un - dis - turbed draw near Thee While Thou dost Thy peo - ple feed.

O how bless - ed is this place, Filled with sol - ace, light, and grace!
To my heart O en - ter Thou, Let it be Thy tem - ple now.
Here of life the foun - tain flows, Here is balm for all our woes. A-MEN.

Alternative tune, Gott des Himmels und der Erden.

OLD HUNDREDTH (*Altered Form*)
Louis Bourgeois
Genevan Psalter, 1551
Descant by Paul Allwardt, 1939

William Kethe, 1561   L. M.

Majestically, but not too slowly

DESCANT stanzas 3 and 4

1. All peo-ple that on earth do dwell, Sing to the Lord with
2. Know that the Lord is God in-deed, With-out our aid He
3. O en-ter then His gates with praise, Ap-proach with joy His
4. For why? the Lord our God is good, His mer-cy is for

cheer-ful voice; Him serve with mirth, His praise forth tell,
did us make; We are His flock, He doth us feed,
courts un-to; Praise, laud, and bless His name al-ways,
ev-er sure; His truth at all times firm-ly stood,

Come ye be-fore Him and re-joice.
And for His sheep He doth us take.
For it is seem-ly so to do.
And shall from age to age en-dure. A-MEN.

Beginning of Worship

PARK STREET

Psalm c
ISAAC WATTS, 1719, alt.

L. M.

FREDERICK M. A. VENUA, c. 1810

With majesty, but not too slowly

1. Be - fore Je - ho - vah's aw - ful throne, Ye na - tions,
2. His sov - ereign power with - out our aid, Made us of
3. We are His peo - ple, we His care, Our souls, and
4. We'll crowd Thy gates with thank - ful songs, High as the
5. Wide as the world is Thy com - mand, Vast as e -

bow with sa - cred joy; Know that the Lord is
clay, and formed us men; And when, like wan - dering
all our mor - tal frame; What last - ing hon - ors
heavens our voi - ces raise; And earth, with her ten
ter - ni - ty Thy love; Firm as a rock Thy

God a - lone, He can cre - ate, and He de - stroy,
sheep, we strayed, He brought us to His fold a - gain,
shall we rear, Al - might - y Mak - er, to Thy name,
thou - sand tongues, Shall fill Thy courts with sound - ing praise,
truth must stand, When roll - ing years shall cease to move,

He can cre - ate, and He de - stroy.
He brought us to His fold a - gain.
Al - might - y Mak - er, to Thy name?
Shall fill Thy courts with sound - ing praise.
When roll - ing years shall cease to move. A - MEN.

Alternative tune, *Old Hundredth.*

Times of Worship

TOBIAS CLAUSNITZER, 1663
TR. CATHERINE WINKWORTH, 1858

LIEBSTER JESU WIR SIND HIER (NÜREMBERG)

7. 8. 7. 8. 8. 8.

JOHANN RUDOLPH AHLE, 1664

In moderate time

1. Bless - ed Je - sus, at Thy word We are gath - ered
2. All our knowl - edge, sense, and sight Lie in deep - est
3. Glo - rious Lord, Thy - self im - part! Light of Light, from

all to hear . . Thee; Let our hearts and souls be stirred
dark - ness shroud - ed, Till Thy Spir - it breaks our night
God pro - ceed - ing, O - pen Thou our ears and heart,

Now to seek and love and fear Thee, By Thy teach - ings
With the beams of truth un - cloud - ed; Thou a - lone to
Help us by Thy Spir - it's plead - ing; Hear the cry Thy

sweet and ho - ly, Drawn from earth to love Thee sole - ly.
God canst win us, Thou must work all good with - in . . us.
peo - ple rais - es, Hear, and bless our prayers and prais - es. A-MEN.

Beginning of Worship

HENRY MONTAGUE BUTLER, 1881   10. 10. 10. 10.   WOODLANDS
W. GREATOREX, 1916

May be sung in unison. With exaltation and majesty

1. "Lift up your hearts!" We lift them, Lord, to Thee;
2. A - bove the lev - el of the for - mer years,
3. Lift ev - ery gift that Thou Thy - self hast given;
4. Then, as the trump - et call, in aft - er years,

Here at Thy feet none oth - er may we see;
The mire of sin, the weight of guilt - y fears,
Low lies the best till lift - ed up to heaven:
"Lift up your hearts!" rings peal - ing in our ears,

"Lift up your hearts!" E'en so, with one ac - cord,
The mist of doubt, the blight of love's de - cay,
Low lie the bound - ing heart, the teem - ing brain,
Still shall those hearts re - spond, with full ac - cord

We lift them up, we lift them to the Lord.
O Lord of Light, lift all our hearts to - day!
Till, sent from God, they mount to God a - gain.
"We lift them up, we lift them to the Lord!" A-MEN.

Music by permission of Mr. W. Greatorex.

Times of Worship

HERR JESUS CHRIST, DICH ZU UNS WEND
(CANTIONALE)

WILHELM AUGUST, II., DUKE of SAXE–WEIMAR, 1638
Tr. CATHERINE WINKWORTH, 1862, alt.   L. M.
Pensum Sacrum, 1648

Reverently

1. Lord Je - sus Christ, be with us now, And
2. O teach our lips to sing Thy praise, Our
3. So shall we join the hosts that cry, Ho -
4. Glo - ry to God, the Fa - ther, Son, And

let Thy Ho - ly Spir - it bow All hearts in love and
hearts in true de - vo - tion raise, Strength-en our faith, in -
ly art Thou, O Lord most High! And in the light of
Ho - ly Spir - it, Three in One! To Thee, O bless - ed

fear to - day, To hear the truth, and keep Thy way.
crease our light, That we may do Thy will a - right.
that blest place Shall gaze up - on Thee face to face.
Trin - i - ty, Be praise through-out e - ter - ni - ty!   A-MEN.

WUNDERBARER KÖNIG

GERHARD TERSTEEGEN, 1729
Tr. Composite

Joachim Neander's *Bundes–Lieder*, 1680

6. 6. 8. 6. 6. 8. 3. 3. 6. 6.

Reverently

1. God Him - self is with us: Let us now a - dore Him,
2. God Him - self is with us: Whom an - gel - ic le - gions
3. Lord, come dwell with - in us, While on earth we tar - ry,

Beginning of Worship

And with awe ap - pear be - fore Him. God is in His
Serve with awe in heaven - ly re - gions. "Ho - ly, Ho - ly,
Make us Thy blest sanc - tu - a - ry, Grant us now Thy

tem - ple, All with - in keep si - lence, And be - fore Him
Ho - ly," Sing the hosts of heav - en, Praise to God be
pres - ence, Un - to us draw near - er, And re - veal Thy -

bow with rev - erence. Him a - lone, God we own; To our Lord and
ev - er giv - en. Bow Thine ear To us here: Hear, O Christ, the
self still clear - er. Where we are, Near or far, Let us see Thy

Sav - iour Prais - es sing for - ev - er.
prais - es That Thy church now rais - es.
pow - er, Ev - ery day and hour. . . . . A-MEN.

Times of Worship

30

ISAAC WATTS, 1709   S. M.   ST. THOMAS
Williams' Psalmody, 1770

Joyously

1. Come, we who love the Lord, And let our joys be known; Join
2. Let those re-fuse to sing Who nev-er knew our God; But
3. The men of grace have found Glo-ry be-gun be-low; Ce-
4. The hill of Zi-on yields A thou-sand sa-cred sweets Be-
5. Then let our songs a-bound, And ev-ery tear be dry; We're

in a song with sweet ac-cord, And thus sur-round the throne.
chil-dren of the heaven-ly King Should speak their joys a-broad.
les-tial fruits on earth-ly ground From faith and hope may grow.
fore we reach the heaven-ly fields, Or walk the gold-en streets.
march-ing through Em-man-uel's ground To fair-er worlds on high. A-MEN.

31

L. E. G. WHITMORE, 1824   10. 10. 10. 10.   LANGRAN
JAMES LANGRAN, 1862

In moderate time

1. Fa-ther, a-gain in Je-sus' name we meet, And bow in pen-i-
2. O we would bless Thee for Thy cease-less care, And all Thy work from
3. A-las, un-wor-thy of Thy bound-less love, Too oft with care-less
4. O by that name in which all ful-ness dwells, O by that love which

tence be-neath Thy feet; A-gain to Thee our fee-ble voi-ces raise,
day to day de-clare: Is not our life with hour-ly mer-cies crowned?
feet from Thee we rove; But now, en-cour-aged by Thy voice, we come,
ev-ery love ex-cels, O by that blood so free-ly shed for sin,

Beginning of Worship

To sue for mer - cy, and to sing Thy praise.
Does not Thine arm en - cir - cle us a - round?
Re - turn - ing sin - ners to a Fa - ther's home.
O - pen blest mer - cy's gate and take us in! A-MEN.

Alternative tune, Ellers.

Close of Worship

32

JOHN ELLERTON, 1866
10. 10. 10. 10.
ELLERS
EDWARD J. HOPKINS, 1869

In moderate time

1. Sav - iour, a - gain to Thy dear name we raise With one ac-cord our
2. Grant us Thy peace up - on our home-ward way; With Thee be - gan, with
3. Grant us Thy peace, Lord, through the com - ing night; Turn Thou for us its
4 Grant us Thy peace through-out our earth - ly life, Our balm in sor - row,

part - ing hymn of praise; We stand to bless Thee ere our wor - ship cease;
Thee shall end the day: Guard Thou the lips from sin, the hearts from shame,
dark - ness in - to light; From harm and dan - ger keep Thy chil - dren free,
and our stay in strife; Then, when Thy voice shall bid our con - flict cease,

Then, low - ly kneel - ing, wait Thy word of peace.
That in this house have called up - on Thy name.
For dark and light are both a - like to Thee.
Call us, O Lord, to Thine e - ter - nal peace. A -MEN.

Alternative tune, Langran.

33

JOHN ELLERTON, 1872   C. M.   FINGAL
JAMES S. ANDERSON, 1885

Not too fast

1. The Lord be with us as we bend, His bless-ing to re-ceive;
2. The Lord be with us as we walk A-long the home-ward road,
3. The Lord be with us till the night Shall close the day of rest;
4. The Lord be with us still, we pray, His night-ly watch to keep;

His gift of peace up-on us send, Be-fore His courts we leave.
In si-lent thought or friend-ly talk Our hearts be still with God.
Be He of ev-ery heart the light, Of ev-ery home the guest.
Crown with His peace His own blest day, And guard His peo-ple's sleep. A-MEN.

Alternative tune, *Belmont.*

34

JOSHUA STEGMANN, 1632, alt.   CHRISTUS DER IST MEIN LEBEN (BREMEN)
     7.6.7.6.   MELCHIOR VULPIUS, 1609

Not too fast, prayerfully

1. A-bide with us, our Sav-iour, Nor let Thy mer-cy cease;
2. A-bide with us, our Sav-iour, Sus-tain us by Thy word,
3. A-bide with us, our Sav-iour, Thou Light of end-less Light;

From Sa-tan's might de-fend us, And grant our souls re-lease.
That we may, now and ev-er, Find peace in Thee, O Lord.
In-crease to us Thy bless-ings, And save us by Thy might. A-MEN.

Close of Worship

35

JOHN FAWCETT, 1773

8. 7. 8. 7. 8. 7.

SICILIAN MARINERS
Sicilian Melody, 1794

In moderate time

1. Lord, dis - miss us with Thy bless - ing; Fill our hearts with
2. Thanks we give and ad - o - ra - tion For Thy gos - pel's

joy and peace; Let us each, Thy love pos - sess - ing,
joy - ful sound; May the fruits of Thy sal - va - tion

Tri - umph in re - deem - ing grace: O re - fresh us,
In our hearts and lives a - bound: Ev - er faith - ful,

O re - fresh us, Trav - 'ling through this wil - der - ness.
ev - er faith-ful To the truth may we be found; A-MEN.

36

JOHN NEWTON, 1779

8. 7. 8. 7.

EVENING PRAYER
JOHN STAINER, 1898

In moderate time

1. May the grace of Christ our Sav - iour And the Fa - ther's bound-less love,
2. Thus may we a - bide in un - ion With each oth - er and the Lord,

With the Ho - ly Spir - it's fa - vor, Rest up - on us from a - bove.
And pos-sess, in sweet com-mun-ion, Joys which earth can-not af - ford.   A-MEN.

The Lord's Day

37

SWABIA
JOHANN M. SPIESS
Davids Harpffen-Spiel, Heidelberg, 1745
Arr. W. H. HAVERGAL, 1847

JOHN ELLERTON, 1867

S. M.

In moderate time

1. This is the day of light: Let there be light to - day;
2. This is the day of rest: Our fail - ing strength re - new;
3. This is the day of peace: Thy peace our spir - its fill;
4. This is the day of prayer: Let earth to heaven draw near;

O Day-spring, rise up - on our night And chase its gloom a - way.
On wea - ry brain and troub-led breast Shed Thou Thy fresh-ening dew.
Bid Thou the blasts of dis - cord cease, The waves of strife be still.
Lift up our hearts to seek Thee there, Come down to meet us here.   A-MEN.

The Lord's Day

CHRISTOPHER WORDSWORTH, 1862

MENDEBRAS
Old German Melody
Arr. LOWELL MASON, 1839

7. 6. 7. 6. D.

38

With joy

1. O day of rest and glad-ness, O day of joy and light,
2. On thee, at the Cre - a - tion, The light first had its birth;
3. New gra - ces ev - er gain - ing From this our day of rest,

O balm of care and sad - ness, Most beau - ti - ful, most bright;
On thee, for our sal - va - tion, Christ rose from depths of earth;
We reach the rest re - main - ing To spir - its of the blest.

On thee the high and low - ly, Through a - ges joined in tune,
On thee our Lord, vic - to - rious, The Spir - it sent from heaven;
To Ho - ly Ghost be prais - es, To Fa - ther, and to Son;

Sing ho - ly, ho - ly, ho - ly, To the great God Tri - une.
And thus on thee, most glo - rious, A tri - ple light was given.
The Church her voice up - rais - es To Thee, blest Three in One. A-MEN.

Times of Worship

39

JOHN NEWTON, 1774

7.7.7.7.7.7.

ST. ATHANASIUS
EDWARD J. HOPKINS, 1872

Joyously

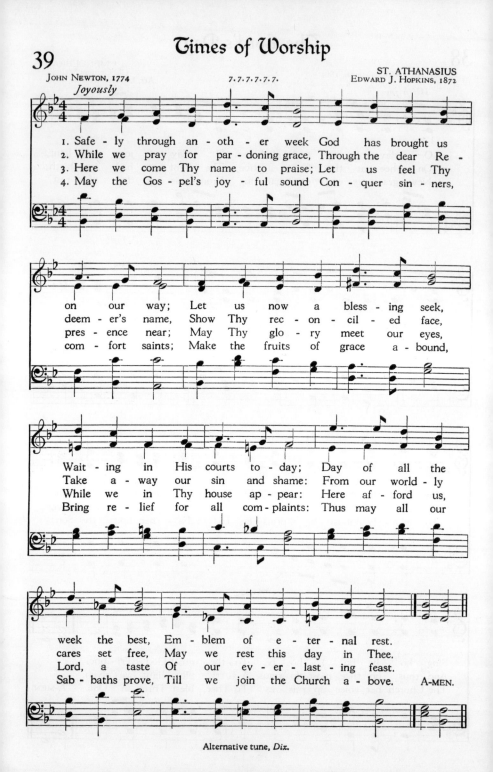

1. Safe - ly through an - oth - er week God has brought us
2. While we pray for par - doning grace, Through the dear Re -
3. Here we come Thy name to praise; Let us feel Thy
4. May the Gos - pel's joy - ful sound Con - quer sin - ners,

on our way; Let us now a bless - ing seek,
deem - er's name, Show Thy rec - on - cil - ed face,
pres - ence near; May Thy glo - ry meet our eyes,
com - fort saints; Make the fruits of grace a - bound,

Wait - ing in His courts to - day; Day of all the
Take a - way our sin and shame: From our world - ly
While we in Thy house ap - pear: Here af - ford us,
Bring re - lief for all com - plaints: Thus may all our

week the best, Em - blem of e - ter - nal rest.
cares set free, May we rest this day in Thee.
Lord, a taste Of our ev - er - last - ing feast.
Sab - baths prove, Till we join the Church a - bove. A-MEN.

Alternative tune, *Dix.*

The Lord's Day

40

GOTT DES HIMMELS UND DER ERDEN (ALBERT)

Jonathan Krause, 1739
Tr. Jane Borthwick, 1858

8.7.8.7.7.7.

Heinrich Albert, 1643

Joyously

1. Al - le - lu - ia, fair - est morn - ing, Fair - er than our
2. In the glad - ness of His wor - ship We will seek our
3. Let the day with Thee be end - ed, As with Thee it

words can say! Down we lay the heav - y bur - den
joy to - day; It is then we learn the ful - ness
has be - gun, And Thy bless - ing, Lord, be grant - ed,

Of life's toil and care to - day, While this morn of
Of the grace for which we pray, When the word of
Till earth's days and weeks are done; That at last Thy

joy and love Brings fresh vig - or from a - bove.
life is given, Like the Sav - iour's voice from heaven.
serv - ants may Keep e - ter - nal Sab - bath - day. A - MEN.

Alternative tune, *Unser Herrscher* (with descant)

Times of Worship

F. R. Daries, 1916

8. 6. 8. 6. D.

RUHETAG
F. R. Daries, 1916

41

In moderate time

1. This day in Thy dear name we meet, Our Lord, Re-deem-er, King,
2. Op-pressed with earth-ly toil and pains The wea-ry week did close,
3. Be with us, as Thy ser-vants ask, Thy mer-cies to pro-long;

This day a-round Thy mer-cy-seat We all Thy glo-ries sing;
Yet God's own day of peace re-mains When spir-its seek re-pose.
Grant that by prayer we know our tasks, Let in-cense rise with song.

Thou gav-est us this day of rest, Of ho-li-ness di-vine;
Let Sun-day's sweet re-fresh-ing dew All with-ering cares dis-pel,
O may this be a day of light To na-tions far and near,

Lend com-fort to each trou-bled breast, And make us ev-er Thine.
Let Sab-bath-joys our strength re-new, Help us Thy good-ness tell.
Let all men see Thy vis-age bright, Thy lov-ing mes-sage hear. A-MEN.

The Lord's Day

42

Benjamin Schmolck, 1715
Tr. Catherine Winkworth, 1858

7.8.7.8.7.7.

MEINEN JESUM LASS ICH NICHT

Johann Ulich, 1674

In moderate time

1. Light of Light, en - light - en me, Now a - new the day is dawn - ing; Sun of grace, the shad - ows flee, Bright - en Thou my Sab - bath morn - ing; With Thy joy - ous sun - shine blest, Hap - py is my day of rest.

2. Fount of all our joy and peace, To Thy liv - ing wa - ters lead me; Thou from earth my soul re - lease, And with grace and mer - cy feed me. Bless Thy word, that it may prove Rich in fruits that Thou dost love.

3. Kin - dle Thou the sac - ri - fice That up - on my lips is ly - ing; Clear the shad - ows from mine eyes, That, from ev - ery er - ror fly - ing, No strange fire may in me glow That Thine al - tar doth not know.

4. Let me with my heart to - day, Ho - ly, Ho - ly, Ho - ly, sing - ing, Rapt a - while from earth a - way, All my soul to Thee up - spring - ing, Have a fore - taste, in - ly given, How they wor - ship Thee in heaven. A - MEN.

Morning

watch - ful, stand we all be - fore Thee; Sing - ing, we of - fer
weak - ness, health and whole-ness send - ing; Bring us to heav - en,
bless - ed, send us Thy sal - va - tion; Thine is the glo - ry

prayer and med - i - ta - tion: Thus we a - dore Thee.
where Thy saints u - nit - ed Joy with-out end - ing.
gleam - ing and re - sound-ing Through all cre - a - tion. A - MEN.

Permission granted by Oxford University Press.

45

GOTT SEI DANK DURCH ALLE WELT

From Psalm xix
JOACHIM NEANDER, 1650–1680   7. 7. 7. 7.   Freylinghausen's *Gesangbuch*, Halle, 1704

May be sung in unison. With spirit

1. Heaven and earth, and sea and air, All their Mak - er's praise de - clare;
2. See the glo - rious orb of day Break-ing through the clouds his way;
3. See how He hath ev - ery-where Made this earth so rich and fair;
4. Lord, great won-ders work-est Thou! To Thy sway all crea - tures bow;

Wake, my soul, a - wake and sing: Now thy grate-ful prais - es bring.
Moon and stars with sil - very light Praise Him through the si - lent night.
Hill and vale and fruit - ful land, All things liv - ing, show His hand.
Write Thou deep - ly in my heart What I am, and what Thou art.   A-MEN.

46

F. R. L. VON CANITZ, 1654-1699
Tr. H. J. BUCKOLL, 1838

8. 4. 7. 8. 4. 7.

HAYDN

JOSEPH HAYDN, 1791

In moderate time

1. Come, my soul, thou must be wak - ing, Now is break - ing
2. Pray that He may pros - per ev - er Each en - deav - or,
3. Think that He thy ways be - hold - eth; He un - fold - eth
4. On - ly God's free gifts a - buse not, Light re - fuse not,

O'er the earth an - oth - er day; Come, to Him who made this splen-dor,
When thine aim is good and true; But that He may ev - er thwart thee,
Ev - ery fault that lurks with-in; He the hid - den shame glossed o - ver
But His Spir - it's voice o - bey; Thou with Him shalt dwell, be - hold-ing

See thou ren - der All thy fee - ble strength can pay.
And con - vert thee, When thou e - vil would'st pur - sue.
Can dis - cov - er, And dis - cern each deed of sin.
Light en - fold - ing All things in un - cloud - ed day. A - MEN.

47

CHRISTIAN KNORR VON ROSENROTH, 1684
Tr. JOHN HENRY HOPKINS, 1866

7. 8. 7. 8. 7. 3.

MORGENGLANZ DER EWIGKEIT
Freylinghausen's *Gesangbuch*,
Halle, 1704

In moderate time

1. Day-spring of E - tern - i - ty, Bright-ness of the Fa - ther's glo - ry,
2. Let Thy grace like morn-ing dew Fall on hearts in Thee con - fid - ing;
3. Give the flame of love, to burn Till the bands of sin it break - eth,
4. Lead us to the gold-en shore, O Thou ris - ing Sun of Morn - ing;

Morning

Dawn on us, that we may see Clouds and dark-ness flee be - fore Thee;
Thy sweet com-fort, ev - er new, Fill our souls with strength a - bid - ing;
Till at each new day's re-turn Pu - rer light my soul a - wak - eth;
Lead where tears shall flow no more, Where all sighs to songs are turn - ing,

Drive a - far with con - quering might All our night.
And Thy quicken - ing eyes be - hold Thy dear fold.
O, ere twi - light come, let me Rise to Thee.
Where Thy glo - ry sheds al - way Per - fect day. A-MEN.

48

AMBROSE of Milan, 340-397
Tr. JOHN CHANDLER, 1837
and LOUIS F. BENSON, 1910

PUER NOBIS NASCITUR

Composed or adapted by
M. PRAETORIUS, 1571-1621

L.M.

Moderately fast. May be sung in unison

1. O splen-dor of God's glo - ry bright, From light e - ter - nal bring-ing light;
2. Con - firm our will to do the right, And keep our hearts from en-vy's blight;
3. O joy-ful be the pass-ing day With thoughts as clear as morn-ing's ray,
4. Dawn's glo - ry gilds the earth and skies; Do thou, our per - fect Morn, a - rise;

Thou Light of life, light's liv - ing Spring, True Day, all days il - lu - min-ing.
Let faith her ea - ger fires re - new, And hate the false, and love the true.
With faith like noon-tide shin-ing bright, Our souls unshadowed by the night.
The Fa-ther's help His chil-dren claim, And sing the Fa-ther's glorious name. A-MEN.

Times of Worship

Paul Gerhardt, 1666
Tr. Richard Massie, 1857

5. 5. 5. 5. 10. 5. 6. 5. 6. 10.

DIE GÜLDNE SONNE

Johann G. Ebeling, 1666

With flowing rhythm

1. Eve-ning and morn-ing, Sun-set and dawn-ing, Wealth, peace, and
2. Fa-ther, O hear me; Par-don and spare me; Calm all my
3. Griefs of God's send-ing Soon have an end-ing; Clouds may be

glad-ness, Com-fort in sad-ness, These are Thy works; all the
ter-rors, Blot out my er-rors, That by Thine eyes they may
pour-ing, Wind and wave roar-ing, Sun-shine will come when the

glo-ry be Thine! Times with-out num-ber, A-wake or in
no more be scanned. Or-der my go-ings; Di-rect all my
tem-pest has past. Joys still in-creas-ing, And peace nev-er

slum-ber, Thou dost ob-serve us, From dan-ger pre-serve us,
do-ings; As it may please Thee, Re-tain or re-lease me;
ceas-ing, Foun-tains that dry not, And ros-es that die not,

Morning

Caus - ing Thy mer - cy up - on us to shine.
All I com - mit to Thy Fa - ther - ly hand.
Bloom - ing in E - den, a - wait me at last. A - MEN.

50

HARRIET BEECHER STOWE, 1835   11. 10. 11. 10.   PERFECT LOVE (SANDRINGHAM)
JOSEPH BARNBY, 1889

In moderate time

1. Still, still with Thee, when pur - ple morn - ing break - eth, When the bird wak - eth,
2. A - lone with Thee, a - mid the mys - tic shad - ows, The sol - emn hush of
3. When sinks the soul, sub - dued by toil, to slum - ber, Its clos - ing eye looks
4. So shall it be at last, in that bright morn - ing, When the soul wak - eth,

and the shad - ows flee; Fair - er than morn - ing, love - lier than the
na - ture new - ly born; A - lone with Thee, in breath - less ad - o -
up to Thee in prayer; Sweet the re - pose be - neath Thy wings o'er -
and life's shad - ows flee; O in that hour, fair - er than day - light

day - light, Dawns the sweet con - scious-ness, I am with Thee.
ra - tion, In the calm dew and fresh-ness of the morn.
shad - ing, But sweet - er still, to wake and find Thee there.
dawn - ing, Shall rise the glo - rious thought, I am with Thee. A-MEN.

Alternative tune, *Consolation*.

Times of Worship

51

HENRY FRANCIS LYTE, 1847   10. 10. 10. 10.   EVENTIDE
WILLIAM H. MONK, 1861

In moderate time

1. A - bide with me: fast falls the e - ven - tide; The dark - ness
2. Swift to its close ebbs out life's lit - tle day; Earth's joys grow
3. I need Thy pres - ence ev - ery pass - ing hour; What but Thy
4. I fear no foe, with Thee at hand to bless: Ills have no
5. Hold Thou Thy cross be - fore my clos - ing eyes; Shine through the

deep - ens; Lord, with me a - bide: When oth - er help - ers
dim, its glo - ries pass a - way; Change and de - cay in
grace can foil the Tempt - er's power? Who like Thy - self my
weight, and tears no bit - ter - ness. Where is death's sting? Where,
gloom, and point me to the skies: Heaven's morn - ing breaks, and

fail, and com-forts flee, Help of the help-less, O a - bide with me.
all a - round I see; O Thou who chang-est not, a - bide with me.
guide and stay can be? Through cloud and sun-shine, O a - bide with me.
grave, thy vic - to - ry? I tri - umph still, if Thou a - bide with me.
earth's vain shadows flee: In life, in death, O Lord, a - bide with me. A-MEN.

52

EWALD KOCKRITZ, 1916, alt.   7. 7. 6. 7. 7. 8.   NUN RUHEN ALLE WÄLDER (INNSBRUCK)
HEINRICH ISAAK, c. 1455–1517

With graceful rhythm

1. As fades the day - light splen - dor, We crave Thy mer - cies ten - der,
2. Thy grace is all - pre - vail - ing, Thy mer - cy nev - er - fail - ing,
3. Some-times the way seems drear - y, And weak-ness makes us wear - y:
4. Lord Je - sus who dost love us, Thy pin - ions spread a - bove us,

Evening

Thou Lord of Life and Light; Thy love for us a-bound-ing, Thy
E'en though our need is great. Though tri-als hard as-sail us, Thy
Do Thou then make us strong; That, pain and grief con-trol-ling, We
And drive all fear a-way; And when this life is end-ed, By

strong arms, us sur-round-ing, De-fend and shield us through the night.
grace shall nev-er fail us If, trust-ful, we Thy help a-wait.
look for Thy con-sol-ing; For Thou wilt nev-er tar-ry long.
an-gel hosts at-tend-ed Bring us to Thine E-ter-nal Day. A-MEN.

Words copyright, 1941, Eden Publishing House.

53

GEORGE W. DOANE, 1824   7.7.7.7.   Arr. from CARL M. VON WEBER, 1826

SEYMOUR

Not too fast

1. Soft-ly now the light of day Fades up-on my sight a-way;
2. Thou, whose all-per-vad-ing eye Naught es-capes, with-out, with-in,
3. Soon for me the light of day Shall for-ev-er pass a-way;
4. Thou who, sin-less, yet hast known All of man's in-firm-i-ty;

Free from care, from la-bor free, Lord, I would com-mune with Thee.
Par-don each in-firm-i-ty, O-pen fault, and se-cret sin.
Then, from sin and sor-row free, Take me, Lord, to dwell with Thee.
Then, from Thine e-ter-nal throne, Je-sus, look with pity-ing eye. A-MEN.

Times of Worship

54

JOHN ELLERTON, 1870   9. 8. 9. 8.   ST. CLEMENT
CLEMENT C. SCHOLEFIELD, 1874

In moderate time; with flowing rhythm

1. The day Thou gav - est, Lord, is end - ed, The dark - ness
2. We thank Thee that Thy Church un - sleep - ing, While earth rolls
3. As o'er each con - ti - nent and is - land The dawn leads
4. The sun that bids us rest is wak - ing Our breth - ren
5. So be it, Lord; Thy throne shall nev - er, Like earth's proud

falls at Thy be - hest; To Thee our morn - ing hymns as -
on - ward in - to light, Through all the world her watch is
on an - oth - er day, The voice of prayer is nev - er
'neath the west - ern sky, And hour by hour fresh lips are
em - pires, pass a - way; But stand, and rule, and grow for -

cend - ed, Thy praise shall hal - low now our rest.
keep - ing, And rests not now by day or night.
si - lent, Nor dies the strain of praise a - way.
mak - ing Thy won - drous do - ings heard on high.
ev - er, Till all Thy crea - tures own Thy sway. A - MEN.

55

JOHN KEBLE, 1820   L. M.   HURSLEY
Katholisches Gesangbuch, Vienna, c. 1774

In moderate time

1. Sun of my soul, Thou Sav - iour dear, It is not night if
2. When the soft dews of kind - ly sleep My wea - ried eye - lids
3. A - bide with me from morn till eve, For with - out Thee I
4. Watch by the sick; en - rich the poor With bless - ings from Thy
5. Come near and bless us when we wake, Ere through the world our

Evening

Thou be near; O may no earth-born cloud a-rise
gen-tly steep, Be my last thought, how sweet to rest
can-not live; A-bide with me when night is nigh,
bound-less store; Be ev-ery mourn-er's sleep to-night,
way we take, Till in the o-cean of Thy love

To hide Thee from Thy ser-vant's eyes.
For-ev-er on my Sav-iour's breast.
For with-out Thee I dare not die.
Like in-fants' slum-bers, pure and light.
We lose our-selves in heaven a-bove. A-MEN.

56

SABINE BARING-GOULD, 1865   6.5.6.5.   MERRIAL
JOSEPH BARNBY, 1868

With graceful rhythm

1. Now the day is o-ver, Night is draw-ing nigh;
2. Je-sus, give the wea-ry Calm and sweet re-pose;
3. Com-fort ev-ery suf-ferer Watch-ing late in pain;
4. Through the long night-watch-es May Thine an-gels spread
5. When the morn-ing wak-ens, Then may I a-rise

Shad-ows of the eve-ning Steal a-cross the sky.
With Thy ten-derest bless-ing May mine eye-lids close.
Those who plan some e-vil From their sin re-strain.
Their white wings a-bove me, Watch-ing round my bed.
Pure and fresh and sin-less In Thy ho-ly eyes. A-MEN.

57

HENRY TWELLS, 1868   L. M.   GEORG JOSEPH, *Heilige Seelenlust*, 1657

ANGELUS

In moderate time

1. At e - ven, when the sun was set, The sick, O
2. Once more 'tis e - ven - tide, and we, Op - pressed with
3. O Sav - iour Christ, our woes dis - pel: For some are
4. O Sav - iour Christ, Thou too art man; Thou hast been
5. Thy touch has still its an - cient power; No word from

Lord, a - round Thee lay; O in what di - vers pains they met!
va - rious ills, draw near: What if Thy form we can - not see?
sick, and some are sad, And some have nev - er loved Thee well,
trou - bled, tempt - ed, tried; Thy kind but search - ing glance can scan
Thee can fruit - less fall: Hear in this sol - emn eve - ning hour,

O with what joy they went a - way!
We know and feel that Thou art here.
And some have lost the love they had.
The ver - y wounds that shame would hide.
And in Thy mer - cy heal us all. A - MEN.

58

PAUL GERHARDT, 1648
Tr. The Yattendon Hymnal, 1899, alt.   7. 7. 6. 7. 7. 8.

NUN RUHEN ALLE WÄLDER (INNSBRUCK)

HEINRICH ISAAK, 1455-1517

Quietly, with flowing rhythm

1. The du - teous day now clos - eth, Each flower and tree re - pos - eth,
2. Now all the heaven - ly splen - dor Breaks forth in star - light ten - der
3. A - while his mor - tal blind - ness May miss God's lov - ing kind - ness,

Evening

Shade creeps o'er wild and wood. Let us as night is fall - ing, On
From myr - iad worlds un-known; And man, Thy mar - vel see - ing, For -
And grope in faith - less strife; But, when life's day is o - ver, Shall

God, our Mak - er, call - ing, Give thanks to Him, the Giv - er good.
gets his self - ish be - ing For joy of beau - ty not his own.
death's fair night dis - cov - er The fields of ev - er last - ing life. A-MEN.

59

THOMAS KEN, 1637-1711   L. M.   TALLIS CANON
                                                        THOMAS TALLIS, c. 1520-1585

With dignity

1. All praise to Thee, my God, this night, For all the bless - ings of the light;
2. For - give me, Lord, for Thy dear Son, The ill that I this day have done,
3. Teach me to live, that I may dread The grave as lit - tle as my bed;
4. O may my soul on Thee re - pose, And with sweet sleep mine eye - lids close;
5. Praise God, from whom all bless - ings flow; Praise Him, all crea - tures here be - low;

Keep me, O keep me, King of kings, Be-neath Thine own almight - y wings.
That with the world, my-self, and Thee, I, ere I sleep, at peace may be.
Teach me to die, that so I may Rise glo-rious at the aw - ful day.
Sleep that may me more vig-orous make To serve my God when I a - wake.
Praise Him a - bove, ye heaven-ly host; Praise Fa-ther, Son, and Ho - ly Ghost. A-MEN.

VESPER HYMN

JAMES EDMESTON, 1820
Verse 3 added by E. H. BICKERSTETH, 1876   8. 7. 8. 7. D.

DIMITRI BORTNIANSKY, 1751–1825

In moderate time

1. Sav - iour, breathe an eve - ning bless-ing Ere re - pose our spir - its seal;
2. Though de - struc-tion walk a - round us, Though the ar - row past us fly,
3. Fa - ther, to Thy ho - ly keep-ing Hum - bly we our-selves re - sign;

Sin and want we come con - fess - ing; Thou canst save, and Thou canst heal.
An - gel-guards from Thee sur - round us, We are safe if Thou art nigh.
Sav - iour, who hast slept our sleep - ing, Make our slum-bers pure as Thine;

Though the night be dark and drear - y, Dark-ness can - not hide from Thee;
Should swift death this night o'er - take us, And our couch be - come our tomb,
Bless - ed Spir - it, brood-ing o'er us, Chase the dark-ness of our night,

Thou art He who, nev - er wear - y, Watch-est where Thy peo-ple be.
May the morn in heaven a - wake us, Clad in light and death-less bloom.
Till the per - fect day be - fore us Breaks in ev - er - last-ing light.   A-MEN.

God the Father

His Eternity and Majesty

61

DANIEL BEN JUDAH, 14th century
Revised version of *The Yigdal*

6. 6. 8. 4. D.

YIGDAL (LEONI)

Hebrew Melody

Majestically

1. The God of Abra-ham praise, All prais-ed be His Name,
2. His spir-it flow-eth free, High sur-ging where it will:
3. He hath e-ter-nal life Im-plant-ed in the soul;

Who was, and is, and is to be, And still the same!
In proph-et's word He spoke of old— He speak-eth still.
His love shall be our strength and stay, While a-ges roll.

The one e-ter-nal God, Ere aught that now ap-pears;
Es-tab-lished is His law, And change-less it shall stand,
Praise to the liv-ing God! All prais-ed be His Name,

The First, the Last: be-yond all thought His time-less years!
Deep writ up-on the hu-man heart, On sea, or land.
Who was, and is, and is to be, And still the same! A-MEN.

God the Father

62

Farkas Kálmán
Tr. from the Hungarian, William Toth, 1938
Metrical version by G. J. Neumann, 1939

9. 9. 9. 9. 6. 6. 9. 9.

KALMAN
Farkas Kálmán

Reverently

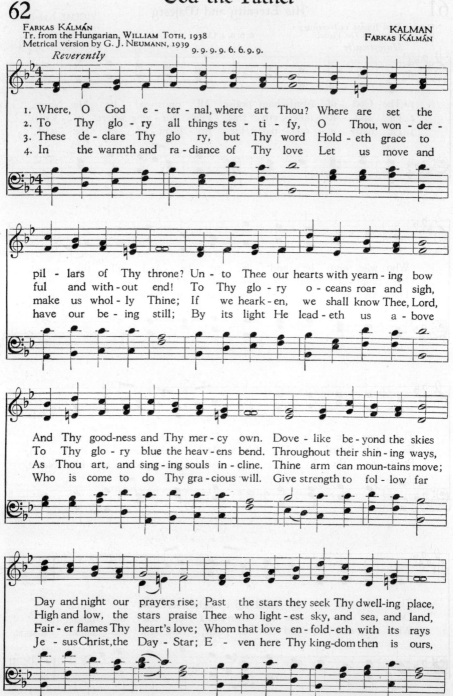

1. Where, O God e - ter - nal, where art Thou? Where are set the
2. To Thy glo - ry all things tes - ti - fy, O Thou, won - der-
3. These de - clare Thy glo - ry, but Thy word Hold - eth grace to
4. In the warmth and ra - diance of Thy love Let us move and

pil - lars of Thy throne? Un - to Thee our hearts with yearn - ing bow
ful and with - out end! To Thy glo - ry o - ceans roar and sigh,
make us whol - ly Thine; If we heark - en, we shall know Thee, Lord,
have our be - ing still; By its light He lead - eth us a - bove

And Thy good - ness and Thy mer - cy own. Dove - like be - yond the skies
To Thy glo - ry blue the heav - ens bend. Throughout their shin - ing ways,
As Thou art, and sing - ing souls in - cline. Thine arm can moun - tains move;
Who is come to do Thy gra - cious will. Give strength to fol - low far

Day and night our prayers rise; Past the stars they seek Thy dwell - ing place,
High and low, the stars praise Thee who light - est sky, and sea, and land,
Fair - er flames Thy heart's love; Whom that love en - fold - eth with its rays
Je - sus Christ, the Day - Star; E - ven here Thy king - dom then is ours,

His Eternity and Majesty

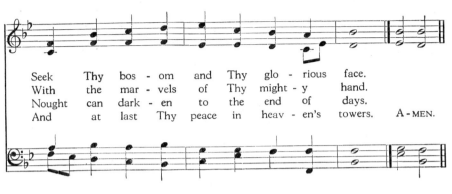

Seek Thy bos - om and Thy glo - rious face.
With the mar - vels of Thy might - y hand.
Nought can dark - en to the end of days.
And at last Thy peace in heav - en's towers. A - MEN.

63

Isaac Watts, 1719   C. M.   ST. ANNE
William Croft, 1708

With majesty

1. Our God, our help in a - ges past, Our hope for years to come,
2. Un - der the shad - ow of Thy throne Thy saints have dwelt se - cure;
3. Be - fore the hills in or - der stood, Or earth re - ceived her frame,
4. A thou - sand a - ges in Thy sight Are like an eve - ning gone;
5. Time, like an ev - er - roll - ing stream, Bears all its sons a - way;
6. Our God, our help in a - ges past, Our hope for years to come,

Our shel - ter from the storm - y blast, And our e - ter - nal home:
Suf - fi - cient is Thine arm a - lone, And our de - fense is sure.
From ev - er - last - ing Thou art God, To end - less years the same.
Short as the watch that ends the night Be - fore the ris - ing sun.
They fly for - got - ten, as a dream Dies at the open - ing day.
Be Thou our guard while trou - bles last, And our e - ter - nal home. A-MEN.

God the Father

64

EDWARD GRUBB, 1925

O GOTT, DU FROMMER GOTT (DARMSTADT)
6. 7. 6. 7. 6. 6. 6. 6.
J. G. C. STÖRL, 1710

In moderate time

1. Our God, to whom we turn When wea-ry with il-lu-sion, Whose
2. Thou art Thy-self the Truth; Though we, who fain would find Thee, Have
3. All beau-ty speaks of Thee—The moun-tains and the riv-ers, The
4. Thou hid-den fount of love, Of peace, and truth, and beau-ty, In-

stars ser-ene-ly burn A-bove this earth's con-fu-sion, Thine
tried, with thoughts un-couth, In fee-ble words to bind Thee, It
line of lift-ed sea, Where spread-ing moon-light quiv-ers, The
spire us from a-bove With joy and strength for du-ty; May

is the might-y plan, The stead-fast or-der sure, In
is be-cause Thou art We're driv-en to the quest; Till
deep-toned or-gan blast That rolls through arch-es dim— Hints
Thy fresh light a-rise With-in each cloud-ed heart, And

which the world be-gan, En-dures, and shall en-dure.
truth from false-hood part, Our souls can find no rest.
of the mu-sic vast Of Thine e-ter-nal hymn.
give us o-pen eyes To see Thee as Thou art. A-MEN.

Words used by permission of Miss Edith Grubb.

His World

65

MALTBIE D. BABCOCK, 1901   S.M.D.

TERRA PATRIS
Melody by FRANKLIN L. SHEPPARD, 1915
Arr. EDWARD SHIPPEN BARNES, 1926

In moderate time and graceful rhythm

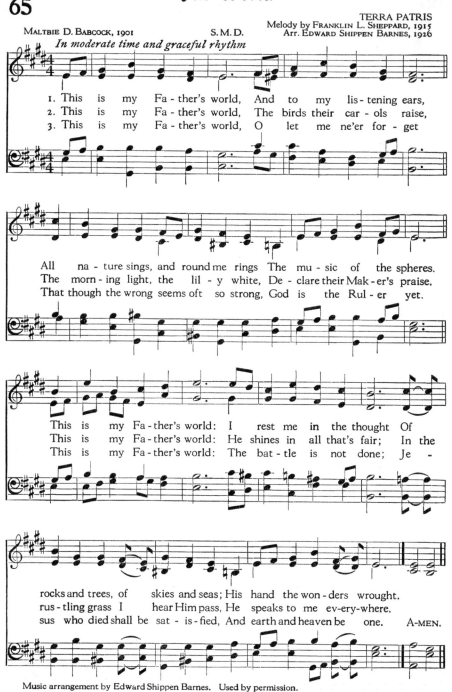

1. This is my Fa-ther's world, And to my lis-tening ears,
2. This is my Fa-ther's world, The birds their car-ols raise,
3. This is my Fa-ther's world, O let me ne'er for-get

All na-ture sings, and round me rings The mu-sic of the spheres.
The morn-ing light, the lil-y white, De-clare their Mak-er's praise.
That though the wrong seems oft so strong, God is the Rul-er yet.

This is my Fa-ther's world: I rest me in the thought Of
This is my Fa-ther's world: He shines in all that's fair; In the
This is my Fa-ther's world: The bat-tle is not done; Je -

rocks and trees, of skies and seas; His hand the won-ders wrought.
rus-tling grass I hear Him pass, He speaks to me ev-ery-where.
sus who died shall be sat-is-fied, And earth and heaven be one. A-MEN.

Music arrangement by Edward Shippen Barnes. Used by permission.
Words from "Thoughts for Every-Day Living." Copyright, 1901, by Charles Scribner's Sons.

God the Father

JOSEPH ADDISON, 1712   L. M. D.   CREATION
FRANZ JOSEPH HAYDN, 1798

Joyously

1. The spa-cious fir-ma-ment on high, With all the
2. Soon as the eve-ning shades pre-vail, The moon takes
3. What though in sol-emn si-lence all Move round this

blue e-the-real sky, And span-gled heavens, a shin-ing frame,
up the won-drous tale, And night-ly to the lis-tening earth
dark ter-res-tri-al ball; What though no re-al voice nor sound

Their great O-rig-i-nal pro-claim: The un-wea-ried sun, from
Re-peats the sto-ry of her birth; Whilst all the stars that
A-midst their ra-diant orbs be found; In rea-son's ear they

day to day, Does his Cre-a-tor's power dis-play, And pub-lish-
round her burn, And all the plan-ets in their turn, Con-firm the
all re-joice, And ut-ter forth a glo-rious voice, For-ev-er

His World

es to ev - ery land The work of an al-might-y hand.
ti - dings as they roll, And spread the truth from pole to pole.
sing - ing, as they shine, "The hand that made us is di - vine." A-MEN.

67

Tr. S. D. RODHOLM

Irregular

IRMER
THEODORE C. HAEUSSLER, 1938

Buoyantly

1. Beau - ty a - round us, Glo - ry a - bove us, Love - ly are
2. A - ges and a - ges Roll on and van - ish, Chil - dren shall
3. Chil - dren of God are we, Liv - ing for vic - tory, Beau - ty re -

earth and the smil - ing skies, Sing - ing we pass a - long, Pil - grims up -
fol - low where fa - thers passed; Nev - er our pil - grim song, Joy - ful and
vealed and glo - ry won; Here strong our voi - ces blend, Sing - ing that

on our way, Through these fair lands of Par - a - dise.
heav - en - born, Shall cease while earth and time shall last.
glo - rious end When life and love and God are one. A-MEN.

Music copyright, 1941, by Theodore C. Haeussler.

God the Father

68

SAMUEL LONGFELLOW, 1864   L. M. with Refrain   PATER OMNIUM
HENRY J. E. HOLMES, 1875

Joyfully

1. God of the earth, the sky, the sea, Mak-er of all a-
2. Thy love is in the sun-shine's glow, Thy life is in the
3. We feel Thy calm at eve-ning's hour, Thy gran-deur in the
4. But high-er far, and far more clear, Thee in man's spir-it

bove, be-low, Cre-a-tion lives and moves in Thee,
quick-ening air; When light-nings flash and storm-winds blow,
march of night; And, when Thy morn-ing breaks in power,
we be-hold; Thine im-age and Thy-self are there,—

REFRAIN

Thy pres-ent life through all doth flow. We give Thee thanks, Thy
There is Thy power; Thy law is there.
We hear Thy word, "Let there be light!"
The in-dwell-ing God, pro-claimed of old.

name we sing, Al-might-y Fa-ther, heaven-ly King. A-MEN.

His World

69

THOMAS PAXTON 7.6.7.6.D. TALYLLYN
Welsh Traditional Melody

Joyously

1. God of the glo-rious sun-shine, God of re-fresh-ing rain,
2. God of the hill and moun-tain, Of val-ley and of dale,
3. God of the bus-y day-time, God of the qui-et night,
4. God of the whole cre-a-tion, God of all life be-low,

Whose voice bids earth a-wak-en And clothe it-self a-gain
Whose fin-ger paints the rain-bows, Thy beau-ties nev-er fail
Whose peace per-vades the dark-ness And greets us with the light,
We seek Thy near-er pres-ence, Thy grand-er life to know;

With life of rich-est beau-ty In plant, in flower, and tree;
To fill our souls with won-der, And turn our thoughts to Thee;
Safe with Thy pres-ence near us, Wher-ev-er we may be,
When we Thy height-ened splen-dor, Thy great-er glo-ries see,

Thou God of light and splen-dor, We rise and wor-ship Thee.
Thou God of liv-ing na-ture We stand and wor-ship Thee.
Thou God, our great Pro-tect-or, We love and wor-ship Thee.
Thou God of all cre-a-tion, We still shall wor-ship Thee. A-MEN.

God the Father

JOHN HAYNES HOLMES, 1909 · C.M.D. · GENEVA · PIERRE WISSMER, 1939

In moderate time

1. O God, whose love is o - ver all The chil - dren of Thy grace,
2. To see Thee in the sun by day And in the stars by night,
3. To see Thee in each qui - et home Where faith and love a - bide,

Whose rich and ten - der bless - ings fall On ev - ery age and place,
In wav - ing grass and o - cean spray And leaves and flow - ers bright;
In school and church, where all may come To seek Thee side by side;

Hear Thou the songs and prayers we raise In ea - ger joy to Thee,
To hear Thy voice, like spo - ken word, In ev - ery breeze that blows,
To see Thee in each hu - man life, Each strug - gling hu - man heart,

And teach us, as we sound Thy praise, In all things Thee to see.
In ev - ery song of ev - ery bird, And ev - ery brook that flows.
Each path by which, in ea - ger strife, Men seek the bet - ter part. A-MEN.

Words used by permission of author.
Music copyright, 1941, by Eden Publishing House.

His World

71

Thomas R. Birks, 1874   7.6.7.6.D.   PEARSALL
Robert L. de Pearsall, 1795–1856

In moderate time; with spirit

1. The heavens de - clare Thy glo - ry, The firm - a - ment Thy power;
2. The sun with roy - al splen - dor Goes forth to chant Thy praise,
3. All heaven on high re - joic - es To do its Ma - ker's will;

Day un - to day the sto - ry Re - peats from hour to hour;
And moon-beams soft and ten - der Their gen - tler an - them raise;
The stars with sol - emn voic - es Re - sound Thy prais - es still;

Night un - to night re - ply - ing, Pro - claims in ev - ery land,
O'er ev - ery tribe and na - tion The mu - sic strange is poured,
So let my whole be - hav - ior, Thoughts, words, and ac - tions be,

O Lord, with voice un - dy - ing, The won - ders of Thy hand.
The song of all cre - a - tion To Thee, cre - a - tion's Lord.
O Lord, my Strength, my Sav - iour, One cease - less song to Thee. A-MEN.

God the Father

72

MARTIN RINKART, 1586–1649
Tr. CATHERINE WINKWORTH, 1858   6. 7. 6. 7. 6. 6. 6. 6.

NUN DANKET ALLE GOTT

JOHANN CRÜGER, 1648

Majestically, but not too slowly

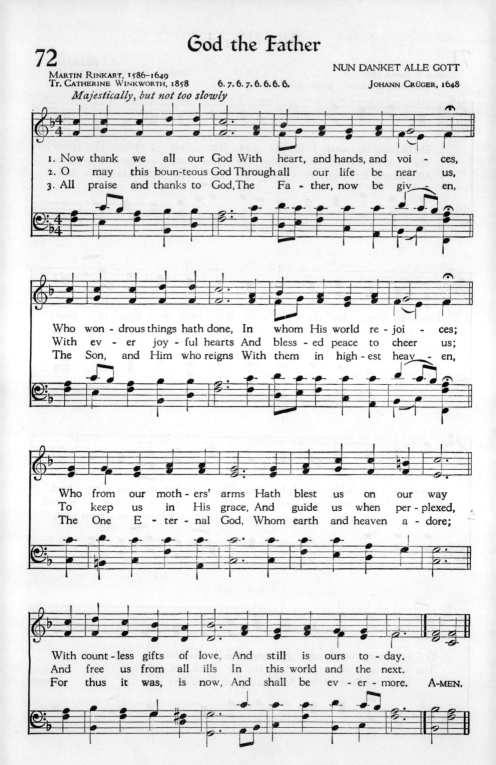

1. Now thank we all our God With heart, and hands, and voi - ces,
2. O may this boun-teous God Through all our life be near us,
3. All praise and thanks to God, The Fa - ther, now be giv - en,

Who won - drous things hath done, In whom His world re - joi - ces;
With ev - er joy - ful hearts And bless - ed peace to cheer us;
The Son, and Him who reigns With them in high - est heav - en,

Who from our moth - ers' arms Hath blest us on our way
To keep us in His grace, And guide us when per - plexed,
The One E - ter - nal God, Whom earth and heaven a - dore;

With count - less gifts of love, And still is ours to - day.
And free us from all ills In this world and the next.
For thus it was, is now, And shall be ev - er - more. A-MEN.

His Providence and Love

NUN DANKET ALLE GOTT

1 Nun danket alle Gott,
  Mit Herzen, Mund und Händen,
Der grosse Dinge tut
  An uns und allen Enden;
Der uns von Mutterleib
  Und Kindesbeinen an
Unzählig viel zu gut
  Bis hieher hat getan.

2 Der ewig reiche Gott
  Woll' uns bei unserm Leben
Ein immer fröhlich Herz
  Und edlen Frieden geben,

Und uns in seiner Gnad'
  Erhalten fort und fort,
Und uns aus aller Not
  Erlösen hier und dort.

3 Lob, Ehr' und Preis sei Gott,
  Dem Vater und dem Sohne,
Und dem, der beiden gleich
  Im höchsten Himmelsthrone:
Ihm, dem dreiein' gen Gott,
  Wie es im Anfang war,
Und ist und bleiben wird
  Jetzund und immerdar!

73

Thomas Tiplady, 1935   8.8.8.4.   ANNISQUAM
T. Tertius Noble, 1938

In moderate time

1. Be - yond the wheel - ing worlds of light, Re -
2. A - bove the earth - quake's aw - ful roar, And
3. A - bove the light - ning's dread - ful flash, And
4. Up - on a cross in an - cient time, There
5. The heights and depths of love di - vine, We
6. As when a bird sinks in its nest, The

vealed to us by si - lent night, There stands, though clad in
smok - ing hills that la - va pour, There stands, though hid from
winds that seas to fu - ry lash, There stands, un - heard a -
suf - fered One in love sub - lime, That men might know, in
can - not mea - sure or de - fine, But from the Cross the
baf - fled mind, with doubts dis - trest, Be - neath the Cross finds

robes of might, A God of love.
rich and poor, A God of love.
mid the crash, A God of love.
ev - ery clime, That God of love.
truth doth shine, That God is love.
per - fect rest, For God is love. A-MEN.

God the Father

74

OLIVER WENDELL HOLMES, 1848   L.M.   GRACE CHURCH
IGNACE PLEYEL, 1815

In flowing rhythm

1. Lord of all be - ing, throned a - far, Thy glo - ry flames from sun and star;
2. Sun of our life, Thy quick-ening ray Sheds on our path the glow of day;
3. Our mid-night is Thy smile with-drawn; Our noon-tide is Thy gra-cious dawn;
4. Lord of all life, be - low, a - bove, Whose light is truth, whose warmth is love,
5. Grant us Thy truth to make us free, And kind-ling hearts that burn for Thee;

Cen-tre and soul of ev - ery sphere, Yet to each lov - ing heart how near.
Star of our hope, Thy soft-ened light Cheers the long watch-es of the night.
Our rain-bow arch, Thy mer-cy's sign: All, save the clouds of sin, are Thine.
Be - fore Thy ev - er-blaz-ing throne We ask no lus-tre of our own.
Till all Thy liv - ing al - tars claim One ho - ly light, one heavenly flame. A-MEN.

Alternative tune, *Louvan.*

75

WILLIAM COWPER, 1774   C.M.   DUNDEE
Scottish Psalter, 1615

In moderate time

1. God moves in a mys - te - rious way His won - ders to per - form;
2. Deep in un - fath - om - a - ble mines Of nev - er - fail - ing skill
3. Ye fear - ful saints, fresh cour - age take; The clouds ye so much dread
4. Blind un - be - lief is sure to err, And scan His work in vain;

He plants His foot-steps in the sea, And rides up - on the storm.
He treas-ures up His bright de - signs, And works His sov-ereign will.
Are big with mer - cy, and shall break In bless - ings on your head.
God is His own in - ter - pre - ter, And He will make it plain. A-MEN.

His Providence and Love

76

JOHN BOWRING, 1825

8.7.8.7.

RATHBUN
ITHAMAR CONKEY, 1851

Not too slowly

1. God is Love; His mer - cy bright-ens All the path in which we rove;
2. Chance and change are bus - y ev - er; Man de-cays and a - ges move;
3. E'en the hour that dark - est seem-eth Will His change-less good-ness prove;
4. He with earth - ly cares en - twin-eth Hope and com - fort from a - bove;

Bliss He makes, and woe He light-ens: God is Wis-dom, God is Love.
But His mer - cy wan - eth nev - er: God is Wis-dom, God is Love.
From the mist His brightness streameth: God is Wis-dom, God is Love.
Ev - ery-where His glo - ry shin-eth: God is Wis-dom, God is Love. A - MEN.

77

INNOCENTS
The Parish Choir, 1850
Arr. from 13th Century French Melody

JOHN MILTON, 1624

7.7.7.7.

In moderate time, joyously

1. Let us with a glad - some mind Praise the Lord, for He is kind:
2. He with all - com-mand - ing might, Filled the new-made world with light;
3. All things liv - ing He doth feed; His full hand sup - plies their need:
4. Let us, then, His praise sing forth, His high ma - jes - ty and worth:

For His mer - cies shall en - dure, Ev - er faith-ful, ev - er sure. A-MEN.

God the Father

Thomas Curtis Clark
In moderate time

10. 10. 10. 10. 6.

FERREE
Carl F. Price

1. God is not far from an - y one of us:
   The wild flower by the way - side speaks His love; Each blithe-some
   bird bears ti - dings from a - bove; Sun - shine and shower His ten - der
   mer - cies prove, And men know not His voice!

2. God is not far from an - y one of us:
   He speaks to us in ev - ery glad sun - rise; His glo - ry
   floods us from the noon - day skies; The stars de - clare His love when
   day - light dies, And men know not His voice!

3. God is not far from an - y one of us:
   He watch - es o'er his chil - dren day and night; On ev - ery
   dark - ened soul He sheds His light; Each bur - dened heart He cheers, and
   lends His might To all who know His voice. A - MEN.

His Providence and Love

79

JOHN HAYNES HOLMES, 1910

C. M. D.

ST. LEONARD
HENRY HILES, 1867

In moderate time

1. O God, whose law from age to age, No chance or change can know,
Whose love for - ev - er - more a - bides, While ae - ons come and go;
From all the strife of earth - ly life, To Thine em - brace we flee,
And 'mid our crowd - ing doubts and fears Would put our trust in Thee.

2. The winds, Thy faith - ful mes - sen - gers, Are guid - ed by Thy hand,
Thy min - is - ters, the flames of fire, O - bey Thy stern com - mand;
The seas re - sound with - in the bound Where Thy do - min - ion reigns,
And wheel - ing plan - ets seek the paths Thy might - y will or - dains.

3. Thy ho - ly pur - pose moves be - fore The na - tions on their way,
And leads the stum - bling hosts of men From dark - ness in - to day.
No cap - tain's sword, no proph - et's word, But Thy great mer - cy prove;
No clime or kin - dred but at - test Thy prov - i - dence of love.

4. Dear Fa - ther, we would learn to trust The do - ing of Thy will,
And in Thy per - fect law of love Our doubts and fears would still.
Help us to know, in joy or woe, Thy ways are al - ways best,
And we, Thy chil - dren ev - er - more, By Thy great good-ness blest. A-MEN.

From *Hymns of the Christian Life.*
Copyright, 1925, by A. S. Barnes and Co.

God the Father

WILLIAM WILLIAMS (Welsh), 1745
Stanza 1 tr. PETER WILLIAMS, 1771
Stanzas 2, 3 tr. WILLIAM WILLIAMS, c. 1772

8.7.8.7.8.7.7.

CWM RHONDDA
Welsh Hymn Melody
JOHN HUGHES, 1907

In moderate time

1. Guide me, O Thou great Je - ho - vah, Pil - grim through this
2. O - pen now the crys - tal foun - tain, Whence the heal - ing
3. When I tread the verge of Jor - dan, Bid my anx - ious

bar - ren land; I am weak, but Thou art might - y; Hold me with Thy
stream doth flow; Let the fire and cloud - y pil - lar Lead me all my
fears sub - side; Death of death, and hell's de - struc-tion, Land me safe on

pow - er - ful hand; Bread of heav - en, Bread of heav - en,
jour - ney through; Strong De - liv - er - er, strong De - liv - er - er,
Ca - naan's side; Songs of prais - es, songs of prais - es

Feed me till I want no more, Feed me till I want no more.
Be Thou still my Strength and Shield, Be Thou still my Strength and Shield.
I will ev - er give to Thee, I will ev - er give to Thee. A-MEN.

Music used by permission of Mrs. John Hughes.

His Providence and Love

81

SWABIA
Johann M. Spiess
Davids Harpffen-Spiel, Heidelberg, 1745
Arr. W. H. Havergal, 1847

Isaac Watts, 1707

S. M.

In moderate time

1. Be - hold what won - drous grace The Fa - ther hath be - stowed
2. Nor doth it yet ap - pear How great we must be made;
3. A hope so much di - vine May tri - als well en - dure,
4. If in my Fa - ther's love I share a fil - ial part,

On sin - ners of a mor - tal race, To call them sons of God.
But when we see our Sa - viour here, We shall be like our Head.
May purge our souls from sense and sin, As Christ the Lord is pure.
Send down Thy Spir - it like a dove, To rest up - on my heart. A-men.

82

GOTT SEI DANK DURCH ALLE WELT

Samuel Johnson, 1864

7. 7. 7. 7.

Freylinghausen's *Gesangbuch*, Halle, 1704

May be sung in unison

1. Life of a - ges, rich - ly poured, Love of God, un - spent and free,
2. Breath - ing in the think - er's creed; Puls - ing in the he - ro's blood;
3. Con - se - crat - ing art and song, Ho - ly book and pil - grim track;
4. Life of a - ges, rich - ly poured, Love of God, un - spent and free,

Flow - ing in the proph - et's word And the peo - ple's lib - er - ty;
Nerv - ing sim-plest thought and deed; Fresh-ening time with truth and good;
Hurl - ing floods of ty - rant wrong From the sa - cred lim - its back—
Flow still in the proph - et's word And the peo - ple's lib - er - ty! A-men.

God the Father

83

United Presbyterian Book of Psalms, U. S. A., 1871

STUTTGART
Arr. from *Psalmodia Sacra*, 1715

8. 7. 8. 7.

In moderate time

1. O my soul, bless God, the Fa-ther; All with-in me bless His name;
2. Who for-giv-eth thy trans-gres-sions, Thy dis-ea-ses all who heals;
3. Far as east from west is dis-tant, He hath put a-way our sin;
4. As it was with-out be-gin-ning, So it lasts with-out an end;
5. Un-to such as keep His cov-enant And are stead-fast in His way;
6. Bless the Fa-ther, all His crea-tures, Ev-er un-der His con-trol;

Bless the Fa-ther, and for-get not All His mer-cies to pro-claim.
Who re-deems thee from de-struc-tion, Who with thee so kind-ly deals.
Like the pit-y of a fa-ther Hath the Lord's com-pas-sion been.
To their chil-dren's children ev-er Shall His right-eous-ness ex-tend;
Un-to those who still re-mem-ber His com-mand-ments and o-bey.
All through-out His vast do-min-ion Bless the Fa-ther, O my soul. A-MEN.

84

JOSEPH ADDISON, 1712

C. M.

TALLIS' ORDINAL
THOMAS TALLIS, 1567

In moderate time

1. When all Thy mer-cies, O my God, My ris-ing soul sur-veys,
2. Un-num-bered com-forts to my soul Thy ten-der care be-stowed,
3. When worn with sick-ness, oft hast Thou With health re-newed my face,
4. Through ev-ery per-iod of my life Thy good-ness I'll pur-sue;

Trans-port-ed with the view, I'm lost In won-der, love, and praise.
Be-fore my in-fant heart could know From whom those com-forts flowed.
And, when in sins and sor-rows bowed, Re-vived my soul with grace.
And af-ter death, in dis-tant worlds, The glo-rious theme re-new. A-MEN.

Alternative tune, *Belmont*.

His Providence and Love

85

FREDERICK W. FABER, 1862   8.7.8.7.D.   HOLMBUSH
G. DARLINGTON RICHARDS, 1938

In flowing rhythm, but with dignity

1. There's a wide-ness in God's mer-cy, Like the wide-ness of the sea;
2. For the love of God is broad-er Than the meas-ure of man's mind;

There's a kind-ness in His jus-tice, Which is more than lib-er-ty.
And the heart of the E-ter-nal Is most won-der-ful-ly kind.

There is no place where earth's sor-rows Are more felt than up in heaven;
If our love were but more sim-ple We should take Him at His word;

There is no place where earth's fail-ings Have such kind-ly judg-ment given.
And our lives would be all sun-shine In the sweet-ness of our Lord. A-MEN.

God the Father

SANDON

From Psalm cxxi. JOHN CAMPBELL,
Duke of Argyll, 1877

10. 4. 10. 4. 10. 10.

CHARLES HENRY PURDAY, 1860

In moderate time

1. Un - to the hills a - round do I lift up My long - ing eyes;
2. He will not suf - fer that thy foot be moved: Safe shalt thou be.
3. Je - ho - vah is Him - self thy keep - er true, Thy change - less shade;
4. From ev - ery e - vil shall He keep thy soul, From ev - ery sin;

O whence for me shall my sal - va - tion come, From whence a - rise?
No care - less slum - ber shall His eye - lids close, Who keep - eth thee.
Je - ho - vah thy de - fense on thy right hand Him - self hath made.
Je - ho - vah shall pre - serve thy go - ing out, Thy com - ing in.

From God the Lord doth come my cer - tain aid,
Be - hold, He sleep - eth not, He slum - bereth ne'er,
And thee no sun by day shall ev - er smite;
A - bove thee watch - ing, He whom we a - dore

From God the Lord who heaven and earth hath made.
Who keep - eth Is - rael in His ho - ly care.
No moon shall harm thee in the si - lent night.
Shall keep thee hence - forth, yea, for - ev - er - more. A-MEN.

His Providence and Love

87

Katharina von Schlegel, 1752
Tr. Jane L. Borthwick, 1855

10. 10. 10. 10. 10. 10.

FINLANDIA

Jean Sibelius

In flowing rhythm

1. Be still, my soul: the Lord is on thy side; . . Bear pa-tient-ly the cross of grief or pain; Leave to thy God to or-der and pro-vide; . . In ev-ery change He faith-ful will re-main. Be still, my soul: thy best, thy heavenly Friend Through thorn-y ways leads to a joy-ful end.

2. Be still, my soul: thy God doth un-der-take . . To guide the fu-ture as He has the past. Thy hope, thy con-fi-dence let noth-ing shake; . All now mys-te-rious shall be bright at last. Be still, my soul: the waves and winds still know His voice who ruled them while He dwelt be-low.

3. Be still, my soul: the hour is has-tening on . . . When we shall be for ev-er with the Lord, When dis-ap-point-ment, grief, and fear are gone, . . Sor-row for-got, love's pur-est joys re-stored. Be still, my soul: when change and tears are past, All safe and bless-ed we shall meet at last. A-men.

Music used by permission of the Presbyterian Board of Christian Education, owner of this special arrangement.

Our Lord Jesus Christ

88

VENI EMMANUEL

From Latin, 12th century
Stanzas 1 and 2 Tr. JOHN MASON NEALE, 1851
Stanza 3 Tr. HENRY S. COFFIN, 1916   8. 8. 8. 8. 8. 8.   Ancient plain song, 13th century (Mode I)

Unison, with spirit

1. O come, O come, Em-man-u-el, And ran-som cap-tive
2. O come, Thou Day-spring, come and cheer Our spir-its by Thine
3. O come, De-sire of na-tions, bind All peo-ples in one

Is-ra-el, That mourns in lone-ly ex-ile here
ad-vent here; Dis-perse the gloom-y clouds of night,
heart and mind; Bid en-vy, strife and dis-cord cease;

HARMONY

Un-til the Son of God ap-pear. Re-joice! Re-joice! Em-
And death's dark shad-ows put to flight. Re-joice! Re-joice! Em-
Fill the whole world with heav-en's peace. Re-joice! Re-joice! Em-

UNISON

man-u-el Shall come to thee, O Is-ra-el!
man-u-el Shall come to thee, O Is-ra-el!
man-u-el Shall come to thee, O Is-ra-el! A-MEN.

His Advent

89

CHARLES WESLEY, 1744

8. 7. 8. 7. D.

IN BABILONE
Dutch Traditional Melody

With dignity and graceful rhythm
May be sung in unison

1. Come, Thou long - ex - pect - ed Je - sus, Born to set Thy peo - ple free;
2. Born Thy peo - ple to de - liv - er, Born a child, yet God, our King;

From our fears and sins re - lease us, Let us find our rest in Thee.
Born to reign in us for ev - er, Now Thy gra - cious king - dom bring.

Is - rael's Strength and Con - so - la - tion, Hope of all the earth Thou art;
By Thine own e - ter - nal Spir - it, Rule in all our hearts a - lone;

Long de - sired of ev - ery na - tion, Joy of ev - ery wait - ing heart.
By Thine all - suf - fi - cient mer - it, Raise us to Thy glo - rious throne. A-MEN.

Our Lord Jesus Christ

90

JOHN OLEARIUS, 1671
Tr. CATHERINE WINKWORTH, 1862

WERDE MUNTER, MEIN GEMÜTE

8. 7. 8. 7. 7. 7. 8. 8.

JOHANN SCHOP, 1642

1. Com - fort, com - fort ye my peo - ple, Speak ye peace, thus saith our God;
2. For the her - ald's voice is cry - ing In the des - ert far and near,
3. Make ye straight what long was crook - ed, Make the rough - er pla - ces plain:

Com - fort those who sit in dark - ness, Mourn-ing 'neath their sor - rows' load.
Bid - ding all men to re - pent - ance, Since the king - dom now is here.
Let your hearts be true and hum - ble, As be - fits His ho - ly reign;

Speak ye to Je - ru - sa - lem Of the peace that waits for them;
O, that warn - ing cry o - bey, Now pre - pare for God a way!
For the glo - ry of the Lord Now o'er earth is shed a - broad,

Tell her that her sins I cov - er, And her war-fare now is o - ver.
Let the val - leys rise to meet Him And the hills bow down to greet Him.
And all flesh shall see the to - ken That His word is nev - er bro - ken. A-MEN.

His Advent

JOHN BOWRING, 1825   7.7.7.7. D.   ST. GEORGE'S, WINDSOR
GEORGE J. ELVEY, 1859

With well defined rhythm

1. Watch-man, tell us of the night, What its signs of prom-ise are:
2. Watch-man, tell us of the night; High - er yet that star as-cends:
3. Watch-man, tell us of the night, For the morn-ing seems to dawn:

Trav - eler, o'er yon moun-tain's height, See that glo - ry-beam-ing star!
Trav - eler, bless - ed - ness and light, Peace and truth, its course por-tends.
Trav - eler, dark - ness takes its flight; Doubt and ter - ror are with-drawn.

Watch-man, doth its beau-teous ray Aught of joy or hope fore-tell?
Watch-man, will its beams a - lone Gild the spot that gave them birth?
Watch-man, let thy wan-derings cease; Hie thee to thy qui - et home.

Trav - eler, yes; it brings the day, Prom-ised day of Is - ra - el.
Trav - eler, a - ges are its own, See, it bursts o'er all the earth!
Trav - eler, lo, the Prince of Peace, Lo, the Son of God is come! A-MEN.

Alternative tune, *Aberystwyth.*

Our Lord Jesus Christ

92

MACHT HOCH DIE TÜR

GEORG WEISSEL, 1642
Tr. CATHERINE WINKWORTH, 1855 8.8.8.8.8.8.6.6. J. A. FREYLINGHAUSEN, 1704

Joyfully; not too slowly

1. Lift up your heads, ye might-y gates, Be - hold the King of Glo - ry waits;
2. The Lord is just, a Help-er tried, Mer - cy is ev - er at His side;
3. O blest the land, the cit - y blest, Where Christ the Ru - ler is con-fessed!
4. Fling wide the por-tals of your heart; Make it a tem-ple, set a - part

The King of kings is draw-ing near, The Sav - iour of the world is here;
His king-ly crown is ho - li - ness, His scep - ter, pi - ty in dis-tress;
O hap - py hearts and hap-py homes To whom this King in tri-umph comes!
From earth-ly use for heaven's em-ploy, A - dorned with prayer, and love, and joy;

Life and sal - va - tion He doth bring, Where-fore re - joice, and glad - ly sing:
The end of all our woe He brings; Where-fore the earth is glad and sings:
The cloud-less Sun of joy He is, Who bring-eth pure de - light and bliss:
So shall your Sov-ereign en - ter in, And new and no - bler life be - gin:

We praise Thee, Fa - ther, now, Cre - a - tor, wise art Thou!
We praise Thee, Sav - iour, now, Might - y in - deed art Thou!
O Com - fort - er di - vine, What bound-less grace is Thine!
To Thee, O God, be praise For word and deed and grace! A - MEN.

His Advent

93

Johann Rist, 1651
Tr. Catherine Winkworth, 1858
C.M.D.
ELLACOMBE
Gesangbuch der Herzogl. Wirtembergischen
Katholischen Hofkapelle, 1784

In marked rhythm

1. A - rise, the king-dom is at hand, The King is draw-ing nigh;
2. Look up, ye droop-ing hearts, to - day, The King is ver - y near;
3. O rich the gifts Thou bring-est us, Thy - self made poor and weak;

A - rise with joy, thou faith - ful band, To meet the Lord most high!
O cast your griefs and fears a - way, For, lo, your help is here!
O love be - yond com - pare that thus Can foes and sin - ners seek!

Look up, ye souls weighed down with care, The Sov-ereign is not far;
Hope on, ye bro - ken hearts, at last The King comes in His might;
For this we raise a glad - some voice On high to Thee a - lone,

Look up, faint hearts, from your de-spair, Be - hold the Morn-ing Star!
He loved us in the a - ges past, When we lay wrapped in night.
And ev - er - more with thanks re-joice Be - fore Thy glo-rious throne. A-MEN.

Our Lord Jesus Christ

J. LEWIS MILLIGAN, 1930 Irregular ASCENSION
H. HUGH BANCROFT, 1938

Unison. With spirit

1. There's a voice in the wil-der-ness cry-ing, A
2. O Zi-on, that bring-est good ti-dings, Get thee
3. But the word of our God en-dur-eth, The
4. There's a voice in the wil-der-ness cry-ing, A

call from the ways un-trod: Pre-pare in the des-ert a high-way,
up to the heights and sing! Pro-claim to a des-o-late peo-ple
arm of the Lord is strong; He stands in the midst of na-tions,
call from the ways un-trod: Pre-pare in the des-ert a high-way,

A high-way for our God! The val-leys shall be ex-alt-ed,
The com-ing of their King: Like the flow'rs of the field they per-ish,
And He will right the wrong: He shall feed His flock like a shep-herd,
A high-way for our God! The val-leys shall be ex-alt-ed,

The loft-y hills brought low; Make straight all the crook-ed
The works of men de-cay, The power and pomp of
And fold the lambs to His breast; In pas-tures of peace He'll
The loft-y hills brought low; Make straight all the crook-ed

Words used by permission of J. Lewis Milligan, and music by H. Hugh Bancroft.

His Advent

pla - ces, Where the Lord our . . God may go!
na - tions Shall pass like a dream a - way.
lead them, And give to the wea - ry rest.
pla - ces, Where the Lord our . . God may go! A - MEN.

Words used by permission of J. Lewis Milligan.

95 CHARLES COFFIN, 1736
Tr. JOHN CHANDLER, 1837   L. M.   WINCHESTER NEW
Musikalisches Handbuch, Hamburg, 1690

Not too slowly

1. On Jor - dan's bank the Bap - tist's cry An -
2. Then cleansed be ev - ery Chris - tian breast, And
3. For Thou art our sal - va - tion, Lord, Our

noun - ces that the Lord is nigh; A - wake and heark - en,
fur - nished for so great a Guest! Yea, let us each his
ref - uge and our great re - ward; Once more up - on Thy

for he brings Glad ti - dings from the King of kings!
heart pre - pare For Christ to come and en - ter there.
peo - ple shine, And fill the world with love di - vine. A - MEN.

Alternative Tune, *Germany.*

Our Lord Jesus Christ

Philipp Nicolai, 1599
Tr. Catherine Winkworth, 1858, alt.

WACHET AUF
Philipp Nicolai, 1599

8. 9. 8. 8. 9. 8. 6. 6. 4. 4. 4. 8.

With spirit

1. Wake, a-wake, for night is fly-ing, The watch-men on the heights are cry-ing,
2. Zi-on hears the watch-men sing-ing, Her heart with deep de-light is spring-ing,
3. Now let all the heavens a-dore Thee, And men and an-gels sing be-fore Thee

A-wake, Je-ru-sa-lem, a-rise! Mid-night's sol-emn hour is toll-ing,
She wakes, she ris-es from her gloom; For her Lord comes down all glo-rious,
With harp and cym-bal's clear-est tone; Of one pearl each shin-ing por-tal,

His char-iot wheels are near-er roll-ing; He comes! O Church, lift up thine eyes!
In grace ar-rayed, by truth vic-to-rious; Her Star is risen, her Light is come!
Where we shall join the choirs im-mor-tal In prais-es round Thy glo-rious throne;

Rise up, with will-ing feet Go forth, the Bride-groom meet: Hal-le-lu-jah!
Ah, come Thou bless-ed One, God's own be-lov-ed Son, Hal-le-lu-jah!
No vi-sion ev-er brought, No ear hath ev-er caught Such great glo-ry!

His Advent

Lo, great and small, We an-swer all; We fol-low where Thy voice shall call.
We haste a-long, An ea-ger throng, And glad-some join the ad-vent song.
There-fore will we, E-ter-nal-ly, Sing hymns of joy and praise to Thee. A-MEN.

97

PHILIP DODDRIDGE, 1735

LOBT GOTT IHR CHRISTEN ALLZUGLEICH (HERMANN)
C. M.
NICOLAUS HERMANN, 1554

Joyfully

1. Hark, the glad sound, the Sav-iour comes, The Sav-iour
2. He comes the pris-oners to re-lease, In Sa-tan's
3. He comes, the bro-ken heart to bind, The bleed-ing
4. Our glad ho-san-nas, Prince of Peace, Thy wel-come

prom-ised long: Let ev-ery heart pre-pare a throne, And
bond-age held: The gates of brass be-fore Him burst, The
soul to cure, And would with treas-ures of His grace En-
shall pro-claim; And heaven's e-ter-nal arch-es ring With

ev-ery voice a song, . . . And ev-ery voice a song.
i-ron fet-ters yield, . . . The i-ron fet-ters yield.
rich the hum-ble poor, . . . En-rich the hum-ble poor.
Thy be-lov-èd name, . . . With Thy be-lov-èd name. A-MEN.

Our Lord Jesus Christ

JOHN S. B. MONSELL, 1862   8. 7. 8. 7. 8. 7.   STÖRL
J. G. C. STÖRL, 1744

In march rhythm

1. O'er the dis - tant mount - ains break - ing Comes the red - dening
2. O, Thou long - ex - pect - ed! wea - ry Waits my an - xious
3. Near - er now my soul's sal - va - tion, Spent the night, the
4. With my lamp well trimmed and burn - ing, Swift to hear and

dawn of day; Rise, my soul, from sleep a - wak - ing,
soul for Thee; Life is dark, and earth is drear - y,
day at hand; Keep me in my low - ly sta - tion,
slow to roam, Watch - ing for Thy glad re - turn - ing

Rise, and sing, and watch, and pray; 'Tis thy Sav - iour,
Where Thy light I do not see; O my Sav - iour,
Watch - ing for Thee, till I stand, O my Sav - iour,
To re - store me to my home; Come, my Sav - iour,

'tis thy Sav - iour, On His bright re - turn - ing way.
O my Sav - iour, When wilt Thou re - turn to me?
O my Sav - iour, In Thy bright, Thy prom - ised land.
come, my Sav - iour, Thou hast prom - ised: quick - ly come! A-MEN.

Alternative tune, *Alleluia Dulce Carmen.*

His Advent

99

LAURENTIUS LAURENTI, 1700
Tr. SARAH B. FINDLATER, 1854

7.6.7.6.D.

LANCASHIRE
HENRY SMART, 1836

In joyous rhythm

1. Re - joice, re - joice, be - liev - ers, And let your lights ap - pear;
2. See that your lamps are burn - ing; Re - plen - ish them with oil,
3. Our Hope and Ex - pec - ta - tion, O Je - sus, now ap - pear!

The eve - ning is ad - van - cing, And dark - er night is near:
And wait for your sal - va - tion, The end of earth - ly toil.
A - rise, Thou Sun so longed for, O'er this be - night - ed sphere!

The Bride-groom is a - ris - ing, And soon He draw - eth nigh;
The watch - ers on the moun - tain Pro-claim the Bride-groom near,
With hearts and hands up - lift - ed, We plead, O Lord, to see

Up, pray, and watch, and wres - tle: At mid-night comes the cry.
Go meet Him as He com - eth, With al - le - lu - ias clear.
The day of earth's re-demp - tion That brings us un - to Thee. A-MEN.

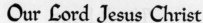

Our Lord Jesus Christ

His Nativity

101

Freely translated from JOSEPH MOHR, 1818

STILLE NACHT
FRANZ GRÜBER, 1818

6.6.8.8.6.6.

Quietly

1. Si - lent night! ho - ly night! All is calm, all is bright;
2. Si - lent night! ho - ly night! Dark - ness flies, all is light;
3. Si - lent night! ho - ly night! Guid - ing Star, lend thy light!
4. Si - lent night! ho - ly night! Won - drous Star, lend thy light!

'Round yon vir - gin moth-er and Child, Ho - ly In-fant so ten-der and mild;
Shep - herds hear the an - gels sing: Al - le - lu - ia! hail the King!
See the east - ern wise men bring Gifts and hom - age to our King!
With the an - gels let us sing Al - le - lu - ia to our King!

Sleep in heav - en - ly peace, Sleep in heav - en - ly peace.
Christ the Sav - iour is born, Christ the Sav - iour is born.
Christ the Sav - iour is born, Christ the Sav - iour is born.
Christ the Sav - iour is born, Christ the Sav - iour is born.

GERMAN TEXT (Stille Nacht, Heilige Nacht)

1 Stille Nacht, heilige Nacht!
Alles schläft, einsam wacht
Nur das heilige Elternpaar,
Das im Stalle zu Bethlehem war
Bei dem himmlischen Kind,
Bei dem himmlischen Kind.

2 Stille Nacht, heilige Nacht!
Hirten erst kund gemacht;
Durch der Engel Halleluja
Tönt es laut von fern und nah':
Christ der Retter ist da,
Christ der Retter ist da!

3 Stille Nacht, heilige Nacht!
Gottes Sohn, o wie lacht
Lieb' aus deinem holdseligen Mund,
Da uns schlägt die rettende Stund',
Christ, in deiner Geburt,
Christ, in deiner Geburt!

Our Lord Jesus Christ

MENDELSSOHN

7.7.7.7. D. with Refrain

CHARLES WESLEY, 1739

FELIX MENDELSSOHN, 1840
Arr. by WILLIAM H. CUMMINGS, 1856

Joyously

1. Hark, the her - ald an - gels sing, "Glo - ry to the new - born King;
2. Christ, by high - est heaven a - dored; Christ, the Ev - er - last - ing Lord!
3. Hail, the heaven-born Prince of peace! Hail, the Sun of Right-eous-ness!

Peace on earth, and mer - cy mild, God and sin - ners rec - on - ciled!"
Late in time be - hold Him come To the earth from heav - en's home;
Light and life to all He brings, Risen with heal - ing in His wings.

Joy - ful, all ye na - tions, rise, Join the tri - umph of the skies;
Veiled in flesh the God - head see; Hail the in - car - nate De - i - ty,
Mild He lays His glo - ry by, Born that man no more may die,

With the an - gel - ic host pro-claim, "Christ is born in Beth - le - hem!"
Pleased as man with men to dwell, Je - sus, our Em-man - u - el.
Born to raise the sons of earth, Born to give them sec - ond birth.

His Nativity

Hark, the her - ald an - gels sing, "Glo - ry to the new-born King."
Hark, the her - ald an - gels sing, "Glo - ry to the new-born King."
Hark, the her - ald an - gels sing, "Glo - ry to the new-born King." A-MEN.

103

ST. AGNES

EDMUND H. SEARS, 1854   C.M.   JOHN BACCHUS DYKES, 1866

In flowing rhythm

1. Calm on   the list - ening   ear   of night Come heav'n's me - lo - dious strains,
2. Ce - les - tial choirs from   courts a - bove Shed   sa - cred glo - ries there;
3. The answer-ing hills   of   Pal - es - tine Send back the glad   re - ply,
4. O'er   the blue depths of   Gal - i - lee There comes a   ho - lier calm;
5. "Glo - ry to God!" the   loft - y strain The realm of   e - ther fills;
6. "Glo - ry to God!" the   sound-ing skies Loud with their an - thems ring:

Where wild Ju - de - a stretch-es   far   Her   sil - ver - man - tled plains.
And   an - gels, with their spark-ling lyres, Make mu - sic on   the   air.
And   greet from all their ho - ly heights The Day-spring from on   high.
And   Shar - on waves in sol - emn praise Her   si - lent groves of palm.
How sweeps the song   of sol - emn joy O'er Ju - dah's sa - cred hills!
"Peace on the earth, good-will to men, From heaven's e - ter - nal King." A-MEN.

Our Lord Jesus Christ

104

JAMES MONTGOMERY, 1816   8. 7. 8. 7. 8. 7.   REGENT SQUARE
HENRY SMART, 1867

Joyfully

1. An - gels, from the realms of glo - ry Wing your flight o'er
2. Shep - herds in the fields a - bid - ing, Watch - ing o'er your
3. Sa - ges, leave your con - tem - pla - tions, Bright - er vi - sions
4. Saints be - fore the al - tar bend - ing, Watch - ing long in

all the earth; Ye who sang cre - a - tion's sto - ry,
flocks by night, God with man is now re - sid - ing,
beam a - far; Seek the great De - sire of na - tions,
hope and fear, Sud - den - ly the Lord, de - scend - ing,

Now pro - claim Mes - si - ah's birth: Come and wor - ship,
Yon - der shines the in - fant Light: Come and wor - ship,
Ye have seen His na - tal star: Come and wor - ship,
In His tem - ple shall ap - pear: Come and wor - ship,

come and wor - ship, Wor - ship Christ, the new - born King.
come and wor - ship, Wor - ship Christ, the new - born King.
come and wor - ship, Wor - ship Christ, the new - born King.
come and wor - ship, Wor - ship Christ, the new - born King. A-MEN.

His Nativity

105

LES ANGES DANS NOS CAMPAGNES (IRIS)

Traditional Carol
Altered by EARL MARLATT, 1937   7. 7. 7. 7. with Refrain   French Carol Melody

Joyously

1. An - gels we have heard on high, Sing - ing sweet - ly through the night,
2. Shep - herds, why this ju - bi - lee? Why these songs of hap - py cheer?
3. Come to Beth - le - hem and see Him whose birth the an - gels sing;

And the moun-tains in re - ply Ech - o - ing their brave de - light.
What great bright-ness did you see? What glad ti - dings did you hear?
Come, a - dore on bend - ed knee Christ, the Lord, the new - born King.

REFRAIN

Glo - - - - - - - - - - - ri - a

in ex - cel - sis De - o, Glo - - - - - - - -

- - - - - ri - a . . in ex - cel - sis De - o. A - MEN.

Our Lord Jesus Christ

106

NAHUM TATE, 1703   C. M.   GEORGE FREDERICK HANDEL, 1728

CHRISTMAS

Joyously

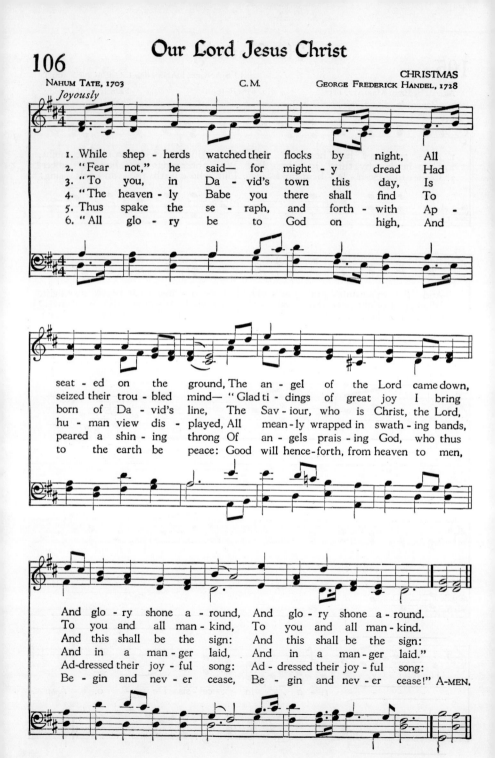

1. While shep - herds watched their flocks by night, All
2. "Fear not," he said— for might - y dread Had
3. "To you, in Da - vid's town this day, Is
4. "The heaven - ly Babe you there shall find To
5. Thus spake the se - raph, and forth - with Ap -
6. "All glo - ry be to God on high, And

seat - ed on the ground, The an - gel of the Lord came down,
seized their trou - bled mind— "Glad ti - dings of great joy I bring
born of Da - vid's line, The Sav - iour, who is Christ, the Lord,
hu - man view dis - played, All mean - ly wrapped in swath - ing bands,
peared a shin - ing throng Of an - gels prais - ing God, who thus
to the earth be peace: Good will hence - forth, from heaven to men,

And glo - ry shone a - round, And glo - ry shone a - round.
To you and all man - kind, To you and all man - kind.
And this shall be the sign: And this shall be the sign:
And in a man - ger laid, And in a man - ger laid."
Ad - dressed their joy - ful song: Ad - dressed their joy - ful song:
Be - gin and nev - er cease, Be - gin and nev - er cease!" A-MEN.

His Nativity

107

Edmund H. Sears, 1850

C.M.D.

CAROL
R. Storrs Willis, 1850

In the style of a carol

1. It came up-on the mid-night clear, That glo-rious song of old,
2. Still through the clo-ven skies they come, With peace-ful wings un-furled,
3. O ye, be-neath life's crush-ing load, Whose forms are bend-ing low,
4. For lo! the days are has-ten-ing on, By proph-et bards fore-told,

From an-gels bend-ing near the earth To touch their harps of gold:
And still their heavenly mu-sic floats O'er all the wear-y world;
Who toil a-long the climb-ing way With pain-ful steps and slow,—
When with the ev-er-cir-cling years Comes round the age of gold,

"Peace on the earth, good-will to men, From heaven's all-gra-cious King!"
A-bove its sad and low-ly plains They bend on hov-ering wing,
Look now! for glad and gold-en hours Come swift-ly on the wing:
When peace shall o-ver all the earth Its an-cient splen-dors fling,

The world in sol-emn still-ness lay, To hear the an-gels sing.
And ev-er o'er its Ba-bel-sounds The bless-ed an-gels sing.
O rest be-side the wea-ry road, And hear the an-gels sing.
And the whole world give back the song Which now the an-gels sing.

A-MEN.

Our Lord Jesus Christ

108

PHILLIPS BROOKS, 1868   8. 6. 8. 6. 7. 6. 8. 6.   ST. LOUIS
LEWIS H. REDNER, 1868

With joy and serenity

1. O lit - tle town of Beth - le - hem, How still we see thee lie;
2. For Christ is born of Ma - ry, And gath - ered all a - bove,
3. How si - lent - ly, how si - lent - ly The won - drous gift is given!
4. O Ho - ly Child of Beth - le - hem! De - scend to us, we pray;

A - bove thy deep and dream-less sleep The si - lent stars go by:
While mor - tals sleep, the an - gels keep Their watch of won-dering love.
So God im - parts to hu - man hearts The bless - ings of His heaven;
Cast out our sin, and en - ter in, Be born in us to - day.

Yet in thy dark streets shin - eth The Ev - er - last - ing Light;
O morn - ing stars, to - geth - er Pro - claim the ho - ly birth!
No ear may hear His com - ing, But in this world of sin,
We hear the Christ-mas an - gels The great glad ti - dings tell;

The hopes and fears of all the years Are met in thee to-night.
And prais - es sing to God the King, And peace to men on earth!
Where meek souls will re - ceive Him, still The dear Christ en - ters in.
O come to us, a - bide with us, Our Lord Em-man - u - el!   A-MEN.

His Nativity

109

Ascribed to MARTIN LUTHER

11. 11. 11. 11.

MÜLLER
CARL MÜLLER

In the style of a carol

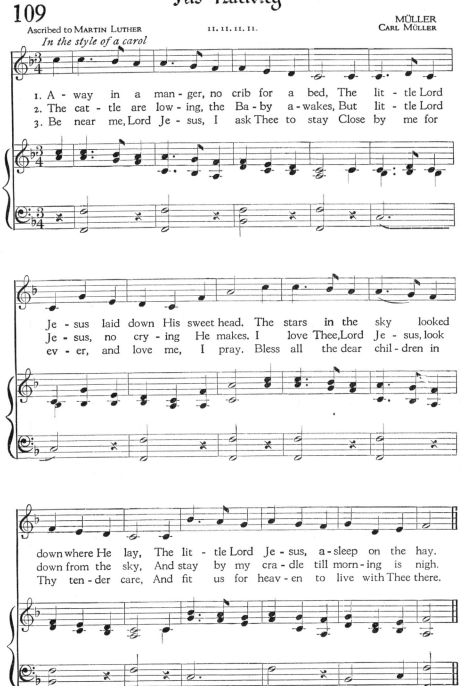

1. A - way in a man - ger, no crib for a bed, The lit - tle Lord
2. The cat - tle are low - ing, the Ba - by a - wakes, But lit - tle Lord
3. Be near me, Lord Je - sus, I ask Thee to stay Close by me for

Je - sus laid down His sweet head. The stars in the sky looked
Je - sus, no cry - ing He makes. I love Thee, Lord Je - sus, look
ev - er, and love me, I pray. Bless all the dear chil - dren in

down where He lay, The lit - tle Lord Je - sus, a - sleep on the hay.
down from the sky, And stay by my cra - dle till morn - ing is nigh.
Thy ten - der care, And fit us for heav - en to live with Thee there.

Our Lord Jesus Christ

110

Croatian Carol

8. 8. with Refrain

CROATIA
XIV Century Croatian Carol

In graceful rhythm

1. Hark, the an - gel voi - ces sing-ing, Through the night their songs are wing - ing.
2. Ev - ery one the word is bring - ing, "Peace, good will" the mes - sage ring - ing.
3. Hark the bells! their mu - sic tell - ing News to earth, all gloom dis - pell - ing.

REFRAIN

Heaven an - noun - ces ti - dings of cheer, Heaven con - firms the news that we hear; Heaven an - noun - ces

His Nativity

ti - dings of cheer, . . Heaven con - firms the news that we hear.

From *Trips Abroad* by Stella Marek Cushing in *Music Highways and Byways,* copyright 1936, Silver Burdett Company, New York.

111

KOMMET IHR HIRTEN

Bohemian Folk Song
Tr. Mari Ruef Hofer, 1912

10. 10. 10. 10. 4.

Bohemian Folk Song

Joyously

1. Come, all ye shep - herds, ye chil - dren of earth, Come ye, bring greet - ings to
2. Hast - en then, hast - en to Beth - le - hem's stall, There to see heav - en de -
3. An - gels and shep - herds to - geth - er we go Seek - ing this Sav - iour from

yon heaven - ly birth. For Christ the Lord to all men is giv - en,
scend to us all. With ho - ly feel - ing, there hum - bly kneel - ing,
all earth - ly woe; While an - gels, wing - ing, His praise are sing - ing,

To be our Sav - iour sent down from heav - en: Come, wel - come Him!
We will a - dore Him, bow down be - fore Him, Wor - ship the King.
Heaven's ech - oes ring - ing, peace on earth bring - ing, Good will to men.

Our Lord Jesus Christ

112

Latin Hymn, 18th century
Tr. FREDERICK OAKELEY, 1841

Irregular

ADESTE FIDELES

WADE'S *Cantus Diversi,* 1751

Joyously

1. O come, all ye faith-ful, Joy-ful and tri-umph-ant, O
2. O sing, choirs of an-gels, Sing in ex-ul-ta-tion! Sing
3. A-men, Lord, we greet Thee, Born this hap-py morn-ing, O

come . ye, O come ye to Beth-le-hem! Come and be-hold Him,
all . . . ye cit-i-zens of heaven a-bove! Now to our God be
Je-sus, for-ev-er be Thy Name a-dored; Word of the Fa-ther,

REFRAIN

Born the King of an-gels! O come, let us a-dore Him, O come, let us a-
Glo-ry in the high-est!
Now in flesh ap-pear-ing!

dore Him, O come, let us a-dore Him, Christ the Lord! A-MEN.

His Nativity

1 Adeste, fideles,
Laeti, triumphantes;
Venite, venite in Bethlehem;
Natum videte
Regem angelorum:
   Venite, adoremus, venite, adoremus,
   Venite, adoremus Dominum.

2 Cantet nunc hymnum
Chorus angelorum;
Cantet nunc aula cœlestium:
Gloria, Gloria
In excelsis Deo!
   Venite, adoremus, venite, adoremus,
   Venite, adoremus Dominum.

3 Ergo qui natus
Die hodierna,
Jesu, tibi sit gloria:
Patris aeterni
Verbum caro factum:
   Venite, adoremus, venite, adoremus
   Venite, adoremus Dominum.

113

Sixteenth Century
Tr. st. 1-4, HARRIET R. KRAUTH, 1879
St. 5, JOHN CASPAR MATTES, 1914

ES IST EIN REIS ENTSPRUNGEN

Traditional Rhenish Folk Song
Alte Kath. Geistliche Kirchengesäng, KÖLN, 1599

7. 6. 7. 6. 6. 7. 6.

In the style of a carol

1. Be - hold a Branch is grow-ing Of love - liest form and grace; As proph-ets
2. I - sa - iah hath fore-told it In words of prom-ise sure, And Ma-ry's
3. The shep-herds heard the sto - ry Pro-claimed by an - gels bright, How Christ, the
4. This Flower, whose fragrance ten-der With sweet-ness fills the air, Dis-pels with
5. O Sav - iour, Child of Ma - ry, Who felt our hu-man woe, O Sav-iour,

sung, fore-know-ing, It springs from Jes - se's race, And bears one lit - tle Flower
arms en - fold It, A vir - gin meek and pure. Through God's e-ter - nal will
Lord of glo - ry Was born on earth this night. To Beth - le - hem they sped,
glo - rious splen-dor The dark-ness ev - ery-where. True Man, yet ver - y God,
King of glo - ry, Who dost our weak-ness know, Bring us at length we pray

In midst of cold - est win - ter, At deep - est mid-night hour.
This Child to her is giv - en, At mid - night calm and still.
And in the man-ger found Him, As an - gel - her - alds said.
From sin and death He saves us And light - ens ev - ery load.
To the bright courts of heav - en, And to the end - less day. A-MEN.

Our Lord Jesus Christ

MARTIN LUTHER, 1535
Tr. CATHERINE WINKWORTH, 1855

L. M.

VOM HIMMEL HOCH (ERFURT)

Geistliche Lieder, LEIPZIG, 1539

In graceful rhythm

1. From heaven a - bove to earth I come, To bear good news to
2. "To you, this night, is born a Child Of Ma - ry, cho - sen
3. "'Tis Christ, our God, who far on high Hath heard your sad and
4. Wel - come to earth, Thou no - ble Guest, Through whom e'en wick - ed
5. Ah, dear - est Je - sus, Ho - ly Child, Make Thee a bed, soft,
6. Glo - ry to God in high - est heaven, Who un - to man His

ev - ery home; Glad ti - dings of great joy I bring,
moth - er mild; This lit - tle Child of low - ly birth,
bit - ter cry; Him - self will your sal - va - tion be,
men are blest! Thou comest to share our mis - er - y;
un - de - filed, With - in my heart, that it may be
Son hath given, While an - gels sing with pi - ous mirth

Where - of I now will say and sing:
Shall be the joy of all your earth.
Him - self from sin will make you free."
What can we ren - der, Lord, to Thee?
A qui - et cham - ber kept for Thee!
A glad New Year to all the earth. A-MEN.

His Nativity

115

JOHN BYROM, 1750

IO. IO. IO. IO. IO. IO.

YORKSHIRE
JOHN WAINWRIGHT, 1750

Joyously

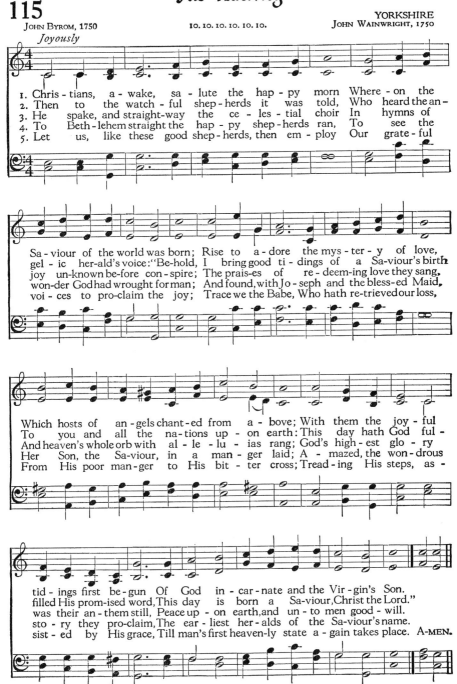

1. Chris - tians, a - wake, sa - lute the hap - py morn Where - on the
2. Then to the watch - ful shep - herds it was told, Who heard the an -
3. He spake, and straight-way the ce - les - tial choir In hymns of
4. To Beth - lehem straight the hap - py shep - herds ran, To see the
5. Let us, like these good shep - herds, then em - ploy Our grate - ful

Sa - viour of the world was born; Rise to a - dore the mys - ter - y of love,
gel - ic her-ald's voice:"Be-hold, I bring good ti - dings of a Sa-viour's birth,
joy un-known be-fore con - spire; The prais-es of re - deem-ing love they sang,
won-der God had wrought for man; And found, with Jo - seph and the bless-ed Maid,
voi - ces to pro-claim the joy; Trace we the Babe, Who hath re-trieved our loss,

Which hosts of an - gels chant-ed from a - bove; With them the joy - ful
To you and all the na - tions up - on earth: This day hath God ful -
And heaven's whole orb with al - le - lu - ias rang; God's high - est glo - ry
Her Son, the Sa - viour, in a man - ger laid; A - mazed, the won - drous
From His poor man - ger to His bit - ter cross; Tread-ing His steps, as -

tid - ings first be-gun Of God in - car-nate and the Vir-gin's Son.
filled His prom-ised word, This day is born a Sa-viour, Christ the Lord."
was their an - them still, Peace up - on earth, and un - to men good - will.
sto - ry they pro-claim, The ear - liest her - alds of the Sa-viour's name.
sist - ed by His grace, Till man's first heaven-ly state a - gain takes place. A-MEN.

Our Lord Jesus Christ

116

Medieval Latin
Tr. John Mason Neale, 1853

6. 6. 7. 7. 7. 8. 5. 5.

IN DULCI JUBILO
14th Century German Melody
Descant by H. A. Chambers

Descant stanza 2

2. Good Chris-tian men, re-joice,   With heart and soul and voice;

1. Good Christian men, re - joice, . . With heart and soul and voice; . .
2. Good Christian men, re - joice, . . With heart and soul and voice; . .
3. Good Christian men, re - joice, . . With heart and soul and voice; . .

Now ye hear of end - less bliss: Je - sus Christ was born for this!

Give ye heed to what we say: Je - sus Christ is born to - day;
Now ye hear of end - less bliss; Je - sus Christ was born for this!
Now ye need not fear the grave; Je - sus Christ was born to save!

He hath oped the heaven-ly door, And man is bless - ed ev - er-more.

Man and beast be - fore Him bow, And He is in the man - ger now.
He hath oped the heaven-ly door, And man is bless - ed ev - er-more.
Calls you one and calls you all, To gain His ev - er - last - ing hall.

His Nativity

Christ is born to-day! . . .   Christ is born to-day!
Christ was born for this! . . .   Christ was born for this!
Christ was born to save! . . .   Christ was born to save!

Christ was born, Christ was born for this.

117

German. Stanza 1, J. Falk; st. 2, 3, Anonymous
Tr. H. Katterjohn, 1919   9. 7. 6. 6. 10.

SICILIAN MARINERS' HYMN
Sicilian Melody, 1794

Joyfully, with flowing rhythm

1. O thou joy - ful, O thou won - der - ful Grace re - veal - ing
2. O thou joy - ful, O thou won - der - ful Love re - veal - ing
3. O thou joy - ful, O thou won - der - ful Peace re - veal - ing

Christ - mas - tide! Je - sus came to win us From all sin with - in us:
Christ - mas - tide! Loud ho - san - nas sing - ing And all prais - es bring - ing,
Christ - mas - tide! Dark - ness dis - ap - pear - eth, God's own light now near - eth,

Glo - ri - fy, glo - ri - fy the Ho - ly Child!
May Thy love, may Thy love with us a - bide.
Peace and joy, peace and joy to all be - tide.   A - MEN.

Our Lord Jesus Christ

118

THE FIRST NOWELL

Traditional melody in W. SANDYS' *Christmas Carols*, 1833

English Carol, 1833   Irregular, with Refrain   Descant by EDWARD SHIPPEN BARNES

DESCANT

In the style of a Carol

1. The first No-well the an-gels did say Was to cer-tain poor shep-herds in fields as they lay, In fields as they lay keep-ing their sheep, On a cold win-ter's night that was so deep. No-well, No-
2. They look-ed up and saw a star, Shin-ing in the east be-yond them far, And to the earth it gave great light, And so it con-tin-ued both day and night.
3. And by the light of that same star, Three Wise Men came from a coun-try a-far, To seek for a king was their in-tent, And to fol-low the star wher-ev-er it went.
4. This star drew nigh to the north-west, O'er Beth-le-hem it took its rest, And there it did both stop and stay, Right o-ver the place where Je-sus lay.
5. Then en-tered in those Wise Men three Full rev-erent-ly up-on their knee, And of-fered there in His pres-ence Their gold, and myrrh, and frank-in-cense.
6. Then let us all with one ac-cord Sing prais-es to our heaven-ly Lord, That hath made heaven and earth of naught, And with His blood man-kind hath bought.

REFRAIN

His Nativity

well, No-well, No-well, Born is the King of Is - ra - el!

119

PAUL GERHARDT, 1653
Tr. CATHERINE WINKWORTH, 1858

WARUM SOLLT ICH MICH DENN GRÄMEN (EBELING; BONN)

8. 3. 3. 6. D.

JOHANN GEORG EBELING, 1666

In the style of a Carol

1. All my heart this night re - joi - ces, As I hear, Far and near,
2. Hark! a voice from yon - der man - ger, Soft and sweet, Doth en - treat,
3. Come, then, let us has - ten yon - der; Here let all, Great and small,

Sweet-est an - gel voi - ces; "Christ is born," the choirs are sing - ing,
"Flee from woe and dan - ger; Breth - ren, come; from all that grieves you
Kneel in awe and won - der, Love Him who with love is yearn - ing;

Till the air, Ev - ery-where, Now with joy is ring - ing.
You are freed; All you need I will sure - ly give you."
Hail the Star That from far Bright with hope is burn - ing. A-MEN.

Our Lord Jesus Christ

From Psalm xcviii. ISAAC WATTS, 1719   C. M.   ANTIOCH
GEORGE FREDERICK HANDEL, 1742

With joy and dignity

1. Joy to the world! the Lord is come: Let earth re-
2. Joy to the earth! the Saviour reigns: Let men their
3. He rules the world with truth and grace, And makes the

ceive her King; Let ev-ery heart pre-pare Him room,
songs em-ploy; While fields and floods, rocks, hills, and plains
na-tions prove The glo-ries of His right-eous-ness,

And heaven and na-ture sing, And heaven and na-ture
Re-peat the sound-ing joy, Re-peat the sound-ing
And won-ders of His love, And won-ders of His

And heaven and na-ture sing,........
Re-peat the sound-ing joy,........
And won-ders of His love,........

And
Re-
And

sing, And heaven, and heaven and na-ture sing.
joy, Re-peat, re-peat the sound-ing joy.
love, And won-ders, won-ders of His love.   A-MEN.

heaven and na-ture sing,
peat the sound-ing joy,
won-ders of His love,

His Epiphany

121

REGINALD HEBER, 1811   11. 10. 11. 10.   MORNING STAR
JOHN P. HARDING, 1850-1911

In the style of a carol

1. Bright - est and best of the sons of the morn - ing,
2. Cold on His cra - dle the dew - drops are shin - ing;
3. Shall we not yield Him, in cost - ly de - vo - tion,
4. Vain - ly we of - fer each am - ple ob - la - tion,

Dawn on our dark - ness and lend us thine aid;
Low lies His head with the beasts of the stall:
O - dors of E - dom and of - ferings di - vine,
Vain - ly with gifts would His fa - vor se - cure;

Star of the East, the ho - ri - zon a - dorn - ing,
An - gels a - dore Him in slum - ber re - clin - ing,
Gems of the moun - tain and pearls of the o - cean,
Rich - er by far is the heart's ad - o - ra - tion,

Guide where our in - fant Re - deem - er is laid.
Mak - er and Mon - arch and Sav - iour of all!
Myrrh from the for - est, or gold from the mine?
Dear - er to God are the prayers of the poor. A - MEN.

Alternative tune, *Wesley.*

Our Lord Jesus Christ

122

WIE SCHÖN LEUCHTET (FRANKFORT)

PHILIPP NICOLAI, 1599
Tr. CATHERINE WINKWORTH, 1829–1878   8.8.7.8.8.7.4.8.4.8.   PHILLIP NICOLAI, 1599

May be sung in unison; with exaltation

1. O   Morn - ing Star, how   fair   and bright Thou beam - est   forth in
2. Thou heaven - ly Bright-ness! Light   di - vine! O   deep with - in   my

truth and light! O   Sov-ereign meek and   low - ly! Thou Root of Jes - se,
heart now shine, And make Thee there an   al - tar! Fill   me with joy and

Da - vid's Son, My   Lord and Mas - ter, Thou hast won My heart to serve Thee
strength to   be Thy mem-ber, ev - er joined to Thee In   love that can - not

sole - ly! Thou   art ho - ly,   Fair and glo-rious, All   vic - to-rious,
fal - ter;   Toward Thee long - ing Doth pos-sess me; Turn and bless me;

His Epiphany

Rich in bless - ing, Rule and might o'er all pos - sess - ing.
Here in sad - ness Eye and heart long for Thy glad - ness! A-MEN.

123

WILLIAM C. DIX, 1861

7. 7. 7. 7. 7. 7.

DIX
Abridged from Chorale, *Treuer Heiland*
CONRAD KOCHER, 1838

Joyously

1. As with glad-ness men of old Did the guid-ing star be-hold;
2. As with joy-ful steps they sped To that low-ly man-ger-bed;
3. As they of-fered gifts most rare At that man-ger rude and bare;
4. Ho-ly Je - sus, ev - ery day Keep us in the nar-row way;
5. In the heaven-ly coun-try bright Need they no cre-a-ted light;

As with joy they hailed its light, Lead-ing on - ward, beam-ing bright;
There to bend the knee be-fore Him whom heaven and earth a - dore;
So may we with ho - ly joy, Pure and free from sin's al - loy,
And, when earth-ly things are past, Bring our ran-somed souls at last
Thou its Light, its Joy, its Crown, Thou its Sun which goes not down,

So, most gra-cious God, may we Ev - er-more be led to Thee.
So may we with will-ing feet Ev - er seek the mer - cy - seat.
All our cost-liest treasures bring, Christ, to Thee our heaven-ly King.
Where they need no star to guide, Where no clouds Thy glo - ry hide.
There for - ev - er may we sing Hal - le - lu - jah to our King. A-MEN.

Our Lord Jesus Christ

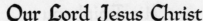

124

JOHN S. B. MONSELL, 1863   7.6.7.6.D.   LIGHT OF THE WORLD
Anonymous

1. Light of the world, we hail Thee Flush-ing the east-ern skies;
Nev-er shall dark-ness veil Thee A-gain from hu-man eyes.
Too long, a-las, with-hold-en, Now spread from shore to shore,
Thy light, so glad and gold-en, Shall set on earth no more.

2. Light of the world, Thy beau-ty Steals in-to ev-ery heart
And glo-ri-fies with du-ty Life's poor-est, hum-blest part;
Thou rob-est in Thy splen-dor The sim-ple ways of men,
And help-est them to ren-der Light back to Thee a-gain.

3. Light of the world, il-lu-mine This dark-ened land of Thine,
Till ev-ery-thing that's hu-man Be filled with what's di-vine;
Till ev-ery tongue and na-tion, From sin's do-min-ion free,
Rise in the new cre-a-tion Which springs from love to Thee. A-MEN.

His Epiphany

125

ARTHUR PENRHYN STANLEY, 1815–1881   L.M.D.

CANTATE DOMINO (JORDAN)
JOSEPH BARNBY, 1872

Joyfully, with well-defined rhythm

1. The Lord is come, on Syr-ian soil, The child of pov-er-ty and toil;
2. The Lord is come! In Him we trace The ful-ness of God's truth and grace;
3. The Lord is come! In ev-ery heart Where truth and mer-cy claim a part;

The Man of Sor-rows, born to know Each vary-ing shade of hu-man woe;
Through-out those words and acts di-vine Gleams of the e-ter-nal splen-dor shine;
In ev-ery land where right is might, And deeds of dark-ness shun the light;

UNISON   HARMONY

His joy, His glo-ry, to ful-fil, In earth and heaven, His Fa-ther's will;
And from His in-most spir-it flow, As from a height of sun-lit snow,
In ev-ery church where faith and love Lift earth-ward thoughts to things a-bove;

UNISON   HARMONY

On lone-ly mount, by fes-tive board, On bit-ter cross, de-spised, a-dored.
The riv-ers of pe-ren-nial life, To heal and sweet-en na-ture's strife.
In ev-ery ho-ly, hap-py home, We bless Thee, Lord, that Thou hast come. A-MEN.

Our Lord Jesus Christ

126

EMILY E. S. ELLIOTT, 1864   Irregular   TIMOTHY R. MATTHEWS, 1876

MARGARET

In moderate time

1. Thou didst leave Thy throne and Thy king - ly crown, When Thou cam - est to
2. Heav-en's arch - es rang when the an - gels sang, Pro - claim-ing Thy
3. Thou cam - est, O Lord, with the liv - ing Word That should set Thy
4. When the heavens shall ring, and the an - gels sing At Thy com - ing to

earth for me; But in Beth - le-hem's home there was found no room
roy - al de-gree; But in low - ly birth didst Thou come to earth,
chil - dren free; But with mock-ing scorn and with crown of thorn
vic - to - ry, Let Thy voice call me home, say - ing, "Yet there is room,

For Thy ho - ly na - tiv - i - ty. O come to my
And in great hu - mil - i - ty. O come to my
They bore Thee to Cal - va - ry. O come to my
There is room at my side for thee." And my heart shall re -

heart, Lord Je - sus: There is room in my heart for Thee!
heart, Lord Je - sus: There is room in my heart for Thee!
heart, Lord Je - sus: There is room in my heart for Thee!
joice, Lord Je - sus: There is room in my heart for Thee! A-MEN.

His Life and Ministry

EDGAR DANIEL KRAMER   7. 6. 7. 6. D.   LONE ACRE
CARL F. MUELLER

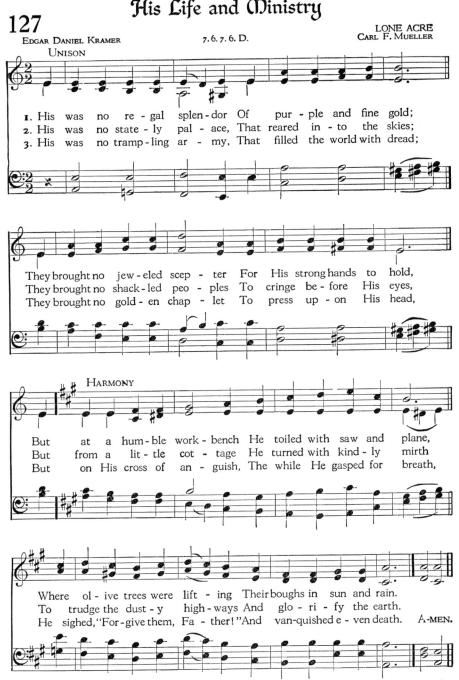

UNISON

1. His was no re-gal splen-dor Of pur-ple and fine gold;
2. His was no state-ly pal-ace, That reared in-to the skies;
3. His was no tramp-ling ar-my, That filled the world with dread,

They brought no jew-eled scep-ter For His strong hands to hold,
They brought no shack-led peo-ples To cringe be-fore His eyes,
They brought no gold-en chap-let To press up-on His head,

HARMONY

But at a hum-ble work-bench He toiled with saw and plane,
But from a lit-tle cot-tage He turned with kind-ly mirth
But on His cross of an-guish, The while He gasped for breath,

Where ol-ive trees were lift-ing Their boughs in sun and rain.
To trudge the dust-y high-ways And glo-ri-fy the earth.
He sighed, "For-give them, Fa-ther!" And van-quished e-ven death. A-MEN.

Our Lord Jesus Christ

128

JAMES R. WOODFORD, 1820–1885   S. M.   ST. ANDREW
JOSEPH BARNBY, 1866

In moderate time

1. With - in the Fa - ther's house The Son hath found His home; And
2. The doc - tors of the law Gaze on the won-drous Child, And
3. Yet not to them is given The might - y truth to know, To
4. The se - cret of the Lord Es - capes each hu - man eye, And
5. Lord, vis - it Thou our souls, And teach us by Thy grace Each
6. Till from our dark - ened sight The cloud shall pass a - way, And

to His tem - ple sud - den - ly The Lord of Life hath come.
mar - vel at His gra - cious words Of wis - dom un - de - filed.
lift the flesh - ly veil which hides In - car - nate God be - low.
faith - ful pon - dering hearts a - wait The full e - piph - an - y.
dim re - veal - ing of Thy-self With lov - ing awe to trace;
on the cleans - èd soul shall burst The ev - er - last - ing day. A-MEN.

129

HENRY S. NINDE, 1859   8. 5. 8. 5.   CAIRNBROOK
EBENEZER PROUT

In moderate time

1. Thou didst teach the throng-ing peo - ple By blue Gal - i - lee;
2. Thou whose touch could heal the lep - er, Make the blind to see;
3. Thou whose word could still the tem - pest, Calm the rag - ing sea;
4. Thou didst sin - less meet the temp - ter; Grant, O Christ, that we

Speak to us, Thy err - ing chil - dren, Teach us pur - i - ty.
Touch our hearts and turn the sin - ning Un - to pur - i - ty.
Hush the storm of hu - man pas - sion; Give us pur - i - ty.
May o'er-come the bent to e - vil By Thy pur - i - ty. A-MEN.

His Life and Ministry

130

WILLIAM J. DAWSON, 1854–1928

8. 7. 11. D.

STOCKWELL NEW
CALVIN W. LAUFER, 1928

Reverently, not too fast

1. When the gold - en eve - ning gath - ered On the shore of Gal - i - lee,
2. Not in robes of pur - ple splen - dor, Not in silk - en soft - ness shod,
3. For He healed their sick at e - ven, And He cured the le - per's sore,
4. Not in robes of pur - ple splen - dor, But in lives that do His will,

When the fish - ing boats lay qui - et by the sea,
But in rai - ment worn with trav - el came their God,
And the sin - ful men and wom - en sinned no more,
And in pa - tient acts of kind - ness He comes still;

Long a - go the peo - ple won - dered, Though no sign was in the sky,
And the peo - ple knew His pres - ence By the heart that ceased to sigh
And the world grew mirth - ful - heart - ed, And for - got its mis - er - y
And the peo - ple cry with won - der, Though no sign is in the sky,

For the glo - ry of the Lord was pass - ing by.
When the glo - ry of the Lord was pass - ing by.
When the glo - ry of the Lord was pass - ing by.
That the glo - ry of the Lord is pass - ing by. A-MEN.

Our Lord Jesus Christ

131

JAY T. STOCKING, 1912   C.M.D.   BETHLEHEM (SERAPH)
GOTTFRIED W. FINK, 1842

In moderate time

1. O Mas - ter Work-man of the race, Thou Man of Gal - i - lee,
2. O Car - pen - ter of Naz - a - reth, Build - er of life di - vine,
3. O Thou who dost the vi - sion send And giv - est each his task,

Who with the eyes of ear - ly youth E - ter - nal things didst see,
Who shap-'est man to God's own law, Thy - self the fair de - sign,
And with the task suf - fi - cient strength, Show us Thy will, we ask;

We thank Thee for Thy boy - hood faith That shone Thy whole life through;
Build us a tower of Christ-like height, That we the land may view,
Give us a con-science bold and good, Give us a pur - pose true,

"Did ye not know it is my work My Fa-ther's work to do?"
And see like Thee our no - blest work Our Fa-ther's work to do.
That it may be our high - est joy Our Fa-ther's work to do.   A-MEN.

132

WILLIAM WALSHAM HOW, 1823-1897 L. M.

OLIVE'S BROW
WILLIAM B. BRADBURY, 1853

Meditatively

1. O Thou through suffering per-fect made, On whom the bit-ter cross was laid,
2. The halt, the maimed, the sick, the blind, Sought not in vain Thy ten-dance kind;
3. O lov-ing Sa-viour, Thou canst cure The pains and woes Thou didst en-dure;
4. O heal the bruis-ed heart with-in! O save our souls all sick with sin!

In hours of sick-ness, grief, and pain, No sufferer turns to Thee in vain.
Now in Thy poor Thy-self we see, And min-is-ter through them to Thee.
For all who need, Phy-si-cian great, Thy heal-ing balm we sup-pli-cate.
Give life and health in bounteous store, That we may praise Thee ev-er-more. A-MEN.

His Triumphal Entry

133

HENRY H. MILMAN, 1827 L. M.

ST. DROSTANE
JOHN B. DYKES, 1862

Majestically

1. Ride on! ride on in maj-es-ty! Hark! all the tribes ho-san-na cry;
2. Ride on! ride on in maj-es-ty! In low-ly pomp ride on to die:
3. Ride on! ride on in maj-es-ty! The wing-ed squad-rons of the skies
4. Ride on! ride on in maj-es-ty! In low-ly pomp ride on to die;

O Sav-iour meek, pur-sue Thy road With palms and scattered garments strowed.
O Christ, Thy triumphs now be-gin O'er cap-tive death and conquered sin.
Look down with sad and wonder-ing eyes To see the ap-proach-ing sac-ri-fice.
Bow Thy meek head to mor-tal pain, Then take, O God, Thy power, and reign. A-MEN.

Alternative tune, *Park Street.*

Our Lord Jesus Christ

134

JAMES GORDON GILKEY, 1915   7.6.7.6.D.   ALL HALLOWS
GEORGE C. MARTIN, 1892

Unison. In march time

1. Out - side the Ho - ly Cit - y Un -'num - bered foot-steps throng,
2. Once more be - side a cit - y The Son of Dav - id waits,
3. The branch - es that we of - fer Are no un - mean - ing sign;
4. A dis - tant mu - sic min - gles With all our songs to - day,

And crowd - ed mart and streets of trade Fling back a swell - ing song.
Once more the chil - dren throng to bring A wel - come at the gates.
Take Thou the hands we lift on high And make them whol - ly Thine.
The cho - rale from a cit - y fair Where sin has passed a - way.

The voic - es ech - o near - er, In flam - ing hope they sing;
With - in are hearts sore bur - dened And feet that go a - stray;
No songs of shal - low wel - come Are these we raise to Thee;
There rides the Christ tri - umph - ant And vic - tor songs ring clear;

HARMONY

"Throw down your branch - es at His feet! Ho - san - na to the King!"
O Christ of God, come near and walk Our cit - y streets to - day!
O give us faith to face the cross And set Thy cit - y free!
O God, give us the strength to build With Christ that cit - y here! A - MEN.

Org.

His Triumphal Entry

135

THEODULPH OF ORLEANS, 820
Tr. JOHN MASON NEALE, 1854

VALET WILL ICH DIR GEBEN (ST. THEODULPH)

7.6.7.6.D.

MELCHIOR TESCHNER, 1615

With well defined rhythm

1. All glo - ry, laud, and hon - or To Thee, Re - deem - er, King,
2. Thou art the King of Is - rael, Thou Da - vid's roy - al Son,
3. Thou didst ac - cept their prais - es; Ac - cept the prayers we bring,

To whom the lips of chil - dren Made sweet ho - san - nas ring!
Who in the Lord's name com - est, The King and bless - ed One!
Who in all good de - light - est, Thou good and gra - cious King!

The peo - ple of the He - brews With palms be - fore Thee went;
To Thee, be - fore Thy pas - sion, They sang their hymns of praise;
All glo - ry, laud, and hon - or To Thee, Re - deem - er, King,

Our praise and prayer and an - thems Be - fore Thee we pre - sent.
To Thee, now high ex - alt - ed Our mel - o - dy we raise.
To whom the lips of chil - dren Made sweet ho - san - nas ring! A-MEN.

Our Lord Jesus Christ

136

JENNETTE THRELFALL, 1873

ELLACOMBE
*Gesangbuch der Herzogl. Wirtembergischen
Katholischen Hofkapelle,* 1784

7. 6. 7. 6. D.

Joyfully

1. Ho - san - na, loud ho - san - na The lit - tle chil - dren sang;
2. From Ol - i - vet they fol - lowed 'Mid an ex - ult - ant crowd,
3. "Ho - san - na in the high - est!" That an - cient song we sing,

Through pil - lared court and tem - ple The love - ly an - them rang;
The vic - tor palm-branch wav - ing, And chant-ing clear and loud;
For Christ is our Re - deem - er, The Lord of heaven our King.

To Je - sus, who had blessed them Close fold - ed to His breast,
The Lord of men and an - gels Rode on in low - ly state,
O may we ev - er praise Him With heart and life and voice,

The chil - dren sang their prais - es, The sim - plest and the best.
Nor scorned that lit - tle chil - dren Should on His bid - ding wait.
And in His bliss - ful pres - ence E - ter - nal - ly re - joice! A-MEN.

His Triumphal Entry

137

ERNEST F. McGREGOR

L. M. D.

CANTATE DOMINO (JORDAN)
JOSEPH BARNBY, 1872

With marked rhythm

1. Lift high the tri - umph song to - day! From Ol - i - vet to Cal - va - ry
2. We climb a - gain the wood - ed slopes Of Ol - i - vet and Cal - va - ry;
3. We join the throng to wel - come Him: From Ol - i - vet and Cal - va - ry—
4. We o - pen wide the gates of love! By Ol - i - vet, by Cal - va - ry,

We tread a - gain that an - cient way Our Sav - iour rode in maj - es - ty.
We share with Him those ra - diant hopes, Which led at last to vic - to - ry.
De - scend the heights to shad - ows dim, Through death with Him to lib - er - ty.
Ac - claim Him Christ, from God a - bove, Our King, through all e - ter - ni - ty.

UNISON   HARMONY

Let now the loud ho - san - nas ring! The Prince of Peace is pass - ing by;
Let now the loud ho - san - nas ring! The Prince of Peace is pass - ing by;
Let now the loud ho - san - nas ring! The Prince of Peace is pass - ing by;
Let now the loud ho - san - nas ring! The Prince of Peace is pass - ing by;

UNISON   HARMONY

The Lord of Life, our Sav - iour King, Goes brave - ly forth, to reign and die.
The Lord of Life, our Sav - iour King, Goes glad - ly forth, to live—and die.
The Lord of Life, our Sav - iour King, Goes hum - bly forth, to serve—and die.
The Lord of Life, our Sav - iour King, Goes no - bly forth, no more to die. A - MEN.

Our Lord Jesus Christ

138

JOHN KING, 1830   7.6.7.6. D.   TOURS   BERTHOLD TOURS, 1872

Moderately fast

1. When, His sal - va - tion bring - ing, To Zi - on Je - sus came,
2. And, since the Lord re - tain - eth His love for chil - dren still,
3. For, should we fail pro - claim - ing Our great Re - deem - er's praise,

The chil - dren all stood sing - ing Ho - san - na to His name;
Though now as King He reign - eth On Zi - on's heaven - ly hill,
The stones, our si - lence sham - ing, Would their ho - san - nas raise.

Nor did their zeal of - fend Him, But, as He rode a - long,
We'll flock a - round His ban - ner Who sits up - on the throne,
But shall we on - ly ren - der The trib - ute of our words?

He let them still at - tend Him, And smiled to hear their song.
And cry a - loud, "Ho - san - na To Da - vid's roy - al Son!"
No! while our hearts are ten - der, They too shall be the Lord's. A-MEN.

His Triumphal Entry

139

John M. Versteeg, 1936   8.7.8.7.D.   HOLMBUSH
G. Darlington Richards, 1938

With great dignity yet not too slowly

1. Does Thy soul leap up with-in Thee, Je - sus, Lord, a - bout to die?
2. Does Thy soul leap up with-in Thee, Je - sus, Lord, a - bout to die?
3. Ah, Thou art my in - spir - a - tion, Great young soul from Gal - i - lee,
4. May my soul leap up with-in me, Je - sus, Lord, who dared to die,

Now Thine eyes be - hold the cit - y, Faith-ful friends with Thee draw nigh;
With their gar-ments, palms, and prais-es, Kept they still, the stones would cry!
Who, for all this dem - on - stra-tion, Keep-est to Thy des - tin - y!
When I, too, ap-proach the cit - y, May I see it with Thine eye.

Does the shout that goes up from them, As the sight their spir - it grips
Can it be that Thou art weep-ing? Weep-ing, Lord, while all these sing!
Grant me grace that when the plau-dits Of the crowd fall on my ears,
If with men's ac - claim I en - ter, On - ly with a cross to end,

And they sing their ex - ul - ta - tion, Find an ech - o on Thy lips?
Dost Thou sense the cit - y's ter - rors, Canst Thou taste its suf - fer - ing?
I shall feel, not thrills of tri-umph, But the pit - y of Thy tears.
May Thy res - o - lute ex - am - ple To my soul Thy val - or lend. A-men.

Our Lord Jesus Christ

140

G. J. Neumann, 1938 — C. M. — SANTA MONICA — T. Tertius Noble, 1938

Words and music copyright, 1941, by Eden Publishing House.

141

Claudia F. Hernaman, 1873 — C. M. — ST. FLAVIAN — Day's Psalter, 1562

His Passion and Crucifixion

HERZLICH TUT MICH VERLANGEN (PASSION CHORALE)
Ascribed to BERNARD OF CLAIRVAUX, 1091–1153
Tr. PAUL GERHARDT, 1656; tr. J. W. ALEXANDER, 1830
HANS LEO HASSLER, 1601
Har. JOH. SEBASTIAN BACH, 1729
7.6.7.6. D.

With great dignity

1. O   Sa - cred Head, now wound-ed,   With grief and shame weighed down,
2. What Thou, my Lord, hast suf - fered   Was all for sin - ners' gain:
3. What lan - guage shall I   bor - row   To thank Thee, dear - est Friend,
4. When strength one day shall fail me,   Lord, fail me not, I   pray:

Now   scorn - ful - ly   sur - round - ed   With thorns, Thine on - ly   crown;
Mine, mine was the trans - gres - sion,   But Thine the dead - ly   pain.
For   this Thy   dy - ing sor - row,   Thy   pit - y   with - out   end?
When pangs of   death as - sail me,   Be - side me, Je - sus, stay:

O   Sa - cred Head, what glo - ry,   What bliss till now was Thine!
Lo, here I   fall, my   Sav - iour,   'Tis   I   de - serve Thy place;
O   make me Thine for - ev - er;   And should I faint - ing   be,
When, head and heart, I   lan - guish,   And hard - ly draw my breath,

Yet, though de - spised and go - ry,   I   joy   to call Thee mine!
Look on   me with Thy fa - vor,   Vouch - safe   to me Thy grace.
Lord, let me nev - er,   nev - er   Out - live my love to Thee.
De - liv - er me from an - guish,   By   vir - tue of Thy death.   A-MEN.

Our Lord Jesus Christ

143

GEORGE HUNT SMYTTAN, 1856
7.7.7.7.
AUS DER TIEFE (HEINLEIN)
Nürnbergisches Gesangbuch, 1677

Rather slowly

1. For - ty days and for - ty nights Thou wast fast - ing in the wild;
2. Shall not we Thy sor - row share, And from earth - ly joys ab - stain,
3. And if Sa - tan, vex - ing sore, Flesh or spir - it should as - sail,
4. Keep, O keep us, Sav - iour dear, Ev - er con - stant by Thy side;

For - ty days and for - ty nights Tempt - ed, and yet un - de - filed.
Fast - ing with un - ceas - ing prayer, Glad with Thee to suf - fer pain?
Thou, his van - quish - er be - fore, Grant we may not faint nor fail.
That with Thee we may ap - pear At the e - ter - nal Eas - ter - tide. A-MEN.

144

JAMES MONTGOMERY, 1820
7.7.7.7.7.7.
REDHEAD 76 (AJALON)
RICHARD REDHEAD, 1853

Rather slowly

1. Go to dark Geth - sem - a - ne, Ye that feel the tempt - er's power;
2. Fol - low to the judg - ment hall, View the Lord of life ar - raigned;
3. Cal - vary's mourn - ful moun - tain climb; There, a - dor - ing at His feet,
4. Ear - ly has - ten to the tomb, Where they laid His breath - less clay;

Your Re - deem - er's con - flict see, Watch with Him one bit - ter hour;
O the worm - wood and the gall, O the pangs His soul sus - tained!
Mark that mir - a - cle of time, God's own Sac - ri - fice com - plete;
All is sol - i - tude and gloom,—Who hath tak - en Him a - way?

His Passion and Crucifixion

Turn not from His griefs a-way, Learn of Je-sus Christ to pray.
Shun not suf-fering, shame, or loss; Learn of Him to bear the cross.
"It is fin-ished!" hear Him cry; Learn of Je-sus Christ to die.
Christ is risen! He meets our eyes! Sav-iour, teach us so to rise. A-MEN.

145

WILLIAM B. TAPPAN, 1822   L. M.   OLIVE'S BROW
WILLIAM B. BRADBURY, 1853

Rather slowly

1. 'Tis mid-night; and on Ol-ive's brow The star is
2. 'Tis mid-night; and, from all re-moved, The Sav-iour
3. 'Tis mid-night; and, for oth-ers' guilt, The Man of
4. 'Tis mid-night; from the heaven-ly plains Is borne the

dimmed that late-ly shone: 'Tis mid-night; in the gar-den now
wres-tles lone with fears; E'en the dis-ci-ple that He loved
Sor-rows weeps in blood; Yet He, who hath in an-guish knelt,
song that an-gels know; Un-heard by mor-tals are the strains

The suf-fering Sav-iour prays a-lone.
Heeds not His Mas-ter's grief and tears.
Is not for-sa-ken by His God.
That sweet-ly soothe the Sav-iour's woe. A-MEN.

Our Lord Jesus Christ

146

FREDERICK WILLIAM FABER, 1840   L.M.   ST. CROSS
JOHN B. DYKES, 1861

Slowly

1. O come and mourn with me a - while; O come ye to the Sav-iour's side;
2. Seven times He spake, seven words of love; And all three hours His si-lence cried
3. O break, O break, hard heart of mine! Thy weak self-love and guilt-y pride
4. A bro-ken heart, a fount of tears, Ask, and they will not be de - nied;
5. O love of God! O sin of man! In this dread act your strength is tried,

O come, to-geth-er let us mourn: Je-sus, our Lord, is cru-ci-fied!
For mer-cy on the souls of men: Je-sus, our Lord, is cru-ci-fied!
His Pi-late and His Ju-das were: Je-sus, our Lord, is cru-ci-fied!
A bro-ken heart love's cra-dle is: Je-sus, our Lord, is cru-ci-fied!
And vic-to-ry re-mains with love: Je-sus, our Lord, is cru-ci-fied! A-MEN.

147

JOHANN HEERMANN, c. 1630
Tr. ROBERT BRIDGES, 1899   11. 11. 11. 5.   HERZLIEBSTER JESU
JOHANN CRÜGER, 1640

Rather slowly and solemnly
May be sung in unison

1. Ah, dear-est Je-sus, how hast Thou of-fend-ed,
2. Who was the guilt-y? Who brought this up-on Thee?
3. For me, dear Je-sus, was Thy in-car-na-tion,
4. There-fore, dear Je-sus, since I can-not pay Thee,

That man to judge Thee hath in hate pre-tend-ed? By foes de-
A-las, my trea-son, Je-sus, hath un-done Thee! 'Twas I, Lord
Thy mor-tal sor-row, and Thy life's ob-la-tion; Thy death of
I do a-dore Thee, and will ev-er pray Thee, Think on Thy

His Passion and Crucifixion

rid - ed, by Thine own re - ject - ed, O most af - flict - ed!
Je - sus, I it was de - nied Thee: I cru - ci - fied Thee.
an - guish and Thy bit - ter pas - sion, For my sal - va - tion.
pit - y and Thy love un-swerv-ing, Not my de - serv - ing. A-MEN.

148

MATTHEW BRIDGES, 1848   6. 6. 6. 4. 8. 8. 4.   ECCE AGNUS
GEORGE WILLIAM WARREN, 1894

In majestic style

1. Be - hold the Lamb of God! O Thou for sin - ners slain,
2. Be - hold the Lamb of God! All hail, In - car - nate Word!
3. Be - hold the Lamb of God! Wor - thy is He a - lone

Let it not be in vain That Thou hast died. Thee for my Sav - iour
Thou ev - er - last - ing Lord, Sav - iour most blest! Fill us with love that
To sit up - on the throne Of God a - bove, One with the An - cient

let me take, My on - ly ref - uge let me make Thy pier-ced side!
nev - er faints, Grant us, with all Thy bless-ed saints, E - ter - nal rest.
of all days, One with the Com-fort-er in praise, All Light, all Love! A - MEN.

Our Lord Jesus Christ

149

CECIL FRANCES ALEXANDER, 1848 C. M. MEDITATION JOHN H. GOWER, 1890

In moderate time

1. There is a green hill far a-way, With-out a cit-y wall,
2. We may not know, we can-not tell, What pains He had to bear;
3. He died that we might be for-given, He died to make us good,
4. There was no oth-er good e-nough To pay the price of sin;
5. O dear-ly, dear-ly has He loved, And we must love Him too,

Where the dear Lord was cru-ci-fied, Who died to save us all.
But we be-lieve it was for us He hung and suf-fered there.
That we might go at last to heaven, Saved by His pre-cious blood.
He on-ly could un-lock the gate Of heaven, and let us in.
And trust in His re-deem-ing blood, And try His works to do. A-MEN.

Alternative version at Hymn 479

150

From the Latin, 13th century STABAT MATER
Tr. compiled by LOUIS F. BENSON, 1855–1930 8. 8. 7. *Mainz Gesangbuch*, 1661

Slowly

1. Near the cross her vig-il keep-ing, Stood the moth-er,
2. Through her soul in an-guish groan-ing, Bowed in sor-row,
3. Near Thy cross, O Christ, a-bid-ing, Grief and love my
4. By Thy guar-dian cross up-hold me, In Thy dy-ing,

worn with weep-ing, Where He hung, the dy-ing Lord.
sigh-ing, moan-ing, Passed the sharp and pierc-ing sword.
heart di-vid-ing, I with her would take my place:
Christ, en-fold me With the death-less arms of grace. A-MEN.

His Passion and Crucifixion

151

G. J. NEUMANN, 1938   4.8.4.8.   GOLGOTHA
K. P. HARRINGTON, 1938

Rather slowly and solemnly

1. Now all is still; Time holds his breath up - on the hill;
2. Un - der the wood I'll kneel in grief and grat - i - tude;

No word is said; The Lord of heaven and earth is dead.
I can but kneel; There are no words for what I feel.

3. Fold, my hands, fold; Beat, O my heart, a prayer un - told;

Tears, have your way; My Lord is dead; I live for aye. A-MEN.

Our Lord Jesus Christ

152

C. R. von Zinzendorf, 1727–1762
Tr. J. C. Hansen, 1916
10. 7. 10. 7. 10. 10. 7. 7.

MARTER CHRISTI
Gnadauer Choralbuch, 1735

Rather slowly and solemnly

1. Man of Sor-rows, now my soul shall greet Thee, Pa - tient Suf - ferer,
2. Thou - sand thanks, Thou Soul so true and ten - der, Thou hast brought the
3. At Thy cross my troub-led heart finds ref - uge, To Thy pierc - èd
4. All of us who here have come to - geth - er Join our hands in

crowned with thorns; There on Cal - vary's height, O Lord, I'll meet Thee
sac - ri - fice! All my heart and soul shall wor - ship ren - der,
side it flees; 'Mid the storm of life and sin's drear del - uge
u - ni - ty; To the cross of Christ our souls we'll teth - er,

At the cross the world still scorns; There I see the
That Thou paid'st in full the price! Ev - ery tongue shall
Let it rest with Thee in peace; And when death's dark
Faith - ful un - to death we'll be. But Thou, bless - èd

Lamb that, un - com - plain - ing, Suf - fers for us all, our par - don gain - ing;
tell re - demp - tion's sto - ry, Ev - ery knee shall bend to Thee in glo - ry,
shad - ows shall en - fold me, Then, O Cru - ci - fied, let me be - hold Thee;
Lord in high-est heav - en, Hear the prom - i - ses that we have giv - en;

His Passion and Crucifixion

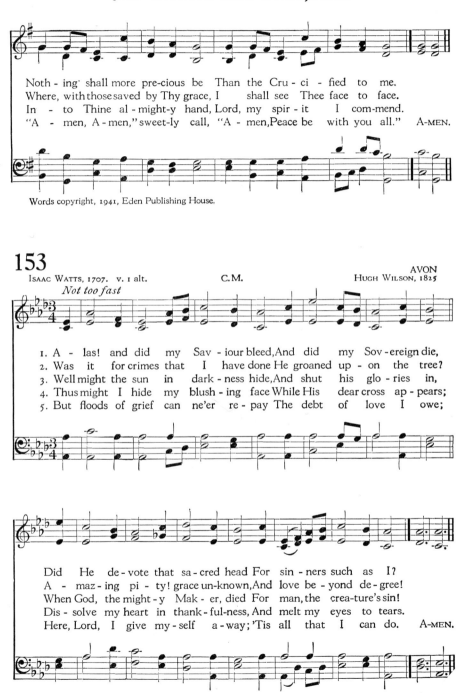

Noth - ing shall more pre-cious be Than the Cru - ci - fied to me.
Where, with those saved by Thy grace, I shall see Thee face to face.
In - to Thine al - might-y hand, Lord, my spir - it I com-mend.
"A - men, A - men," sweet-ly call, "A - men, Peace be with you all." A-MEN.

153

Isaac Watts, 1707. v. 1 alt.   C.M.   AVON
Hugh Wilson, 1825

Not too fast

1. A - las! and did my Sav - iour bleed, And did my Sov - ereign die,
2. Was it for crimes that I have done He groaned up - on the tree?
3. Well might the sun in dark - ness hide, And shut his glo - ries in,
4. Thus might I hide my blush - ing face While His dear cross ap - pears;
5. But floods of grief can ne'er re - pay The debt of love I owe;

Did He de - vote that sa - cred head For sin - ners such as I?
A - maz - ing pi - ty! grace un-known, And love be - yond de - gree!
When God, the might - y Mak - er, died For man, the crea - ture's sin!
Dis - solve my heart in thank - ful-ness, And melt my eyes to tears.
Here, Lord, I give my - self a - way; 'Tis all that I can do. A-MEN.

Our Lord Jesus Christ

154

G. J. Neumann, 1938   C. M. D.   MILBURN
Carl F. Price, 1938

In moderate time

1. King of my soul, a crown of thorns And wo - ven of my wrong
2. King of my soul, a crown of grace Thy dy - ing hands did lay
3. King of my soul, a crown of love And wo - ven through the years

They twined a - round Thy bleed - ing brow, And sang their scorn - ful song;
Up - on the mal - e - fac - tor's head And all his ow - ing pay;
I lay on Thine im - mor - tal head And dew it with my tears;

And Thou wast pur - est of the pure, And past all prais - ing mild,
And e - ven me, who hum - bly bow And Thee as Lord con - fess,
Sav - iour and Lord, my joy and peace, My per - fect life to be,

And lov - ing un - to death, that I And God be rec - on - ciled.
Thou lead - est to Thy Fa - ther's house In robes of right-eous-ness.
All to Thy bound-less grace I owe And con - se - crate to Thee! A-men.

Alternative tune, *St. Leonard.*

His Passion and Crucifixion

155

ALLE MENSCHEN MÜSSEN STERBEN (DARMSTADT)

GIROLAMO SAVONAROLA, 1452–1498
TR. JANE FRANCESCA WILDE, 1826–1896   8.7.8.7.8.8.7.7.   H. MÜLLER, 1687

In moderate time

1. Je - sus, ref - uge of the wear - y, Ob - ject of the spir - it's love,
2. Do we pass that cross un - heed - ing, Breath - ing no re - pent - ant vow,
3. Je - sus, may our hearts be burn - ing With more fer - vent love for Thee;

Foun - tain in life's des - ert drear - y, Sav - iour from the world a - bove,
Though we see Thee wound - ed, bleed - ing, See Thy thorn - en - cir - cled brow?
May our eyes be ev - er turn - ing To Thy cross of ag - o - ny;

Though Thy heart was oft of - fend - ed, E'en up - on the cross ex - tend - ed
Yet Thy won - drous grace hath taught us What Thy sin - less death hath brought us,
Till in glo - ry, part - ed nev - er, One with Thee in love for - ev - er,

Thou didst mourn the sin - ners' fall, And didst bear the pain of all.
Life e - ter - nal, peace, and rest On the gen - tle Sav - iour's breast.
At the bless - ed Sav - iour's side We u - nit - ed shall a - bide. A-MEN.

156

Stopford A. Brooke, 1832–1916   7.7.7.7.   AUS DER TIEFE (HEINLEIN)
Nürnbergisches Gesangbuch, 1677

Slowly and solemnly

1. "It is fin-ished," all the pain, All the sor-row, all the strain;
2. "It is fin-ished," all the days, Led through man-y wear-y ways;
3. "It is fin-ished," all the love, Deep as His that dwells a-bove;
4. "It is fin-ished!" Hark! the cry, Ut-tered in love's ag-o-ny,

Death has freed the Lord of life From the bur-den of His strife.
Now at last His eye-lids close On the ha-tred of His foes.
Sav-ing oth-ers, all He gave, But Him-self He could not save.
Is the seal, be-low, a-bove, Of the vic-to-ry of love. A-MEN.

157

William D. Maclagan, 1875   10.10.10.10.   TOULON
Genevan Psalter, 1551

With dignity

1. "Lord, when Thy king-dom comes, re-mem-ber me!" Thus spake the
2. No king-ly sign de-clares that glo-ry now; No ray of
3. Yet hear the words the dy-ing Sav-iour saith, "Thou too shalt
4. Lord, when with dy-ing lips my prayer is said, Grant that in

dy-ing lips to dy-ing ears; O faith, which in that dark-est
hope lights up that aw-ful hour; A thorn-y crown sur-rounds the
rest in Par-a-dise to-day;" O words of love to an-swer
faith Thy king-dom I may see, And, think-ing on Thy cross and

His Passion and Crucifixion

hour could see The prom-ised glo-ry of the far-off years!
bleed-ing brow; The hands are stretched in weak-ness, not in power.
words of faith! O words of hope for those who live to pray!
thorn-crowned head, May breathe my part-ing words, "Re-mem-ber me." A-MEN.

158

ISAAC WATTS, 1707   L. M.   HAMBURG
LOWELL MASON, 1825

In moderate time

1. When I sur-vey the won-drous cross On which the
2. For-bid it, Lord, that I should boast, Save in the
3. See, from His head, His hands, His feet, Sor-row and
4. Were the whole realm of na-ture mine, That were a

Prince of Glo-ry died, My rich-est gain I
death of Christ, my God; All the vain things that
love flow min-gled down: Did e'er such love and
pres-ent far too small; Love so a-maz-ing,

count but loss, And pour con-tempt on all my pride.
charm me most, I sac-ri-fice them to His blood.
sor-row meet, Or thorns com-pose so rich a crown?
so di-vine, De-mands my soul, my life, my all. A-MEN.

Alternative tune, *Rockingham Old.*

Our Lord Jesus Christ

159

E. W. EDDIS, 1825–1905   10. 10. 10. 10.   LANGRAN
JAMES LANGRAN, 1862

In moderate time

1. Our sins, our sor - rows, Lord, were laid on Thee;
2. Now hast Thou laid Thee down in per - fect peace
3. Yet in Thy glo - ry, on the throne a - bove,
4. E'en now our place is with Thee on the throne,
5. O, by Thy life with - in us, set us free!

Thy stripes have healed, Thy bonds have set us free;
Where all the wick - ed from their trou - bling cease,
Thou wast a - bid - ing ev - er, Love of Love,
For Thou a - bid - est ev - er with Thine own;
Re - veal the glo - ry that is hid with Thee!

And now Thy toil is o'er; Thy grief and pain
Thy tran - quil Sab - bath in the grave to keep;
E - ter - nal, fill - ing all cre - a - ted things
Yet in the tomb with Thee, we watch for day;
Glo - ry to God the Fa - ther, God the Son,

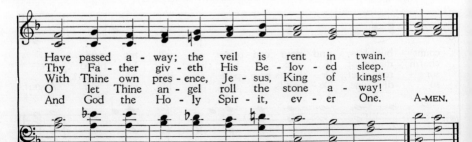

Have passed a - way; the veil is rent in twain.
Thy Fa - ther giv - eth His Be - lov - ed sleep.
With Thine own pres - ence, Je - sus, King of kings!
O let Thine an - gel roll the stone a - way!
And God the Ho - ly Spir - it, ev - er One. A-MEN.

His Passion and Crucifixion

J. MONTGOMERY, 1834, alt.　　　　6.5.6.5.D.　　　　PENITENCE (LANE)
SPENCER LANE, 1879

In moderate time

1. In the hour of tri - al, Je - sus, plead for me,
2. With for - bid - den pleas - ures Would this vain world charm,
3. Should Thy mer - cy send me Sor - row, toil, or woe,

Lest by base de - ni - al I de - part from Thee;
Or its sor - did treas - ures Spread to work me harm,
Or should pain at - tend me On my path be - low,

When Thou see'st me wa - ver, With a look re - call,
Bring to my re - mem - brance Sad Geth - sem - a - ne,
Grant that I may nev - er Fail Thy hand to see;

rall.

Nor for fear or fa - vor Suf - fer me to fall.
Or, in dark - er sem - blance, Cross-crowned Cal - va - ry.
Grant that I may ev - er Cast my care on Thee. A - MEN.

Our Lord Jesus Christ

161

ELIZABETH CLEPHANE, 1872   7. 6. 8. 6. 8. 6. 8. 6.   ST. CHRISTOPHER
FREDERICK C. MAKER, 1881

In moderate time

1. Be - neath the cross of Je - sus I fain would take my stand,
2. Up - on that cross of Je - sus Mine eye at times can see
3. I take, O cross, thy shad - ow For my a - bid - ing - place;

The shad - ow of a might - y rock With - in a wear - y land;
The ver - y dy - ing form of One Who suf - fered there for me;
I ask no oth - er sun-shine than The sun - shine of His face;

A home with - in the wil - der - ness, A rest up - on the way,
And from my smit - ten heart with tears Two won - ders I con - fess,
Con - tent to let the world go by, To know no gain nor loss,

From the burn - ing of the noon-tide heat And the bur - den of the day.
The won - ders of His glo-rious love And my own worth-less-ness.
My sin - ful self my on - ly shame, My glo - ry all the cross. A-MEN.

His Passion and Crucifixion

162

ARTHUR T. RUSSELL, 1851

HERZLICH TUT MICH VERLANGEN (PASSION CHORALE)
HANS LEO HASSLER, 1601
7.6.7.6. D.
Har. J. SEBASTIAN BACH, 1729

With great dignity

1. O Je - sus, we a - dore Thee, Up - on the cross, our King!
2. Yet doth the world dis - dain Thee, Still pass - ing by the cross;
3. O glo - rious King, we bless Thee, No lon - ger pass Thee by;

We bow our hearts be - fore Thee, Thy gra - cious Name we sing.
Lord, may our hearts re - tain Thee; All else we count but loss.
O Je - sus, we con - fess Thee The Son en - throned on high.

That Name hath brought sal - va - tion, That Name in life our stay,
Ah, Lord, our sins ar - raigned Thee, And nailed Thee to the tree:
Lord, grant to us re - mis - sion; Life through Thy death re - store;

Our peace, our con - so - la - tion When life shall fade a - way.
Our pride, our Lord, dis - dained Thee; Yet deign our Hope to be.
Yea, grant us the fru - i - tion Of life for - ev - er - more. A-MEN.

Music in Key of C, No. 142.

Our Lord Jesus Christ

163

JAMES S. SIMPSON, 1886

8. 7. 8. 7.

CROSS OF JESUS
JOHN STAINER, 1887

Not too fast; with solemnity

1. Cross of Je-sus, cross of sor-row, Where the blood of Christ was shed,
2. Here the King of all the a-ges, Throned in light ere worlds could be,
3. O mys-te-rious con-de-scend-ing! O a-ban-don-ment sub-lime!
4. Ev-er-more for hu-man fail-ure By His pas-sion we can plead;

Per-fect man on thee did suf-fer, Per-fect God on thee has bled!
Robed in mor-tal flesh is dy-ing, Cru-ci-fied by sin for me.
Ver-y God Him-self is bear-ing All the suf-fer-ings of time!
God has borne all mor-tal an-guish, Sure-ly He will know our need. A-MEN.

Alternative tune, *Dorrnance.*

164

JOHN BOWRING, 1825

8. 7. 8. 7.

RATHBUN
ITHAMAR CONKEY, 1851

Not too slowly

1. In the cross of Christ I glo-ry, Tow-ering o'er the wrecks of time;
2. When the woes of life o'er-take me, Hopes de-ceive, and fears an-noy,
3. When the sun of bliss is beam-ing Light and love up-on my way,
4. Bane and bless-ing, pain and pleas-ure, By the cross are sanc-ti-fied;

All the light of sa-cred sto-ry Gath-ers round its head sub-lime.
Nev-er shall the cross for-sake me; Lo, it glows with peace and joy.
From the cross the ra-diance stream-ing Adds more lus-ter to the day.
Peace is there that knows no meas-ure, Joys that through all time a-bide. A-MEN.

His Resurrection

165

John of Damascus, 8th century
Tr. John Mason Neale, 1862

7.6.7.6.D.

LANCASHIRE

Henry Smart, 1836

Jubilantly

1. The day of res - ur - rec - tion! Earth, tell it out a - broad,
2. Our hearts be pure from e - vil, That we may see a - right
3. Now let the heavens be joy - ful, Let earth her song be - gin;

The Pass - o - ver of glad - ness, The Pass - o - ver of God!
The Lord in rays e - ter - nal Of res - ur - rec - tion - light;
Let the round world keep tri - umph, And all that is there - in;

From death to life e - ter - nal, From this world to the sky,
And, lis - tening to His ac - cents, May hear, so calm and plain,
In - vis - i - ble and vis - i - ble, Their notes let all things blend,

Our Christ hath brought us o - ver With hymns of vic - to - ry.
His own "All hail!" and, hear - ing, May raise the vic - tor strain.
For Christ the Lord is ris - en, Our Joy that hath no end. A - men.

Our Lord Jesus Christ

166

Based on a 14th century Latin Hymn
4th stanza, CHARLES WESLEY, 1740   7.7.7.7. with Alleluias

LLANFAIR

ROBERT WILLIAMS, 1817

Jubilantly

1. Je - sus Christ is risen to - day, Al - - le - lu - ia!
2. Hymns of praise then let us sing, Al - - le - lu - ia!
3. But the pains which He en - dured, Al - - le - lu - ia!
4. Sing we to our God a - bove, Al - - le - lu - ia!

Our tri - um - phant ho - ly day, Al - - le - lu - ia!
Un - to Christ, our heaven - ly King, Al - - le - lu - ia!
Our sal - va - tion have pro - cured; Al - - le - lu - ia!
Praise e - ter - nal as His love; Al - - le - lu - ia!

Who did once up - on the cross, Al - - le - lu - ia!
Who en - dured the cross and grave, Al - - le - lu - ia!
Now a - bove the sky He's King, Al - - le - lu - ia!
Praise Him, all ye heaven - ly host, Al - - le - lu - ia!

Suf - fer to re - deem our loss. Al - - le - lu - ia!
Sin - ners to re - deem and save. Al - - le - lu - ia!
Where the an - gels ev - er sing. Al - - le - lu - ia!
Fa - ther, Son, and Ho - ly Ghost. Al - - le - lu - ia!   A-MEN.

His Resurrection

167

CHARLES WESLEY, 1739

7.7.7.7. with Alleluias

EASTER HYMN (WORGAN)
Lyra Davidica, 1708

Jubilantly

1. Christ the Lord is risen to - day, Al - - le - lu - ia!
2. Lives a - gain our glo - rious King, Al - - le - lu - ia!
3. Love's re - deem - ing work is done, Al - - le - lu - ia!
4. Soar we now where Christ has led, Al - - le - lu - ia!

Sons of men and an - gels say, Al - - le - lu - ia!
Where, O death, is now thy sting? Al - - le - lu - ia!
Fought the fight, the bat - tle won, Al - - le - lu - ia!
Fol - lowing our ex - alt - ed Head, Al - - le - lu - ia!

Raise your joys and tri - umphs high, Al - - le - lu - ia!
Once He died, our souls to save, Al - - le - lu - ia!
Death in vain for - bids Him rise, Al - - le - lu - ia!
Made like Him, like Him we rise, Al - - le - lu - ia!

Sing, ye heavens, and earth re - ply, Al - - le - lu - ia!
Where's thy vic - to - ry, O grave? Al - - le - lu - ia!
Christ has o - pened Par - a - dise, Al - - le - lu - ia!
Ours the cross, the grave, the skies, Al - - le - lu - ia! A-MEN.

Our Lord Jesus Christ

168

CHRISTIAN F. GELLERT, 1715–1769
Tr. Anon.

JESUS MEINE ZUVERSICHT (RATISBON)
From JOHANN CRÜGER'S
Praxis Pietatis Melica, c. 1653

7. 8. 7. 8. 7. 7.

Jubilantly

1. Je - sus lives and so shall I; Death, thy sting is
2. Je - sus lives, and God ex - tends Grace to each re -
3. Je - sus lives, and by His grace Vic - tory o'er my
4. Je - sus lives, and death is now But my en - try

gone for - ev - er. He who deigned for me to die
turn - ing sin - ner. Reb - els He re - ceives as friends,
pas - sions giv - ing, I will cleanse my heart and ways,
in - to glo - ry. Cour - age, then, my soul, for thou

Lives the bands of death to sev - er. He shall raise me
And ex - alts to high - est hon - or. God is true as
Ev - er to His glo - ry liv - ing. Th' weak He rais - es
Hast a crown of life be - fore thee; Thou shalt find thy

with the just: Je - sus is my hope and trust.
He is just: Je - sus is my hope and trust.
from the dust: Je - sus is my hope and trust.
hopes were just: Je - sus is my hope and trust. A - MEN.

His Resurrection

169

John of Damascus, 8th century
Tr. John Mason Neale, 1859

7.6.7.6. D.

ST. KEVIN

Arthur Sullivan, 1872

Jubilantly

1. Come, ye faith-ful, raise the strain Of tri-um-phant glad-ness:
2. 'Tis the spring of souls to-day: Christ hath burst His pris-on,

God hath brought His peo-ple forth In-to joy from sad-ness.
And from three days' sleep in death As a sun hath ris-en;

Now re-joice, Je-ru-sa-lem, And with true af-fec-tion
All the win-ter of our sins, Long and dark, is fly-ing

Wel-come in un-wea-ried strains Je-sus' res-ur-rec-tion.
From His light, to whom we give Laud and praise un-dy-ing. A-MEN.

Our Lord Jesus Christ

170

HERMAS

Venantius Fortunatus, before 582
Tr. John Ellerton, 1869

6. 5. 6. 5. D. with Refrain

Frances Ridley Havergal, 1871

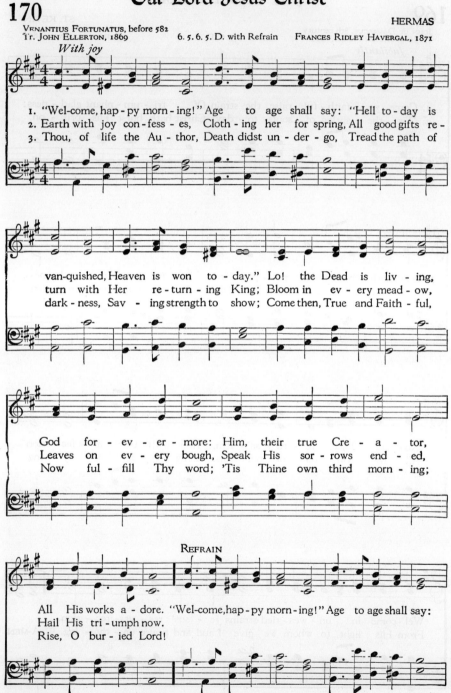

With joy

1. "Wel-come, hap-py morn-ing!" Age to age shall say: "Hell to-day is van-quished, Heaven is won to-day." Lo! the Dead is liv-ing, God for-ev-er-more: Him, their true Cre-a-tor, All His works a-dore.

2. Earth with joy con-fess-es, Cloth-ing her for spring, All good gifts re-turn with Her re-turn-ing King; Bloom in ev-ery mead-ow, Leaves on ev-ery bough, Speak His sor-rows end-ed, Hail His tri-umph now.

3. Thou, of life the Au-thor, Death didst un-der-go, Tread the path of dark-ness, Sav-ing strength to show; Come then, True and Faith-ful, Now ful-fill Thy word; 'Tis Thine own third morn-ing; Rise, O bur-ied Lord!

REFRAIN

"Wel-come, hap-py morn-ing!" Age to age shall say:

His Resurrection

"Hell to-day is van-quished, Heaven is won to-day." A-men.

171

WILLIAM WALSHAM HOW, 1872

6. 6. 6. 6. 8. 8.

MANSFIELD
JOSEPH BARNBY, 1893

Jubilantly

1. On wings of liv - ing light, At ear - liest dawn of day, Came
2. Then rose from death's dark gloom, Un - seen by mor - tal eye, Tri -
3. Ye chil - dren of the light, A - rise with Him, a - rise: See,
4. Leave in the grave be - neath The old things passed a - way; Bur -

down the an - gel bright, And rolled the stone a - way. Your
um - phant o'er the tomb, The Lord of earth and sky. Your
how the Day - Star bright Is burn - ing in the skies! Your
ied with Him in death, O live with Him to - day! Your

voic - es raise with one ac - cord To bless and praise your ris - en Lord.
voic - es raise with one ac - cord To bless and praise your ris - en Lord.
voic - es raise with one ac - cord To bless and praise your ris - en Lord.
voic - es raise with one ac - cord To bless and praise your ris - en Lord. A-MEN.

Our Lord Jesus Christ

172

J. P. LANGE, 1851
Tr. H. HARBAUGH

7.6.7.6.D.

RESURRECTION

ALICE NEVIN, 1837-1925

Jubilantly

1. The Lord of life is ris - en; Sing, Eas - ter her - alds, sing!
2. The Lord of life is ris - en, And love no lon - ger grieves;
3. A - round Thy tomb, O Je - sus, How sweet the Eas - ter breath;
4. O pub - lish this sal - va - tion, Ye her - alds, through the earth,
5. Hail, hail, our Je - sus ris - en! Sing, ran-somed breth-ren, sing!

He bursts His rock - y pris - on; Wide let the tri - umph ring!
In ru - in lies death's pris - on, Sing, her - alds, Je - sus lives!
Hear we not in the breez - es, "Where is thy sting, O death?"
To ev - ery bur - ied na - tion Pro - claim the day of birth!
Through death's dark, gloom - y pris - on Let Eas - ter cho - rals ring!

In death no long - er ly - ing, He rose, the Prince, to - day;
We hear Thy bless - ed greet - ing; Sal - va - tion's work is done!
Dark hell flies in com - mo - tion, The heavens their an - thems sing;
Till, ris - ing from their slum - bers In long and an - cient night,
Haste, haste, ye cap - tive le - gions, Ac - cept your glad re - prieve;

Life of the dead and dy - ing, He tri - umphed o'er de - cay.
We wor - ship Thee, re - peat - ing, "Life for the dead is won!"
While far o'er earth and o - cean Glad hal - le - lu - jahs ring!
The count-less hea - then num - bers Shall hail the Eas - ter light.
Come forth from sin's dark re - gions; In Je - sus' king - dom live! A-MEN.

His Resurrection

173

Latin; tr. FRANCIS POTT, 1861

VICTORY
PALESTRINA, 1591
Adapted by W. H. MONK

8. 8. 8. 4. with Alleluias

Jubilantly. With majesty

Al - le - lu - ia! Al - le - lu - ia! Al - le - lu - ia!

1. The strife is o'er, the bat - tle done;
2. The powers of death have done their worst,
3. The three sad days have quick - ly sped;
4. He closed the yawn - ing gates of hell,
5. Lord, by the stripes which wound - ed Thee,

The vic - to - ry of life is won; The song of
But Christ their le - gions hath dis - persed: Let shouts of
He ris - es glo - rious from the dead: All glo - ry
The bars from heaven's high por - tals fell: Let hymns of
From death's dread sting Thy serv - ants free, That we may

tri - umph has be - gun. Al - le - lu - ia!
ho - ly joy out - burst. Al - le - lu - ia!
to our ris - en Head! Al - le - lu - ia!
praise His tri - umphs tell! Al - le - lu - ia!
live and sing to Thee. Al - le - lu - ia! A - MEN.

Our Lord Jesus Christ

CHRISTOPHER WORDSWORTH, 1872   8. 7. 8. 7. D.   HYFRYDOL
ROWLAND HUGH PRICHARD, 1811–1887

With joy; in moderate time

1. Al - le - lu - ia! Al - le - lu - ia! Hearts to heaven and voic -es raise;
2. Now the i - ron bars are bro - ken, Christ from death to life is born,
3. Al - le - lu - ia! Al - le - lu - ia! Glo - ry be to God on high;

Sing to God a hymn of glad - ness, Sing to God a hymn of praise.
Glo - rious life, and life im - mor - tal, On this ho - ly Eas - ter morn;
Al - le - lu - ia to the Sav - iour Who has won the vic - to - ry;

He who on the cross as Sav - iour For the world's sal - va - tion bled,
Christ has tri - umphed, and we con - quer By His might - y en - ter - prise,
Al - le - lu - ia to the Spir - it, Fount of love and sanc - ti - ty;

Je - sus Christ, the King of Glo - ry, Now is ris - en from the dead.
We with Him to life e - ter - nal By His res - ur - rec - tion rise.
Al - le - lu - ia! Al - le - lu - ia! To the Tri - une Ma - jes - ty. A-MEN.

His Ascension and Reign

175

CHARLES WESLEY, 1739   7.7.7.7. with Alleluias

ASCENSION
WILLIAM HENRY MONK, 1861

Jubilantly

1. Hail the day that sees Him rise, Al - le - lu - ia!
2. There the glo - rious tri - umph waits: Al - le - lu - ia!
3. Him though high - est heaven re - ceives, Al - le - lu - ia!

To His throne a - bove the skies! Al - le - lu - ia!
Lift your heads, e - ter - nal gates, Al - le - lu - ia!
Still He loves the earth He leaves; Al - le - lu - ia!

Christ, a - while to mor - tals given, Al - le - lu - ia!
Wide un - fold the ra - diant scene, Al - le - lu - ia!
Though re - turn - ing to His throne, Al - le - lu - ia!

Re - as - cends His na - tive heaven. Al - le - lu - ia!
Take the King of Glo - ry in! Al - le - lu - ia!
Still He calls man - kind His own. Al - le - lu - ia!   A-MEN.

Our Lord Jesus Christ

176

Matthew Bridges, 1851   S. M. D.   DIADEMATA
George J. Elvey, 1868

Joyously, but with great dignity

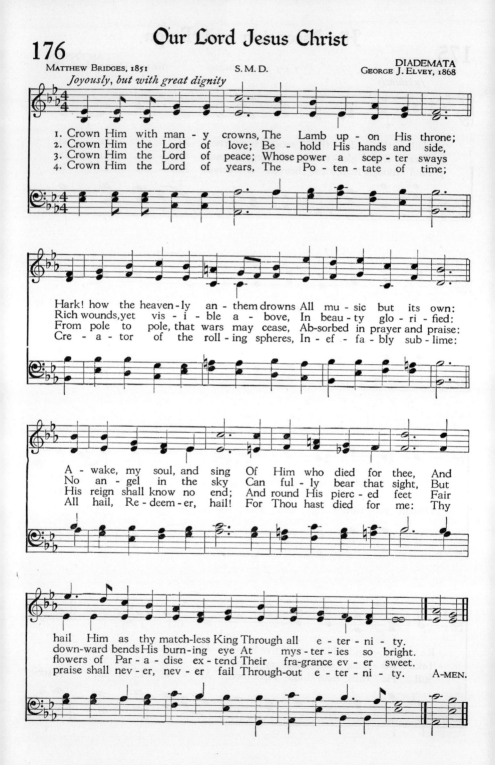

1. Crown Him with man - y crowns, The Lamb up - on His throne;
2. Crown Him the Lord of love; Be - hold His hands and side,
3. Crown Him the Lord of peace; Whose power a scep - ter sways
4. Crown Him the Lord of years, The Po - ten - tate of time;

Hark! how the heaven - ly an - them drowns All mu - sic but its own:
Rich wounds, yet vis - i - ble a - bove, In beau - ty glo - ri - fied:
From pole to pole, that wars may cease, Ab - sorbed in prayer and praise:
Cre - a - tor of the roll - ing spheres, In - ef - fa - bly sub - lime:

A - wake, my soul, and sing Of Him who died for thee, And
No an - gel in the sky Can ful - ly bear that sight, But
His reign shall know no end; And round His pierc - ed feet Fair
All hail, Re - deem - er, hail! For Thou hast died for me: Thy

hail Him as thy match - less King Through all e - ter - ni - ty.
down - ward bends His burn - ing eye At mys - ter - ies so bright.
flowers of Par - a - dise ex - tend Their fra - grance ev - er sweet.
praise shall nev - er, nev - er fail Through - out e - ter - ni - ty.

A-MEN.

His Ascension and Reign

177

WILLIAM JOSEPH IRONS, 1875   8. 7. 8. 7. D.   HYMN TO JOY   LUDWIG VAN BEETHOVEN, 1824

With exultation

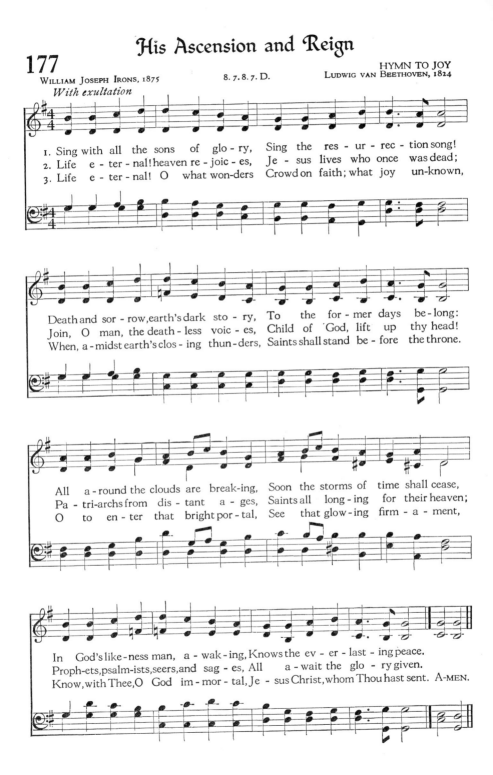

1. Sing with all the sons of glo - ry, Sing the res - ur - rec - tion song!
2. Life e - ter - nal! heaven re - joic - es, Je - sus lives who once was dead;
3. Life e - ter - nal! O what won - ders Crowd on faith; what joy un - known,

Death and sor - row, earth's dark sto - ry, To the for - mer days be - long:
Join, O man, the death - less voic - es, Child of God, lift up thy head!
When, a - midst earth's clos - ing thun - ders, Saints shall stand be - fore the throne.

All a - round the clouds are break - ing, Soon the storms of time shall cease,
Pa - tri - archs from dis - tant a - ges, Saints all long - ing for their heaven;
O to en - ter that bright por - tal, See that glow - ing firm - a - ment,

In God's like - ness man, a - wak - ing, Knows the ev - er - last - ing peace.
Proph - ets, psalm - ists, seers, and sag - es, All a - wait the glo - ry given.
Know, with Thee, O God im - mor - tal, Je - sus Christ, whom Thou hast sent. A-MEN.

Our Lord Jesus Christ

178

HORATIUS BONAR, 1808–1889   10. 10. 10. 10.   La Feillée's *Méthode du Plain Chant*, 1808

O QUANTA QUALIA

In moderate time and with majestic rhythm

1. Bless - ing and hon - or and glo - ry and power,
2. Sound - eth the heaven of the heavens with His Name;
3. Ev - er as - cend - eth the song and the joy;
4. Give we the glo - ry and praise to the Lamb;

Wis - dom and rich - es and strength ev - er - more
Ring - eth the earth with His glo - ry and fame;
Ev - er de - scend - eth the love from on high;
Take we the robe and the harp and the palm;

Give ye to Him who our bat - tle hath won,
O - cean and moun - tain, stream, for - est, and flower
Bless - ing and hon - or and glo - ry and praise—
Sing we the song of the Lamb that was slain,

Whose are the King - dom, the crown, and the throne.
Ech - o His prais - es and tell of His power.
This is the theme of the hymns that we raise.
Dy - ing in weak - ness, but ris - ing to reign.   A-MEN.

His Ascension and Reign

179

John Bakewell, 1760

8.7.8.7.D.

PLEADING SAVIOUR
Plymouth Collection, 1855

Jubilantly, but with dignity

1. Hail, Thou once de - spis - ed Je - sus, Crowned in mock - er - y a King!
2. Je - sus, hail! en - throned in glo - ry, There for - ev - er to a - bide;
3. Wor - ship, hon - or, power, and bless-ing Thou art wor - thy to re - ceive;

Thou didst suf - fer to re - lease us; Thou didst free sal - va - tion bring.
All the heaven-ly hosts a - dore Thee, Seat - ed at Thy Fa-ther's side:
Loud - est prais - es, with-out ceas-ing, Meet it is for us to give.

Hail, Thou ag - o - niz - ing Sav - iour, Bear - er of our sin and shame!
There for sin - ners Thou art plead - ing; There Thou dost our place pre - pare:
Help, ye bright an - gel - ic spir - its, Bring your sweet-est, no - blest lays;

By Thy mer - its we find fav - or; Life is giv - en through Thy Name.
Ev - er for us in - ter - ce - ding, Till in glo - ry we ap - pear.
Help to sing our Sav-iour's mer-its; Help to chant Im - man-uel's praise. A-men.

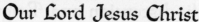

Our Lord Jesus Christ

180

THOMAS KELLY, 1809   8.7.8.7.4.7.   CORONAE
WILLIAM H. MONK, 1871

With exultation

1. Look, ye saints, the sight is glo - rious; See the Man of Sor - rows now,
2. Crown the Sav - iour, an - gels, crown Him, Rich the tro - phies Je - sus brings;
3. Sin - ners in de - ri - sion crowned Him, Mock - ing thus the Sav-iour's claim:
4. Hark, those bursts of ac - cla - ma - tion! Hark, those loud tri - um-phant chords!

From the fight re - turned vic - to - rious, Ev - ery knee to Him shall bow:
In the seat of power en - throne Him, While the vault of heav - en rings:
Saints and an - gels crowd a - round Him, Own His ti - tle, praise His Name:
Je - sus takes the high - est sta - tion; O what joy the sight af - fords!

Crown Him! Crown Him! Crowns be - come the Vic - tor's brow.
Crown Him! Crown Him! Crown the Sav - iour King of kings.
Crown Him! Crown Him! Spread a - broad the Vic - tor's fame.
Crown Him! Crown Him! King of kings, and Lord of lords. A-MEN.

181

CHARLES WESLEY, 1739   C. M.   RICHMOND
T. HAWEIS, 1734-1820
Arr. S. WEBBE, the younger

With joy, but not too fast

1. O for a thou - sand tongues to sing My great Re - deem-er's praise,
2. Je - sus, the Name that charms our fears, That bids our sor - rows cease;
3. He breaks the power of reign - ing sin, He sets the pris-oner free;
4. My gra - cious Mas - ter and my God, As - sist me to pro - claim,

His Ascension and Reign

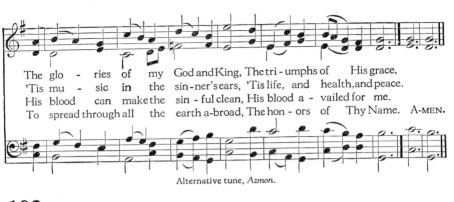

The glo - ries of my God and King, The tri - umphs of His grace.
'Tis mu - sic in the sin - ner's ears, 'Tis life, and health, and peace.
His blood can make the sin - ful clean, His blood a - vailed for me.
To spread through all the earth a-broad, The hon - ors of Thy Name. A-MEN.

Alternative tune, *Azmon.*

182

German, 17th century   Irregular

SCHÖNSTER HERR JESU (CRUSADERS' HYMN)
Silesian Folksong Melody
Arr. RICHARD S. WILLIS, 1850

In moderate time and graceful rhythm

1. Fair - est Lord Je - sus! Rul - er of all na - ture!
2. Fair are the mead - ows, Fair - er still the wood - lands,
3. Fair is the sun - shine, Fair - er still the moon - light,

O Thou of God and man the Son! Thee will I cher - ish,
Robed in the bloom - ing garb of spring: Je - sus is fair - er,
And all the twink - ling star - ry host; Je - sus shines bright - er,

Thee will I hon - or, Thou, my soul's glo - ry, joy, and crown!
Je - sus is pur - er, Who makes the woe - ful heart to sing.
Je - sus shines pur - er Than all the an - gels heaven can boast! A-MEN.

Our Lord Jesus Christ

183

SAMUEL STENNETT, 1787

C.M.

NUN DANKET ALL' (GRÄFENBERG)
JOHANN CRÜGER'S
Praxis Pietatis Melica, 1653

May be sung in unison. Majestically

1. Ma - jes - tic sweet-ness sits en-throned Up - on the Sav - iour's brow;
2. No mor - tal can with Him com-pare A - mong the sons of men;
3. To Him I owe my life and breath, And all the joys I have;
4. To heaven, the place of His a - bode, He brings my wea - ry feet;
5. Since from His boun - ty I re - ceive Such proofs of love di - vine,

His head with ra - diant glo-ries crowned, His lips with grace o'er - flow.
Fair - er is He than all the fair That fill the heaven-ly train.
He makes me tri - umph o - ver death, And saves me from the grave.
Shows me the glo - ries of my God, And makes my joys com - plete.
Had I a thou-sand hearts to give, Lord, they should all be Thine. A-MEN.

184

EDWARD PERRONET, 1785, alt.
Stanza 5, JOHN RIPPON, 1787

C.M.
First Tune

CORONATION

OLIVER HOLDEN, 1793

With dignity; but in moderate time

1. All hail the power of Je - sus' name, Let an - gels pros-trate fall!
2. Crown Him, ye mar - tyrs of your God Who from His al - tar call;
3. Sin - ners, whose love can ne'er for - get The worm-wood and the gall,
4. Let ev - ery kin - dred, ev - ery tribe On this ter - res - trial ball,
5. O that with yon - der sa - cred throng We at His feet may fall;

Bring forth the roy - al di - a - dem, And crown Him Lord of all;
Ex - tol the Stem of Jes - se's rod, And crown Him Lord of all;
Go, spread your tro - phies at His feet, And crown Him Lord of all;
To Him all maj - es - ty as - cribe, And crown Him Lord of all;
We'll join the ev - er - last - ing song, And crown Him Lord of all;

His Ascension and Reign

Bring forth the roy-al di - a - dem, And crown Him Lord of all.
Ex - tol the Stem of Jes - se's rod, And crown Him Lord of all.
Go, spread your tro-phies at His feet, And crown Him Lord of all.
To Him all ma-jes-ty as - cribe, And crown Him Lord of all.
We'll join the ev - er - last-ing song, And crown Him Lord of all. A-men.

185

MILES' LANE

EDWARD PERRONET, 1785, alt.
Verse 5, JOHN RIPPON, 1787

C. M.
Second Tune

WILLIAM SHRUBSOLE, 1785

With dignity; but in moderate time

1. All hail the power of Je - sus' name! Let an - gels pros-trate fall;
2. Crown Him, ye mar-tyrs of your God Who from His al - tar call;
3. Sin - ners, whose love can ne'er for - get The worm-wood and the gall,
4. Let ev - ery kin-dred, ev - ery tribe, On this ter - res - trial ball,
5. O that with yon-der sa - cred throng We at His feet may fall,

Bring forth the roy - al di - a - dem, And crown Him,
Ex - tol the Stem of Jes - se's rod, And crown Him,
Go spread your tro - phies at His feet, And crown Him,
To Him all maj - es - ty as - cribe, And crown Him,
Join in the ev - er - last - ing song, And crown Him,

crown Him, crown Him, crown Him Lord of all! A-men.

186

The Holy Spirit

MICHAEL SCHIRMER, 1640
Tr. CATHERINE WINKWORTH, 1862

WIE SCHÖN LEUCHTET (FRANKFORT)

PHILIPP NICOLAI, 1599

8. 8. 7. 8. 8. 7. 8. 4. 4. 8.

In moderate time; reverently

1. O Ho - ly Spir - it, en - ter in, A - mong these hearts Thy work be - gin,
2. Left to our - selves, we shall but stray; O lead us in the nar - row way,
3. O might - y Rock, O Source of Life, Let Thy dear word 'mid doubt and strife
4. Grant that our days, while life shall last, In pu - rest ho - li - ness be passed;

Thy tem - ple deign to make us; Sun of the soul, Thou Light di - vine,
With wis - est coun - sel guide us; And give us sted - fast - ness, that we
Be so with - in us burn - ing, That we be faith - ful un - to death,
Our minds so rule and strength - en That they may rise o'er things of earth,

A - round and in us bright - ly shine, To strength and glad - ness wake us.
May hence - forth tru - ly fol - low Thee, What - ev - er woes be - tide us:
In Thy pure love and ho - ly faith, From Thee true wis - dom learn - ing!
The hopes and joys that here have birth; And if our course Thou length - en,

Where Thou shin - est, life from heav - en There is giv - en;
Heal Thou gen - tly hearts now bro - ken, Give some to - ken
Lord, Thy gra - ces on us show - er; By Thy pow - er
Keep Thou pure, Lord, from of - fen - ses, Heart and sen - ses;

The Holy Spirit

We be - fore Thee For that pre - cious gift im - plore Thee.
Thou art near us, Whom we trust to light and cheer us.
Christ con - fess - ing, Let us win His grace and bless - ing.
Bless - ed Spir - it, Bid us thus true life in - her - it. A-MEN.

187

LAWRENCE TUTTIETT, 1864   L. M.   QUEBEC
HENRY BAKER, 1862

In moderate time

1. O grant us light, that we may know The wis - dom
2. O grant us light, that we may see Where er - ror
3. O grant us light, that we may learn How dead is
4. O grant us light, when, soon or late, All earth - ly

Thou a - lone canst give; That truth may guide wher -
lurks in hu - man lore, And turn our seek - ing
life from Thee a - part, How sure is joy for
scenes shall pass a - way, In Thee to find the

e'er we go, And vir - tue bless wher - e'er we live.
minds to Thee, And love Thy ho - ly Word the more.
all who turn To Thee an un - di - vid - ed heart.
o - pen gate To death - less home and end - less day. A - MEN.

The Holy Spirit

SAMUEL LONGFELLOW, 1864

Arr. from LOUIS M. GOTTSCHALK, 1829–1869

MERCY

7.7.7.7.

Not too fast

1. Ho - ly Spir - it, Truth di - vine, Dawn up - on this soul of mine;
2. Ho - ly Spir - it, Love di - vine, Glow with - in this heart of mine;
3. Ho - ly Spir - it, Power di - vine, Fill and nerve this will of mine;
4. Ho - ly Spir - it, Right di - vine, King with - in my con - science reign;

Word of God, and in - ward Light, Wake my spir - it, clear my sight.
Kin - dle ev - ery high de - sire; Per - ish self in Thy pure fire.
By Thee may I strong-ly live, Brave-ly bear, and no - bly strive.
Be my Law, and I shall be Firm - ly bound, for-ev - er free. A-MEN.

189

GEORGE RAWSON, 1853

7.7.7.5.

CAPETOWN

FRIEDRICH FILITZ, 1847

In moderate time

1. Ho - ly Ghost, the In - fi - nite, Shine up - on our na - ture's night
2. We are sin - ful, cleanse us, Lord; We are faint, Thy strength af - ford;
3. Like the dew, Thy peace dis - til; Guide, sub-due our way - ward will,
4. In us "Ab - ba, Fa - ther," cry, Ear - nest of our bliss on high,
5. Search for us the depths of God; Bear us up the star - ry road,

With Thy bless - ed in - ward light, Com-fort - er Di - vine.
Lost, un - til by Thee re - stored, Com-fort - er Di - vine.
Things of Christ un - fold - ing stili, Com-fort - er Di - vine.
Seal of im - mor - tal - i - ty, Com-fort - er Di - vine.
To the height of Thine a - bode, Com-fort - er Di - vine. A-MEN.

Alternative Tune, *Irene.*

The Holy Spirit

190

Henry Hallam Tweedy

C. M. D.

ST. MATTHEW
William Croft, 1708

Not too slowly

1. O Spir - it of the Liv - ing God, Thou Light and Fire Di - vine:
2. Blow, Wind of God! With wis - dom blow Un - til our minds are free
3. Teach us to ut - ter liv - ing words Of truth which all may hear,
4. So shall we know the power of Him Who came man - kind to save;

De - scend up - on Thy Church once more And make it tru - ly Thine!
From mists of er - ror, clouds of doubt, Which blind our eyes to Thee!
The lan - guage all men un - der - stand When love speaks, loud and clear;
So shall we rise with Him to life Which soars be - yond the grave;

Fill it with love and joy and power, With right - eous - ness and peace,
Burn, Wing - ed Fire! In - spire our lips With flam - ing love and zeal,
Till ev - ery age and race and clime Shall blend their creeds in one,
And earth shall win true ho - li - ness, Which makes Thy chil - dren whole,

Till Christ shall dwell in hu - man hearts, And sin and sor - row cease.
To preach to all Thy great Good News, God's glo - rious Com - mon - weal!
And earth shall form one broth - er - hood By whom Thy will is done.
Till, per - fect - ed by Thee, we reach Cre - a - tion's glo - rious goal! A - MEN.

Words used by permission of the author.

191

EDWIN HATCH, 1886   S. M.   TRENTHAM
ROBERT JACKSON, 1894

Rather slowly

1. Breathe on me, Breath of God, Fill me with life a - new,
2. Breathe on me, Breath of God, Un - til my heart is pure,
3. Breathe on me, Breath of God, Till I am whol - ly Thine,
4. Breathe on me, Breath of God, So shall I nev - er die,

That I may love what Thou dost love, And do what Thou wouldst do.
Un - til with Thee I will one will, To do and to en - dure.
Un - til this earth - ly part of me Glows with Thy fire di - vine.
But live with Thee the per - fect life Of Thine e - ter - ni - ty. A-MEN.

192

THOMAS T. LYNCH, 1855   7.7.7.7.7.7.   REDHEAD (AJALON)
RICHARD REDHEAD, 1853

In moderate time

1. Gra - cious Spir - it, dwell with me; I my - self would gra - cious be;
2. Truth - ful Spir - it, dwell with me; I my - self would truth - ful be;
3. Might - y Spir - it, dwell with me; I my - self would might - y be;
4. Ho - ly Spir - it, dwell with me; I my - self would ho - ly be;

And, with words that help and heal, Would Thy life in mine re - veal;
And, with wis - dom kind and clear, Let Thy life in mine ap - pear;
Might - y so as to pre - vail Where, un - aid - ed, man must fail;
Sep - a - rate from sin, I would Choose and cher - ish all things good,

The Holy Spirit

And, with ac-tions bold and meek, Would for Christ my Sav-iour speak.
And, with ac-tions broth-er-ly, Speak my Lord's sin-cer-i-ty.
Ev-er by a might-y hope, Press-ing on and bear-ing up.
And what-ev-er I can be Give to Him who gave me Thee! A-MEN.

193

GEORGE CROLY, 1854   10. 10. 10. 10.   FREDERICK C. ATKINSON, 1880

MORECAMBE

In moderate time, with deep reverence

1. Spir - it of God, de - scend up - on my heart; Wean it from earth, through
2. I ask no dream, no proph - et - ec - sta - cies, No sud-den rend - ing
3. Hast Thou not bid us love Thee, God and King? All, all Thine own, soul,
4. Teach me to feel that Thou art al-ways nigh; Teach me the strug - gles
5. Teach me to love Thee as Thine an-gels love, One ho - ly pas - sion

all its puls - es move; Stoop to my weak - ness, might-y as Thou art,
of the veil of clay, No an - gel - vis - i - tant, no open - ing skies;
heart, and strength, and mind; I see Thy cross—there teach my heart to cling:
of the soul to bear, To check the ris - ing doubt, the reb - el sigh;
fill ing all my frame; The bap - tism of the heaven-de-scend-ed Dove,

And make me love Thee as I ought to love.
But take the dim - ness of my soul a - way.
O let me seek Thee, and O let me find.
Teach me the pa - tience of un - an - swered prayer.
My heart an al - tar, and Thy love the flame. A-MEN.

The Holy Trinity

194

HORATIUS BONAR, 1808–1889   8. 7. 8. 7. 8. 7.   ST. PETER'S WESTMINSTER
JAMES TURLE, 1802–1882

With marked and joyous rhythm

1. Glo-ry be to God the Fa-ther, Glo-ry be to God the Son,
2. Glo-ry be to Him who loved us, Washed us from each spot and stain,
3. Glo-ry to the King of an-gels, Glo-ry to the Church's King,
4. "Glo-ry, bless-ing, praise e-ter-nal!" Thus the choir of an-gels sings;

Glo-ry be to God the Spir-it— Great Je-ho-vah, Three in One!
Glo-ry be to Him who bought us, Made us kings with Him to reign!
Glo-ry to the King of na-tions! Heaven and earth, your prais-es bring;
"Hon-or, rich-es, power, do-min-ion!" Thus its praise cre-a-tion brings;

Glo-ry, glo-ry, Glo-ry, glo-ry, While e-ter-nal a-ges run!
Glo-ry, glo-ry, Glo-ry, glo-ry, To the Lamb that once was slain!
Glo-ry, glo-ry, Glo-ry, glo-ry, To the King of glo-ry bring!
Glo-ry, glo-ry, Glo-ry, glo-ry, Glo-ry to the King of kings! A-MEN.

Alternative tune, *Regent Square.*

195

LOUIS F. BENSON, 1907   8. 4. 8. 4. 8. 4.   WENTWORTH
FREDERICK C. MAKER, 1876

Joyfully

1. The sun is on the land and sea, The day be-gun;
2. Thy love was ev-er in our view, Like stars by night;
3. We do not know what grief or care The day may bring,
4. All glo-ry to the Fa-ther be, With Christ the Son,

The Holy Trinity

Our morn - ing hymn be - gins with Thee, Blest Three in One;
Thy gifts are ev - ery morn - ing new, O God of light;
The heart shall find some glad - ness there That loves its King;
And, Ho - ly Spir - it, un - to Thee, For - ev - er One;

Our praise shall rise con - tin - ual - ly Till day is done.
Thy mer - cy, like the heav - ens' blue, Fills all our sight.
The life that serves Thee ev - ery-where Can al - ways sing.
All glo - ry to the Trin - i - ty While a - ges run. A-MEN.

Words used by permission of Mrs. Barbara Benson Jeffery

196

EDWARD COOPER, 1805   L. M.   WARRINGTON
R. HARRISON, 1784

In moderate time

1. Fa - ther of heaven, Whose love pro-found A ran-som for our souls hath found,
2. Al - might-y Son, In - car - nate Word, Our Prophet, Priest, Re-deem - er, Lord!
3. E - ter - nal Spir - it, By whose breath The soul is raised from sin and death,
4. Thrice Ho - ly! Fa - ther, Spir - it, Son, Mys-ter-ious God-head, Three in One!

Be-fore Thy throne we sin - ners bend: To us Thy pardoning love ex-tend.
Be-fore Thy throne we sin - ners bend: To us Thy sav-ing grace ex-tend.
Be-fore Thy throne we sin - ners bend: To us Thy quickening power extend.
Be-fore Thy throne we sin - ners bend: Grace, par-don, life, to us ex-tend. A-MEN.

The Holy Trinity

197

WILLIAM DOANE, 1886 · 11. 10. 11. 10. · ANCIENT OF DAYS · J. ALBERT JEFFERY, 1886

With marked rhythm

1. An-cient of Days, who sit-test throned in glo-ry;
2. O Ho-ly Fa-ther, who hast led Thy chil-dren
3. O Ho-ly Je-sus, Prince of Peace and Sav-iour,
4. O Ho-ly Ghost, the Lord and the Life Giv-er,
5. O Tri-une God, with heart and voice a-dor-ing,

Introduction 1st stanza

Accompaniment

To Thee all knees are bent, all voic-es pray;
In all the a-ges, with the fire and cloud,
To Thee we owe the peace that still pre-vails,
Thine is the quick-ening power that gives in-crease;
Praise we the good-ness that doth crown our days;

The Holy Trinity

Thy love has blest the wide world's won-drous sto-ry
Through seas dry-shod, through wea-ry wastes be-wil-dering;
Still-ing the rude wills of men's wild be-hav-ior,
From Thee have flowed, as from a pleas-ant riv-er,
Pray we that Thou wilt hear us, still im-plor-ing

With light and life since E-den's dawn-ing day.
To Thee, in rev-erent love, our hearts are bowed.
And calm-ing pas-sion's fierce and storm-y gales.
Our plen-ty, wealth, pros-per-i-ty, and peace.
Thy love and fa-vor, kept to us al-ways. A-MEN.

The Holy Trinity

198

James Montgomery, 1832

7.7.7.7. D.

SPANISH HYMN
Arr. Benjamin Carr, 1824

In moderate time

1. Ho - ly, Ho - ly, Ho - ly Lord, God of Hosts, when heaven and earth
2. Ho - ly, Ho - ly, Ho - ly! Thee, One Je - ho - vah ev - er - more,
3. Ho - ly, Ho - ly, Ho - ly! All Heaven's tri - um - phant choir shall sing,

Out of dark - ness, at Thy word, Is - sued in - to glo - rious birth,
Fa - ther, Son, and Spir - it, we, Dust and ash - es, would a - dore:
While the ran - somed na - tions fall At the foot - stool of their King:

All Thy works be - fore Thee stood, And Thine eyes be - held them good,
Light - ly by the world es - teemed, From that world by Thee re - deemed,
Then shall saints and ser - a - phim, Harps and voic - es swell one hymn,

While they sang with sweet ac - cord, Ho - ly, Ho - ly, Ho - ly Lord!
Sing we here with glad ac - cord, Ho - ly, Ho - ly, Ho - ly Lord!
Blend - ing in sub - lime ac - cord, Ho - ly, Ho - ly, Ho - ly Lord! A-men.

The Word of God

199

MUNICH
Neuvermehrtes Meiningsches Gesangbuch, 1693
Harmonized by MENDELSSOHN

WILLIAM WALSHAM HOW, 1867

7.6.7.6. D.

With joyous feeling

1. O Word of God In - car - nate, O Wis - dom from on high,
2. The Church from her [dear Mas - ter Re - ceived the gift di - vine,
3. It float - eth like a ban - ner Be - fore God's host un - furled;
4. O make Thy Church, dear Sav - iour, A lamp of pur - est gold,

O Truth un-changed, un - chang - ing, O Light of our dark sky;
And still that light she lift - eth O'er all the earth to shine.
It shin - eth like a bea - con A - bove the dark - ling world;
To bear a - mong the na - tions Thy true light as of old.

We praise Thee for the ra - diance That from the hal - lowed page,
It is the gold - en cas - ket Where gems of truth are stored;
It is the chart and com - pass That o'er life's surg - ing sea,
O teach Thy wan-dering pil - grims By this their path to trace,

A lan - tern to our foot - steps, Shines on from age to age.
It is the heaven-drawn pic - ture Of Christ, the liv - ing Word.
'Mid mists, and rocks, and quick - sands Still guides, O Christ, to Thee.
Till, clouds and dark - ness end - ed, They see Thee face to face. A-MEN.

Alternative tune, *Aurelia*.

The Word of God

200

CHRISTIAN GREGOR, 1723–1801
V. 2, C. G. CLEMENS
V. 3, J. SWERTNER

FAHRE FORT
JOH. EUSEBIUS SCHMIDT, 1704

6. 7. 8. 7. 8. 9. 6.

Joyfully, with dignity

1. Ho - ly Lord, Ho - ly Lord, Ho - ly and Al - might - y Lord,
2. Thanks and praise, thanks and praise, Thanks and praise be ev - er Thine,
3. Lord, our God, Lord, our God, May Thy pre - cious sav - ing word,

Thou, who, as the great Cre - a - tor, Art by all Thy works a - dored;
That Thy word to us is giv - en, Teach-ing us with power di - vine,
Till our race is here com - plet - ed, Light un - to our path af - ford;

Source of u - ni - ver - sal na - ture, And to man, re -
That the Lord of earth and heav - en, Ev - er - last - ing
And, when in Thy pres - ence seat - ed, We to Thee will

deemed by Je - sus' blood, Sov - ereign Good, sov - ereign Good.
life for us to gain, Once was slain, once was slain.
ren - der for Thy grace Cease-less praise, cease - less praise. A-MEN.

The Word of God

201

Washington Gladden, 1897   C.M.D.   FOREST GREEN
English traditional melody

In moderate time; brightly

1. Be - hold a Sow - er! from a - far He go - eth forth with might;
2. O Lord of life, to Thee we lift Our hearts in praise for those,
3. Shine forth, O Light, that we may see, With hearts all un - a - fraid,
4. Light up Thy Word; the fet - tered page From kill - ing bond - age free:

The roll - ing years His fur - rows are, His seed, the grow - ing light;
Thy proph - ets, who have shown Thy gift Of grace that ev - er grows,
The mean - ing and the mys - ter - y Of things that Thou hast made:
Light up our way; lead forth this age In love's large lib - er - ty.

For all the just His word is sown, It spring - eth up al - way;
Of truth that spreads from shore to shore, Of wis - dom's wid - ening ray,
Shine forth, and let the dark - ling past, Be - neath Thy beam grow bright;
O Light of light! with - in us dwell, Through us Thy ra - diance pour,

The ten - der blade is hope's young dawn, The har - vest, love's new day.
Of light that shin - eth more and more Un - to Thy per - fect day.
Shine forth, and touch the fu - ture vast With Thine un - trou - bled light.
That word and life Thy truths may tell, And praise Thee ev - er - more. A-men.

The Word of God

202

JOHN BURTON, 1805

7. 7. 7. 7.

MERCY

Arr. from LOUIS M. GOTTSCHALK, 1867

Not too fast

1. Ho - ly Bi - ble, book di - vine, Pre - cious treas - ure, thou art mine;
2. Mine to chide me when I rove, Mine to show a Sav - iour's love;
3. Mine to com - fort in dis - tress, If the Ho - ly Spir - it bless;
4. Mine to tell of joys to come, In that bless - ed heav'n-ly home;

Mine to tell me whence I came, Mine to teach me what I am.
Mine art thou to guide my feet, Mine to judge, con - demn, ac - quit.
Mine to show by liv - ing faith, Man can tri - umph o - ver death.
Ho - ly Bi - ble, book di - vine, Pre - cious treas - ure, thou art mine. A - MEN.

203

PERCY DEARMER, 1925

7. 8. 7. 8. 8. 8.

LIEBSTER JESU WIR SIND HIER (NÜREMBERG)

JOHANN RUDOLPH AHLE, 1664

In moderate time

1. Book of books, our peo - ple's strength, States - man's, teach - er's, he - ro's treas - ure,
2. Thank we those who toiled in thought, Man - y di - verse scrolls com - plet - ing,
3. Praise we God, who hath in - spired Those whose wis - dom still di - rects us;

Bring - ing free - dom, speed - ing truth, Shed - ding light that none can meas - ure;
Po - ets, proph - ets, schol - ars, saints, Each his word from God re - peat - ing;
Praise Him for the Word made flesh, For the Spir - it who pro - tects us.

The Word of God

Wis-dom comes to those who know thee, All the best we have we owe thee.
Till they came, who told the sto-ry Of the Word, and showed His glo-ry.
Light of Knowl-edge, ev-er burn-ing, Shed on us thy death-less learn-ing. A-MEN.

204

MARY A. LATHBURY, 1877   6. 4. 6. 4. D.

BREAD OF LIFE
WILLIAM F. SHERWIN, 1877

Rather slowly, in flowing rhythm

1. Break Thou the bread of life, Dear Lord, to me, As Thou didst
2. Bless Thou the truth, dear Lord, To me— to me, As Thou didst

break the loaves Be-side the sea; Be-yond the sa-cred page
bless the bread By Gal-i-lee; Then shall all bond-age cease,

I seek Thee, Lord; My spir-it pants for Thee, O liv-ing Word.
All fet-ters fall; And I shall find my peace, My All in all. A-MEN.

The Christian Life

205

WASHINGTON GLADDEN, 1880
L.M.
MARYTON
HENRY PERCY SMITH, 1874

In moderate time

1. O Mas-ter, let me walk with Thee In low-ly
2. Help me the slow of heart to move By some clear,
3. Teach me Thy pa-tience; still with Thee In clos-er,
4. In hope that sends a shin-ing ray Far down the

paths of serv-ice free; Tell me Thy se-cret,
win-ning word of love; Teach me the way-ward
dear-er com-pan-y, In work that keeps faith
fu-ture's broad-ening way, In peace that on-ly

help me bear The strain of toil, the fret of care.
feet to stay, And guide them in the homeward way.
sweet and strong, In trust that tri-umphs o-ver wrong.
Thou canst give, With Thee, O Mas-ter, let me live. A-MEN.

206

LUCY LARCOM, 1892
6.4.6.4.6.6.6.4.
ST. EDMUND
ARTHUR S. SULLIVAN, 1872

In moderate time

1. Draw Thou my soul, O Christ, Clos-er to Thine; Breathe in-to
2. Lead forth my soul, O Christ, One with Thine own, Joy-ful to
3. Not for my-self a-lone May my prayer be; Lift Thou Thy

Call to Discipleship

ev - ery wish Thy will di - vine: Raised my low self a-bove, Won by Thy
fol - low Thee Through paths unknown: In Thee my strength re-new; Give me Thy
world, O Christ, Clos - er to Thee: Cleanse from its guilt and wrong, Teach it sal -

death-less love, Ev - er, O Christ, through mine Let Thy life shine.
work to do; Through me Thy truth be shown, Thy love made known.
va - tion's song, Till earth, as heaven, ful - fil God's ho - ly will. A-MEN.

Words used by permission of Houghton Mifflin Co.

207

CECIL FRANCES ALEXANDER, 1852   8.7.8.7.   GALILEE
                                              WILLIAM H. JUDE, 1887

In moderate time

1. Je - sus calls us: o'er the tu - mult Of our life's wild, rest - less sea,
2. Je - sus calls us from the wor - ship Of the vain world's gold - en store;
3. In our joys and in our sor - rows, Days of toil and hours of ease,
4. Je - sus calls us! By Thy mer - cies, Sav - iour, may we hear Thy call;

Day by day His sweet voice soundeth, Say - ing, "Christian, fol - low Me!"
From each i - dol that would keep us, Say - ing, "Christian, love Me more!"
Still He calls, in cares and pleas-ures, "Chris-tian, love Me more than these!"
Give our hearts to Thy o - be-dience, Serve and love Thee best of all! A-MEN.

208

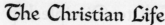

FREDERICK MANN, 1846-1928   8.8.8.4   FIRENZE
LINDSAY B. LONGACRE

Not too slowly

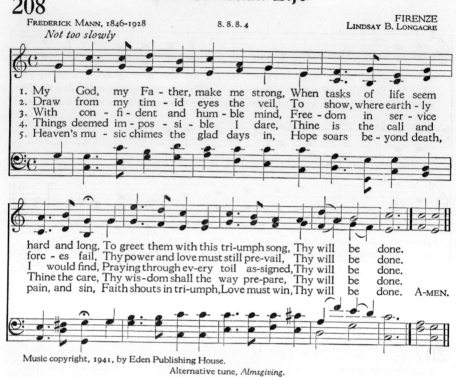

1. My God, my Fa-ther, make me strong, When tasks of life seem
2. Draw from my tim-id eyes the veil, To show, where earth-ly
3. With con-fi-dent and hum-ble mind, Free-dom in ser-vice
4. Things deemed im-pos-si-ble I dare, Thine is the call and
5. Heaven's mu-sic chimes the glad days in, Hope soars be-yond death,

hard and long, To greet them with this tri-umph song, Thy will be done.
forc-es fail, Thy power and love must still pre-vail, Thy will be done.
I would find, Praying through ev-ery toil as-signed, Thy will be done.
Thine the care, Thy wis-dom shall the way pre-pare, Thy will be done.
pain, and sin, Faith shouts in tri-umph, Love must win, Thy will be done. A-MEN.

Music copyright, 1941, by Eden Publishing House.

Alternative tune, *Almsgiving*.

209   ### Sin and Repentance

CHARLES WESLEY, 1740   7.7.7.7.   SEYMOUR
CARL M. VON WEBER, 1826

Not too fast

1. Depth of mer-cy! can there be Mer-cy still re-served for me?
2. I have long with-stood His grace, Long pro-voked Him to His face;
3. Still for me the Sav-iour stands, Shows His wounds, and spreads His hands;

Can my God His wrath for-bear? Me, the chief of sin-ners spare?
Would not heark-en to His calls, Grieved Him by a thou-sand falls.
God is love! I know, I feel; Je-sus weeps, and loves me still. A-MEN.

Sin and Repentance

AUS TIEFER NOT (HERR, WIE DU WILLT)

MARTIN LUTHER, 1523
Tr. as in New Congregational Hymn Book, 1859

Teutsch Kirchenampt, Strassburg, 1525

8.7.8.7.8.8.7.

With quiet confidence

1. Out of the depths I cry to Thee; Lord, hear me, I im-
2. Thy sov - ereign grace and bound-less love Make Thee, O Lord, for -
3. Thou canst be mer - ci - ful while just, This is my hope's foun -
4. Wher - e'er the great - est sins a - bound, By grace they are ex -

plore Thee; Bend down Thy gra - cious ear to me, Let my prayer come be -
giv - ing; My pur - est thoughts and deeds but prove, Sin in my heart is
da - tion; On Thy re - deem - ing grace I trust, Grant me, then, Thy sal -
ceed - ed; Thy help - ing hand is al - ways found With aid, where aid is

fore Thee! On my mis - deeds in mer - cy look, O
liv - ing: None guilt - less in Thy sight ap - pear, All
va - tion. Shield - ed by Thee, I stand se - cure; Thy
need - ed: Thy hand, the on - ly hand to save, Will

deign to blot them from Thy book, Or who can stand be - fore Thee?
who approach Thy throne must fear, And hum - bly trust Thy mer - cy.
word is firm, Thy prom-ise sure, And I re - ly up - on Thee.
save the sin - ner from the grave, And par-don his trans-gres-sion. A-MEN.

211

WILLIAM WALSHAM HOW, 1867

7. 6. 7. 6. D.

ST. HILDA (ST. EDITH)
JUSTIN H. KNECHT, 1799
EDWARD HUSBAND, 1871

In moderate time

1. O Je - sus, Thou art stand - ing Out - side the fast-closed door,
2. O Je - sus, Thou art knock - ing; And lo, that hand is scarred,
3. O Je - sus, Thou art plead - ing In ac - cents meek and low,

In low - ly pa - tience wait - ing To pass the thresh - old o'er:
And thorns Thy brow en - cir - cle, And tears Thy face have marred:
"I died for you, My chil - dren, And will ye treat Me so?"

Shame on us, Chris - tian broth - ers, His name and sign who bear,
O love that pass - eth knowl - edge, So pa - tient - ly to wait!
O Lord, with shame and sor - row We o - pen now the door;

O shame, thrice shame up - on us, To keep Him stand - ing there.
O sin that hath no e - qual, So fast to bar the gate!
Dear Sav - iour, en - ter, en - ter, And leave us nev - er - more. A - MEN.

Sin and Repentance

212

Thomas Benson Pollock, 1870

7.7.7.6.

AGNES
Edward Bunnett, 1877

Not too fast

1. Je - sus, we are far a - way From the light of heaven - ly day;
2. Help us to be - wail our sin, And, in heaven-ly strength, be - gin
3. May Thy wis - dom be our guide, Com - fort, rest, and peace pro - vide
4. Fix our hearts on things on high; Let no e - vil thoughts come nigh;
5. May Thy grace with - in the soul Na - ture's way - ward - ness con - trol,

Lost in paths of sin we stray: Lord, in mer - cy hear us.
Dai - ly vic - to - ries to win: Lord, in mer - cy hear us.
Near to Thy pro - tect - ing side: Lord, in mer - cy hear us.
Purge from sin our mem - o - ry: Lord, in mer - cy hear us.
Guid - ing toward the heaven - ly goal: Lord, in mer - cy hear us. A-MEN.

213

John Marckant, 1562
Alt. Reginald Heber, 1827

C.M.

MANOAH
Henry W. Greatorex's
Collection, Boston, 1851

Slowly

1. O Lord, turn not Thy face a - way From them that low - ly lie,
2. Thy mer - cy-gates are o - pen wide To them that mourn their sin;
3. And need we, then, O Lord, re - peat The bless - ing which we crave,
4. Mer - cy, O Lord, mer - cy we ask, This is the to - tal sum;

La - ment-ing sore their sin - ful life With tears and bit - ter cry.
O shut them not a - gainst us, Lord, But let us en - ter in.
When Thou dost know, be - fore we speak, The thing that we would have?
For mer - cy, Lord, is all our prayer, O let Thy mer - cy come! A-MEN.

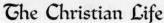

214

Charlotte Elliott, 1836   L. M.   WOODWORTH   William B. Bradbury, 1849

In moderate time

1. Just as I am, with-out one plea But that Thy blood was shed for me, And that Thou bidd'st me come to Thee, O Lamb of God, I come, I come!
2. Just as I am, and wait-ing not To rid my soul of one dark blot, To Thee, whose blood can cleanse each spot, O Lamb of God, I come, I come!
3. Just as I am, though tossed a-bout, With many a con-flict, many a doubt, Fight-ings and fears with-in, with-out, O Lamb of God, I come, I come!
4. Just as I am, poor, wretch-ed, blind, Sight, rich-es, heal-ing of the mind, Yea, all I need in Thee to find, O Lamb of God, I come, I come!
5. Just as I am, Thou wilt re-ceive, Wilt wel-come, par-don, cleanse, re-lieve; Be-cause Thy prom-ise I be-lieve, O Lamb of God, I come, I come!
6. Just as I am, Thy love un-known Has bro-ken ev-ery bar-rier down; Now to be Thine, yea, Thine a-lone, O Lamb of God, I come, I come! A-men.

215

Theodore Monod, 1874   8. 7. 8. 8. 7.   ST. AUGUSTINE   Pietro Yon, 1939

1. O the bit-ter shame and sor-row, That a time could ev-er be
2. Yet He found me; I be-held Him Bleed-ing on th' ac-curs-ed tree,
3. Day by day His ten-der mer-cy, Heal-ing, help-ing, full and free,
4. High-er than the high-est heav-ens, Deep-er than the deep-est sea,

Sin and Repentance

When I let the Saviour's pit-y   Plead in vain, and proud-ly an-swered,
Heard Him pray,"For-give them,Fa-ther!" And my wist-ful heart said faint-ly,
Sweet and strong,and, ah! so pa-tient, Brought me low-er, while I whis-pered,
Lord, Thy love at last hath con-quered;Grant me now my sup-pli-ca-tion,

"All of self, all of self, all of self,
"Some of self, some of self, some of self,
"Less of self, less of self, less of self,
"None of self, ? none of self, none of self,

"All of self, all of self, all of self and none of Thee!"
"Some of self, some of self, some of self and some of Thee."
"Less of self, less of self, less of self and more of Thee."
"None of self, none of self, none of self and all of Thee!" A-MEN.

"All of self, . . . all of self, . . .
"Some of self, . . . some of self, . . .
"Less of self, . . . less of self, . . .
"None of self, . . . none of self, . . .

Tune used by permission of the composer.

216

MARY ANN SIDEBOTHAM, 1881   8.7.8.7.   RINGE RECHT (BATTY)
                                                      JOHANN THOMMEN'S, *Choralbuch*, 1745

Rather slowly

1. Lord, Thy mer-cy now en-treat-ing, Low be-fore Thy throne we fall;
2. Sin-ful thoughts and words un-lov-ing Rise a-gainst us one by one;
3. Hearts that far from Thee were stray-ing, While in prayer we bowed the knee;
4. Lord, Thy mer-cy still en-treat-ing, We with shame our sins would own;
5. Heaven-ly Fa-ther, bless Thy chil-dren;Hear-ken from Thy throne on high;

Our mis-deeds to Thee con-fess-ing, On Thy Name we hum-bly call.
Acts un-wor-thy, deeds un-think-ing, Good that we have left un-done.
Lips that,while Thy prais-es sound-ing, Lift-ed not the soul to Thee.
From hence-forth,the time re-deem-ing, May we live to Thee a-lone.
Lov-ing Sav-iour, Ho-ly Spir-it, Hear and heed our hum-ble cry. A-MEN.

The Christian Life

TOPLADY

Augustus M. Toplady, 1776
Stanza 4, line 2, alt. by
Thomas Cotterill, 1815

7. 7. 7. 7. 7. 7.
First Tune

Thomas Hastings, 1830

In moderate time

1. Rock of A - ges, cleft for me, Let me
2. Not the la - bors of my hands Can ful -
3. Noth - ing in my hand I bring, Sim - ply
4. While I draw this fleet - ing breath, When my

hide my - self in Thee; Let the wa - ter and the blood,
fil Thy law's de - mands; Could my zeal no res - pite know,
to Thy cross I cling; Na - ked, come to Thee for dress,
eye - lids close in death, When I soar to worlds un - known,

From Thy riv - en side which flowed, Be of
Could my tears for - ev - er flow, All for
Help - less, look to Thee for grace; Foul, I
See Thee on Thy judg - ment throne, Rock of

sin the dou - ble cure, Cleanse me from its guilt and power.
sin could not a - tone; Thou must save, and Thou a - lone.
to the foun - tain fly; Wash me, Sav - iour, or I die.
A - ges, cleft for me, Let me hide my - self in Thee. A - MEN.

Sin and Repentance

218

Augustus M. Toplady, 1776
Stanza 4, line 2, alt. by
Thomas Cotterill, 1815

7. 7. 7. 7. 7. 7.
Second Tune

REDHEAD (AJALON)

Richard Redhead, 1853

In moderate time

1. Rock of A - ges, cleft for me, Let me hide my-
2. Not the la - bors of my hands Can ful - fil Thy
3. Noth - ing in my hand I bring, Sim - ply to Thy
4. While I draw this fleet - ing breath, When my eye - lids

self in Thee; Let the wa - ter and the blood,
law's de - mands; Could my zeal no res - pite know,
cross I cling; Na - ked, come to Thee for dress,
close in death, When I soar to worlds un - known,

From Thy riv - en side which flowed, Be of sin the
Could my tears for - ev - er flow, All for sin could
Help - less, look to Thee for grace; Foul, I to the
See Thee on Thy judg - ment throne, Rock of A - ges,

dou - ble cure, Cleanse me from its guilt and power.
not a - tone; Thou must save, and Thou a - lone.
foun - tain fly; Wash me, Sav - iour, or I die.
cleft for me, Let me hide my - self in Thee. A-MEN.

The Christian Life

219

ROBERT GRANT, 1815

7.7.7.7. D.

SPANISH HYMN
Arr. BENJAMIN CARR, 1826

Not too fast

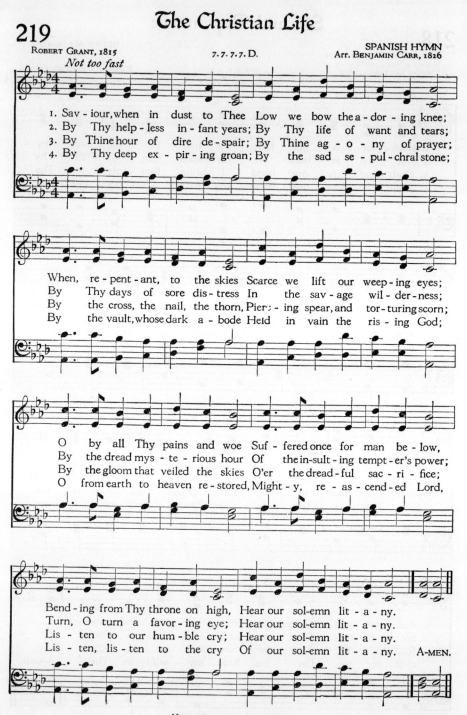

1. Sav - iour, when in dust to Thee Low we bow the a - dor - ing knee;
2. By Thy help - less in - fant years; By Thy life of want and tears;
3. By Thine hour of dire de - spair; By Thine ag - o - ny of prayer;
4. By Thy deep ex - pir - ing groan; By the sad se - pul - chral stone;

When, re - pent - ant, to the skies Scarce we lift our weep - ing eyes;
By Thy days of sore dis - tress In the sav - age wil - der - ness;
By the cross, the nail, the thorn, Pierc - ing spear, and tor - turing scorn;
By the vault, whose dark a - bode Held in vain the ris - ing God;

O by all Thy pains and woe Suf - fered once for man be - low,
By the dread mys - te - rious hour Of the in - sult - ing tempt - er's power;
By the gloom that veiled the skies O'er the dread - ful sac - ri - fice;
O from earth to heaven re - stored, Might - y, re - as - cend - ed Lord,

Bend - ing from Thy throne on high, Hear our sol - emn lit - a - ny.
Turn, O turn a favor - ing eye; Hear our sol - emn lit - a - ny.
Lis - ten to our hum - ble cry; Hear our sol - emn lit - a - ny.
Lis - ten, lis - ten to the cry Of our sol - emn lit - a - ny. A - MEN.

Alternative tune, *Aberystwyth.*

Faith and Forgiveness

220

James Edmeston, 1821

8. 7. 8. 7. 8. 7.

ALLELUIA DULCE CARMEN (corinth)
Essay on the Church Plain Chant, 1782

In march rhythm

1. Lead us, heaven-ly Fa - ther, lead us O'er the world's tem - pes - tuous sea; Guard us, guide us, keep us, feed us, For we have no help but Thee; Yet pos - sess - ing ev - ery bless - ing, If our God our Fa - ther be.

2. Sav - iour, breathe for - give - ness o'er us, All our weak - ness Thou dost know; Thou didst tread this earth be - fore us, Thou didst feel its keen - est woe; Lone and drear - y, faint and wea - ry, Through the des - ert Thou didst go.

3. Spir - it of our God, de - scend - ing, Fill our hearts with heaven - ly joy, Love with ev - ery pas - sion blend - ing, Pleas - ure that can nev - er cloy; Thus pro - vid - ed, par - doned, guid - ed, Noth - ing can our peace de - stroy. A - men.

The Christian Life

221

RAY PALMER, 1830   6. 6. 4. 6. 6. 6. 4.   OLIVET
                                            LOWELL MASON, 1832

In moderate time; not too slowly

1. My faith looks up to Thee, Thou Lamb of Cal - va - ry,
2. May Thy rich grace im - part Strength to my faint - ing heart,
3. While life's dark maze I tread, And griefs a - round me spread,
4. When ends life's tran - sient dream, When death's cold, sul - len stream

Sav - iour di - vine: Now hear me while I pray, Take all my
My zeal in - spire; As Thou hast died for me, O may my
Be Thou my Guide; Bid dark - ness turn to day, Wipe sor - row's
Shall o'er me roll, Blest Sav - iour, then, in love, Fear and dis -

guilt a - way, O let me from this day Be whol - ly Thine!
love to Thee Pure, warm, and change-less be, A liv - ing fire!
tears a - way, Nor let me ev - er stray From Thee a - side.
trust re - move; O bear me safe a - bove, A ran-somed soul!
                                                     A-MEN.

222

                                    ST. BERNARD
                            Neues Kirchen-und Hauss-gesangbuch
JOHN HAMPDEN GURNEY, 1838   C. M.   *der Tochter Sion,*COLOGNE, 1741

In moderate time

1. Lord, as to Thy dear cross we flee And plead to be for-given,
2. Help us through good re - port and ill Our dai - ly cross to bear;
3. If joy shall at Thy bid - ding fly And grief's dark day come on,
4. Should friends mis-judge, or foes de - fame, Or breth - ren faith-less prove,
5. Kept peace - ful in the midst of strife, For - giv - ing and for-given,

Faith and Forgiveness

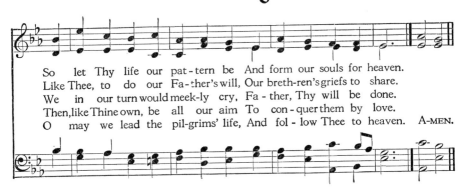

So let Thy life our pat-tern be And form our souls for heaven.
Like Thee, to do our Fa-ther's will, Our breth-ren's griefs to share.
We in our turn would meek-ly cry, Fa-ther, Thy will be done.
Then, like Thine own, be all our aim To con-quer them by love.
O may we lead the pil-grims' life, And fol-low Thee to heaven. A-MEN.

223

ELIZA FANNY MORRIS, 1857, alt.   7.7.7.5.   CAPETOWN
                                                  FRIEDRICH FILITZ, 1847

In moderate time

1. God of pit-y, God of grace, When we hum-bly seek Thy face,
2. When we in Thy tem-ple meet, Spread our wants be-fore Thy feet,
3. When Thy love our hearts shall fill, And we long to do Thy will,
4. Should we wan-der from Thy fold, And our love to Thee grow cold,
5. And what-e'er our cry may be, When we lift our hearts to Thee,

Bend from heaven, Thy dwell-ing - place, Hear, for - give and save.
Plead-ing at Thy mer - cy - seat, Look from heaven and save.
Turn-ing to Thy ho - ly hill, Lord, ac - cept and save.
With a pity-ing eye be - hold; Lord, for - give and save.
From our bur-den set us free: Heal, for - give, and save. A-MEN.

The Christian Life

224

Johann Andreas Rothe, 1728
Tr. Henry Mills, 1850

9. 8. 9. 8. 8. 8.

MIR IST ERBARMUNG WIDERFAHREN
F. L. F. Hainlin, c. 1790
Alt. 1819

1. I now have found for hope of heav - en, An an - chor -
2. 'Tis God's own mer - cy nev - er end - ing, Its meas - ure
3. This love's a deep, our fol - lies hid - ing; The death of
4. Up - on this ground I rest most firm - ly, Long as the

ground that firm will hold; 'Twas through the cross of Je - sus
all our thoughts ex - ceeds; While Je - sus, too, His arms ex -
Christ, a match - less grace, To life and peace our spir - its
earth my dwell - ing prove; And wish to serve my God and

giv - en, By God ap - point - ed from of old; A ground that
tend - ing, Whose heart for guilt - y sin - ners bleeds, Now with com -
guid - ing, Where wrath no more shall find a place; His blood for
Sav - iour, Till, dy - ing, I shall rise a - bove, And there, re -

shall en - dur - ing stay, When earth and skies have
pas - sion calls His foes To flee from sin and
us is plead - ing still, "Let mer - cy all its
joic - ing, shall a - dore Un - bound - ed mer - cy

Faith and Forgiveness

passed a - way, When earth and skies have passed a - way.
end - less woes, To flee from sin and end - less woes.
work ful - fil, Let mer - cy all its work ful - fil!"
ev - er - more, Un - bound - ed mer - cy ev - er - more. A-MEN.

225

ST. CRISPIN
ALFRED TENNYSON, 1850   L. M.   GEORGE J. ELVEY, 1862

In moderate time and majestic style

1. Strong Son of God, im - mor - tal Love, Whom we, that
2. Thou seem - est hu - man and di - vine, The high - est,
3. Our lit - tle sys - tems have their day; They have their
4. Let knowl - edge grow from more to more, But more of

have not seen Thy face, By faith, and faith a -
ho - liest man - hood, Thou: Our wills are ours, we
day and cease to be; They are but bro - ken
rev - erence in us dwell: That mind and soul, ac -

lone, em - brace, Be - liev - ing where we can - not prove:
know not how; Our wills are ours, to make them Thine.
lights of Thee, And Thou, O Lord, art more than they.
cord - ing well, May make one mu - sic as be - fore. A-MEN.

The Christian Life

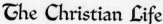

226

JOHN GREENLEAF WHITTIER, 1872   8. 6. 8. 8. 6.   REST (ELTON)
FREDERICK C. MAKER, 1887

In moderate time

1. Dear Lord and Fa - ther of man - kind, For - give our fool - ish ways;
2. In sim - ple trust like theirs who heard, Be - side the Syr - ian sea,
3. O Sab - bath rest by Gal - i - lee! O calm of hills a - bove,
4. Drop Thy still dews of qui - et - ness, Till all our striv - ings cease;
5. Breathe through the heats of our de - sire Thy cool - ness and Thy balm;

Re - clothe us in our right - ful mind, In pur - er lives Thy
The gra - cious call - ing of the Lord, Let us, like them, with -
Where Je - sus knelt to share with Thee The si - lence of e -
Take from our souls the strain and stress, And let our or - dered
Let sense be dumb, let flesh re - tire; Speak through the earth-quake,

serv - ice find, In deep - er rev - erence, praise.
out a word Rise up and fol - low Thee.
ter - ni - ty, In - ter - pret - ed by love!
lives con - fess The beau - ty of Thy peace.
wind, and fire, O still small voice of calm! A - MEN.

Music used by permission of the Psalms and Hymns Trust.

227

Berwick Hymnal, 1886   11. 11. 11. 5.   ISTE CONFESSOR
Angers Church Melody

May be sung in unison. *With stately movement*

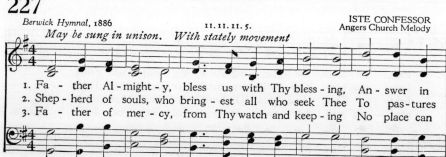

1. Fa - ther Al - might - y, bless us with Thy bless - ing, An - swer in
2. Shep - herd of souls, who bring - est all who seek Thee To pas - tures
3. Fa - ther of mer - cy, from Thy watch and keep - ing No place can

Prayer and Aspiration

love Thy chil-dren's sup-pli-ca-tion: Hear Thou our prayer, the
green, be-side the peace-ful wa-ters; Ten-der-est Guide, in
part, nor hour of time re-move us: Give us Thy good, and

spo-ken and un-spo-ken; Hear us, our Fa-ther.
ways of cheer-ful du-ty Lead us, good Shep-herd.
save us from our e-vil, In-fi-nite Spir-it! A-MEN.

Alternative tune, Integer Vitae.

228

JOHN ELLERTON, 1870   C. M.   WINCHESTER OLD
Este's Psalter, 1592

In moderate time

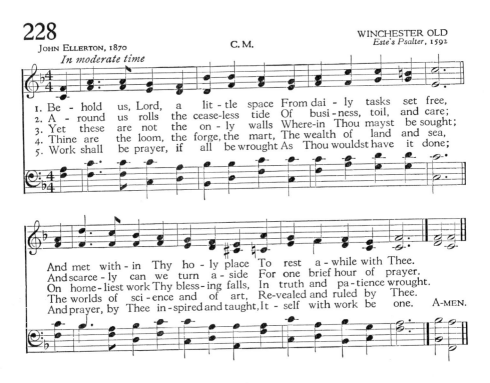

1. Be-hold us, Lord, a lit-tle space From dai-ly tasks set free,
2. A-round us rolls the cease-less tide Of busi-ness, toil, and care;
3. Yet these are not the on-ly walls Where-in Thou mayst be sought;
4. Thine are the loom, the forge, the mart, The wealth of land and sea,
5. Work shall be prayer, if all be wrought As Thou wouldst have it done;

And met with-in Thy ho-ly place To rest a-while with Thee.
And scarce-ly can we turn a-side For one brief hour of prayer.
On home-liest work Thy bless-ing falls, In truth and pa-tience wrought.
The worlds of sci-ence and of art, Re-vealed and ruled by Thee.
And prayer, by Thee in-spired and taught, It-self with work be one. A-MEN.

229

ANNE STEELE, 1716-1786

C. M.

MANOAH
HENRY W. GREATOREX'S
Collection, Boston, 1851

In moderate time

1. Dear Fa - ther, to Thy mer - cy - seat My soul for shel - ter flies;
2. My cheer - ful hope can nev - er die, If Thou, my God, art near;
3. My great Pro - tect - or, and my Lord, Thy con-stant aid im - part;
4. O nev - er let my soul re - move From this di - vine re - treat;

'Tis here I find a safe re - treat When storms and tem-pests rise.
Thy grace can raise my com-forts high, And ban - ish ev - ery fear.
O let Thy kind, Thy gra-cious word Sus - tain my trem-bling heart.
Still let me trust Thy power and love And dwell be-neath Thy feet.

A-MEN.

230

JOHN NEWTON, 1769

C. M.

KILMARNOCK
NEIL DOUGALL, 1831

In moderate time

1. Dear Shep-herd of Thy peo - ple, hear; Thy pres - ence now dis - play;
2. With - in these walls let ho - ly peace And love and con - cord dwell;
3. May we in faith re - ceive Thy word, In faith pre - sent our prayers,
4. The hear-ing ear, the see - ing eye, The hum - bled mind be - stow;

As Thou hast given a place for prayer, So give us hearts to pray.
Here give the trou-bled con-science ease, The wounded spir - it heal.
And in the pres-ence of our Lord Un-bos - om all our cares.
And shine up - on us from on high, To make our grac-es grow.

A-MEN.

Prayer and Aspiration

231

Horatius Bonar, 1867, alt.

Irregular

RUHE IST DAS BESTE GUT
Johann Georg Stötzel, 1777

In moderate time

1. When the wear - y, seek - ing rest, To Thy good - ness flee;
2. When the world - ling, sick at heart, Lifts his soul a - bove;
3. When the stran - ger asks a home, All his toils to end;
4. When the child with lov - ing heart, Youth or maid - en fair,

When the heav - y - la - den cast All their load on Thee;
When the prod - i - gal looks back To his Fa - ther's love;
When the hun - gry crav - eth food, And the poor a friend;
When the a - ged, trust - ing still, Seek Thy face in prayer;

When, crav - ing peace, Sin - ners on Thy Name shall call,
When from their pride Proud men stoop to seek Thy face,
When in their pain Un - to Thee the sick do flee,
When, worn and sad, Fal - tering steps to Thee do turn,

At Thy feet re - pent - ant fall, Lord, hear their cry!
And the bur - dened ask for grace, Lord, hear their cry!
Lift to Thee their hum - ble plea, Lord, hear their cry!
Home-sick hearts for Thee do yearn, Lord, hear their cry! A-MEN.

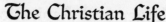

The Christian Life

232

JOHN OXENHAM, 1917   C.M.   ST. AGNES
JOHN B. DYKES, 1866

In rather slow time

1. 'Mid all the traf - fic of the ways— Tur - moils with-out, with - in—
2. A lit - tle shrine of qui - et - ness, All sa - cred to Thy-self,
3. A lit - tle shel - ter from life's stress, Where I may lay me prone,
4. A lit - tle place of mys - tic grace, Of self and sin swept bare,

Make in my heart a qui - et place, And come and dwell there - in:
Where Thou shalt all my soul pos-sess, And I may find my - self;
And bare my soul in lone - li - ness, And know as I am known;
Where I may look up-on Thy face, And talk with Thee in prayer. A-MEN.

Words used by permission of John Oxenham.

233

OLIVER HOLDEN, 1835   7.7.7.7.   UNIVERSITY COLLEGE
HENRY J. GAUNTLETT, 1852

Quietly

1. They who seek the throne of grace Find that throne in ev - ery place;
2. In our sick - ness and our health, In our want or in our wealth,
3. When our earth - ly com - forts fail, When the woes of life pre - vail,
4. Then, my soul, in ev - ery strait, To thy Fa - ther come, and wait;

If we live a life of prayer, God is pres-ent ev - ery-where.
If we look to God in prayer, God is pres-ent ev - ery-where.
'Tis the time for ear - nest prayer; God is pres-ent ev - ery-where.
He will an - swer ev - ery prayer; God is pres-ent ev - ery-where. A-MEN.

Prayer and Aspiration

234

Psalm xlii
Christine Curtis

8. 7. 8. 7. 7. 8. 8.

FREU' DICH SEHR (COMME UN CERF)
Louis Bourgeois
Genevan Psalter, 1551

With flowing rhythm. May be sung in unison.

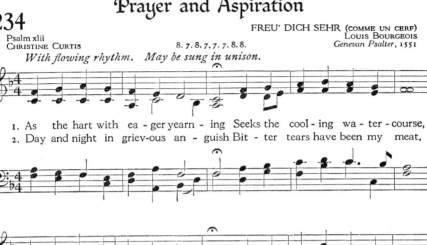

1. As the hart with ea - ger yearn - ing Seeks the cool - ing wa - ter - course,
2. Day and night in griev-ous an - guish Bit - ter tears have been my meat,

So my soul with ar - dor burn - ing Longs for God, its heaven-ly source;
While my long-ing soul doth lan - guish To par - take His man - na sweet:

When shall I be - hold His face? When shall I re - ceive His grace?
O, my soul, be not dis-mayed: Trust in God, who is our aid:

When shall I a - bide re - joic - ing In His pres-ence, His praise voic - ing?
Hope and joy His love pro - vides thee; 'Tis His hand a - lone that guides thee. A-MEN.

The Christian Life

HENRY HALLAM TWEEDY, 1925   C. M. D.   ST. LEONARD
HENRY HILES, 1867

In moderate time

1. O gra-cious Fa-ther of man-kind, Our spir-its' un-seen Friend,
2. Thou hear-est these—the good and ill—Deep bur-ied in each breast;
3. Our best is but Thy-self in us, Our high-est thought Thy will;
4. Thou seek-est us in love and truth More than our minds seek Thee;

High heav-en's Lord, our hearts' dear Guest, To Thee our prayers as-cend.
The se-cret thought, the hid-den plan, Wrought out or un-ex-pressed.
To hear Thy voice we need but love, And lis-ten, and be still.
Through o-pen gates Thy power flows in Like flood-tides from the sea.

Thou dost not wait till hu-man speech Thy gifts di-vine im-plore;
O, cleanse our prayers from hu-man dross! At-tune our lives to Thee,
We would not bend Thy will to ours, But blend our wills with Thine;
No more we seek Thee from a-far, Nor ask Thee for a sign,

Our dreams, our aims, our work, our lives Are prayers Thou lov-est more.
Un-til we la-bor for those gifts We ask on bend-ed knee.
Not beat with cries on heav-en's doors, But live Thy life di-vine.
Con-tent to pray in life and love And toil, till all are Thine. A-MEN.

The New Life in Christ

236

Horatius Bonar, 1846   C. M. D.   VOX DILECTI
John B. Dykes, 1868

In moderate time

1. I heard the voice of Je-sus say, "Come un-to Me and rest;
2. I heard the voice of Je-sus say, "Be-hold, I free-ly give
3. I heard the voice of Je-sus say, "I am this dark world's Light;

Lay down, thou wea-ry one, lay down Thy head up-on My breast."
The liv-ing wa-ter; thirst-y one, Stoop down and drink, and live."
Look un-to Me, thy morn shall rise, And all thy day be bright."

I came to Je-sus as I was, Wea-ry and worn and sad,
I came to Je-sus, and I drank Of that life-giv-ing stream;
I looked to Je-sus, and I found In Him my Star, my Sun;

I found in Him a rest-ing place, And He has made me glad.
My thirst was quenched, my soul re-vived, And now I live in Him.
And in that Light of life I'll walk, Till trav-el-ing days are done. A-MEN.

Consult index for alternative version.

The Christian Life

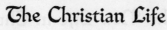

237

Anonymous, 1904   10. 10. 10. 6.   ARTAVIA
EDWARD J. HOPKINS, 1887

Not too fast

1. I sought the Lord, and aft-er-ward I knew He moved my soul to seek Him, seek-ing me; It was not I that found, O Sav-iour true; No, I was found of Thee.
2. Thou didst reach forth Thy hand and mine en-fold; I walked and sank not on the storm-vexed sea, 'Twas not so much that I on Thee took hold, As Thou, dear Lord, on me.
3. I find, I walk, I love, but O the whole Of love is but my an-swer, Lord, to Thee! For Thou wert long be-fore-hand with my soul; Al-ways Thou lov-edst me. A-MEN.

238

GEORGE WASHINGTON DOANE, 1824   C.M.   NUN DANKET ALL (GRÄFENBERG)
JOHANN CRÜGER'S
Praxis Pietatis Melica, 1653

May be sung in unison. **With dignity**

1. Thou art the Way: to Thee a-lone From sin and death we flee;
2. Thou art the Truth: Thy word a-lone True wis-dom can im-part;
3. Thou art the Life: the rend-ing tomb Pro-claims Thy con-quering arm;
4. Thou art the Way, the Truth, the Life: Grant us that Way to know,

The New Life in Christ

And he who would the Fa-ther seek, Must seek Him, Lord, by Thee.
Thou on-ly canst in-form the mind And pur-i-fy the heart.
And those who put their trust in Thee Nor death nor hell shall harm.
That Truth to keep, that Life to win, Whose joys e-ter-nal flow. A-MEN.

239

HENDON

JOHANN C. SCHWEDLER, 1672–1730
Tr. BENJAMIN H. KENNEDY, 1863   7.7.7.7.   H. A. CÉSAR MALAN, 1827

With exaltation

1. Ask ye what great thing I know That de-lights and
2. Who de-feats my fier-cest foes? Who con-soles my
3. Who is life in life to me? Who the death of
4. This is that great thing I know; This de-lights and

stirs me so? What the high re-ward I win? Whose the name I
sad-dest woes? Who re-vives my faint-ing heart, Heal-ing all its
death will be? Who will place me on His right, With the count-less
stirs me so: Faith in Him who died to save, Him who tri-umphed

glo-ry in? Je-sus Christ, the Cru-ci-fied.
hid-den smart? Je-sus Christ, the Cru-ci-fied.
hosts of light? Je-sus Christ, the Cru-ci-fied.
o'er the grave, Je-sus Christ, the Cru-ci-fied. A-MEN.

The Christian Life

240

J. Franck, 1618–1677
Tr. Catherine Winkworth, 1863

JESU, MEINE FREUDE
German Traditional Melody
From J. Crüger's *Praxis Pietatis Melica*, 1656

6. 6. 5. 6. 6. 5. 7. 8. 6.

Slowly and with dignity

1. Je - sus, price - less treas - ure, Source of pur - est pleas-ure,
2. In Thine arm I rest me; Foes who would mo - lest me
3. Hence, all thoughts of sad - ness! For the Lord of glad -ness,

Tru-est friend to me; Long my heart hath pant-ed, Till it well-nigh
Can-not reach me here. Though the earth be shak-ing, Ev - ery heart be
Je - sus, en - ters in: Those who love the Fa - ther, Though the storms may

faint - ed, Thirst-ing aft - er Thee. Thine I am, O spot-less Lamb,
quak-ing, God dis - pels our fear; Sin and hell in con-flict fell
gath - er, Still have peace with-in; Yea, what-e'er we here must bear,

I will suf-fer nought to hide Thee, Ask for nought be-side Thee.
With their heav-iest storms as - sail us: Je - sus will not fail us.
Still in Thee lies pur - est pleas - ure, Je - sus, price-less treas - ure! A-men.

The New Life in Christ

241

HARRY WEBB FARRINGTON, 1910

C.M.

MIRON
PIERRE WISSMER, 1939

In the style of a carol

1. I know not how that Bethlehem's Babe Could in the God-head be;
2. I know not how that Cal - vary's cross A world from sin could free;
3. I know not how that Jo - seph's tomb Could solve death's mys - ter - y;

I on - ly know the Man - ger Child Has brought God's life to me.
I on - ly know its match-less love Has brought God's love to me.
I on - ly know a liv - ing Christ, Our im - mor - tal - i - ty. A-MEN.

Words used by permission of Mrs. Harry Webb Farrington.
Music copyright, 1941, by Eden Publishing House.

242

JOHN G. WHITTIER, 1866

C.M.

SERENITY
Arr. from WILLIAM V. WALLACE, 1856

In flowing rhythm, with dignity

1. Im - mor - tal Love, for - ev - er full, For - ev - er flow - ing free,
2. We may not climb the heaven - ly steeps To bring the Lord Christ down;
3. But warm, sweet, ten - der, e - ven yet A pres - ent help is He;
4. The heal - ing of His seam - less dress Is by our beds of pain;
5. O Lord and Mas - ter of us all, What-e'er our name or sign,

For - ev - er shared, for - ev - er whole, A nev - er-ebb - ing sea!
In vain we search the low - est deeps, For Him no depths can drown.
And faith has still its Ol - i - vet, And love its Gal - i - lee.
We touch Him in life's throng and press, And we are whole a - gain.
We own Thy sway, we hear Thy call, We test our lives by Thine. A-MEN.

The Christian Life

243

GEORGE MATHESON, 1890

S. M. D.

LEOMINSTER
GEORGE WILLIAM MARTIN, 1862
Har. ARTHUR SULLIVAN, 1874

In moderate time

1. Make me a cap-tive, Lord, And then I shall be free;
   Force me to ren-der up my sword, And I shall con-queror be.
   I sink in life's a-larms, When by my-self I stand;
   Im-pris-on me with-in Thine arms, And strong shall be my hand.

2. My heart is weak and poor Un-til it mas-ter find;
   It has no spring of ac-tion sure, It va-ries with the wind;
   It can-not free-ly move Till Thou hast wrought its chain;
   En-slave it with Thy match-less love, And death-less it shall reign.

3. My power is faint and low Till I have learned to serve;
   It wants the need-ed fire to glow, It wants the breeze to nerve;
   It can-not drive the world Un-til it-self be driven;
   Its flag can on-ly be un-furled When Thou shalt breathe from heaven.

4. My will is not my own Till Thou hast made it Thine;
   If it would reach a mon-arch's throne It must its crown re-sign;
   It on-ly stands un-bent A-mid the clash-ing strife,
   When on Thy bos-om it has leant, And found in Thee its life. A-MEN.

The New Life in Christ

244

Edward H. Plumptre, 1864

8.8.8.8.8.8.

ST. CHRYSOSTOM
Joseph Barnby, 1871

In moderate time

1. O Light, whose beams il - lu - mine all From twi - light dawn to per - fect day, Shine Thou be - fore the shad - ows fall That lead our wan - dering feet a - stray; At morn and eve Thy ra - diance pour, That youth may love and age a - dore.

2. O Way, through whom our souls draw near To yon e - ter - nal home of peace, Where per - fect love shall cast out fear, And earth's vain toil and wan - dering cease; In strength or weak - ness may we see Our heaven-ward path, O Lord, through Thee.

3. O Truth, be - fore whose shrine we bow, Thou price - less pearl for all who seek, To Thee our ear - liest strength we vow, Thy love will bless the pure and meek; When dreams or mists be - guile our sight, Turn Thou our dark - ness in - to light.

4. O Life, the well that ev - er flows To slake the thirst of those that faint, Thy power to bless, what ser - aph knows? Thy joy su - preme, what words can paint? In earth's last hour of fleet - ing breath Be Thou our Con - queror o - ver death. A - men.

The Christian Life

PAX TECUM
GEORGE T. CALDBECK
and CHARLES J. VINCENT, 1877

EDWARD H. BICKERSTETH, 1875   10. 10.

In rather slow time

1. Peace, per - fect peace, in this dark world of sin?
2. Peace, per - fect peace, by throng - ing du - ties pressed?
3. Peace, per - fect peace, with sor - rows sur - ging round?
4. Peace, per - fect peace, our fu - ture all un - known?
5. Peace, per - fect peace, death shadow - ing us and ours?
6. It is e - nough: earth's strug - gles soon shall cease,

The blood of Je - sus whis - pers peace with - in.
To do the will of Je - sus, this is rest.
On Je - sus' bos - om naught but calm is found.
Je - sus we know, and He is on the throne.
Je - sus has van-quished death and all its powers.
And Je - sus call us to heaven's per - fect peace. A-MEN.

246

MERCY
LOUIS GOTTSCHALK, 1829–1869
Arr. EDWIN P. PARKER, 1888

JAMES MONTGOMERY, 1808   7. 7. 7. 7.

Not too fast

1. Fa - ther of e - ter - nal grace, Glo - ri -
2. Hap - py on - ly in Thy love, Poor, un -
3. Hum - ble, ho - ly, all - re - signed To Thy
4. Count - ing gain and glo - ry loss, May I

The New Life in Christ

fy Thy - self in me; Beam - ing bright - ly
friend - ed, or un - known; Fix my thoughts on
will: Thy will be done! Give me, Lord, the
tread the path He trod; Die with Je - sus

in my face, May the world Thine im - age see.
things a - bove, Stay my heart on Thee a - lone.
per - fect mind Of Thy well - be - lov - ed Son.
on the cross, Rise with Him, to Thee, my God! A - MEN.

247

FRANCONIA
JOHANN B. KÖNIG, 1738
Arr. WILLIAM H. HAVERGAL, 1840

JOHN KEBLE, 1819, alt.
S. M.

In moderate time

1. Blest are the pure in heart, For they shall see our God;
2. The Lord, who left the heavens Our life and peace to bring,
3. He to the low - ly soul Doth still Him - self im - part;
4. Lord, we Thy pres - ence seek; May ours this bless - ing be;

The se - cret of the Lord is theirs; Their soul is Christ's a - bode.
To dwell in low - li - ness with men Their pat - tern and their King;
And for His dwell - ing and His throne Choos - eth the pure in heart.
Give us a pure and low - ly heart, A tem - ple meet for Thee. A - MEN.

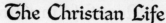

The Christian Life

248

G. J. NEUMANN, 1939

8. 8. 8. 8. 8. 8.

SAN VICENTE
EDWARD SHIPPEN BARNES, 1939

In moderate time

1. Heal - er Di - vine, who walk - est still By sea and cit - y,
2. Heal - er Di - vine, un - wor - thy now As ev - er, at Thy
3. Heal - er Di - vine, we know Thy power, We who have felt it

field and hill, Un - seen of man - y in Thy round, But
feet we bow! Weak are our souls to see the light, Weak
many an hour; Heal - er Di - vine, we trust in Thee; Who

by the faith - ful sought and found, Hear us! We come to
are our souls to walk a - right, Weak are our souls to
gave His life to set us free Sure - ly will hear our

Thee a - gain, Whose help we nev - er seek in vain.
hear and do: Each day, O Lord, our strength re - new!
prayers, and give Un - to our souls the strength to live. A - MEN.

Consecration and Stewardship

249

ELLESDIE
W. A. MOZART, 1756-1791
Arr. H. P. MAIN, 1873

HENRY F. LYTE, 1824   8.7.8.7. D.

In moderate time

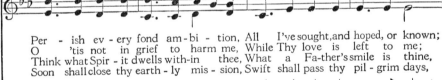

1. Je - sus, I my cross have ta - ken, All   to leave, and fol - low Thee;
2. Man may trou-ble and dis - tress me, 'Twill but drive me to Thy breast;
3. Take, my soul, thy full sal - va - tion, Rise o'er sin, and fear, and care,
4. Haste, then, on from grace to glo - ry, Armed by faith and winged by prayer;

Des - ti-tute, de-spised, for - sa - ken, Thou from hence my All shalt be:
Life with tri - als hard may press me, Heaven will bring me sweet - er rest;
Joy to find in ev - er - y sta - tion, Some-thing still to do or bear;
Heaven's e - ter - nal day's be - fore thee, God's own hand shall guide thee there:

Per - ish ev - er - y fond am - bi - tion, All I've sought, and hoped, or known;
O 'tis not in grief to harm me, While Thy love is left to me;
Think what Spir - it dwells with-in thee, What a Fa-ther's smile is thine,
Soon shall close thy earth - ly mis - sion, Swift shall pass thy pil - grim days,

Yet how rich is my con-di - tion, God and heaven are still my own!
O 'twere not in joy to charm me, Were that joy un-mixed with Thee.
What a Sav - iour died to win thee: Child of heaven, shouldst thou repine?
Hope soon change to glad fru-i - tion, Faith to sight, and prayer to praise. A-MEN.

250

Walter J. Mathams

6. 4. 6. 4. 10. 10.

SURSUM CORDA
George Lomas, 1876

In moderate time

1. Christ of the Up-ward Way, My Guide di-vine, Where Thou hast
2. Give me the heart to hear Thy voice and will, That with-out
3. Give me the good stout arm To shield the right, And wield Thy
4. Christ of the Up-ward Way, My Guide di-vine, Where Thou hast

set Thy feet May I place mine; And move and march wher-ev-er
fault or fear I may ful-fill Thy pur-pose with a glad and
sword of truth With all my might, That, in the war-fare I must
set Thy feet, May I place mine; And when Thy last call comes se-

Thou hast trod, Keep-ing face for-ward up the hill of God.
ho-ly zest, Like one who would not bring less than his best.
wage for Thee, More than a vic-tor I may ev-er be.
rene and clear, Calm may my an-swer be, "Lord, I am here." A-men.

251

Lauchlan MacLean Watt

6. 7. 7. 7.

ST. QUINTIN
Henry Parr, 1834

May be sung in unison. Solemnly

1. I bind my heart this tide To the Gal-i-læ-an's side,
2. I bind my soul this day To the broth-er far a-way,
3. I bind my heart in thrall To the God, the Lord of all,
4. I bind my-self to peace, To make strife and en-vy cease,

Consecration and Stewardship

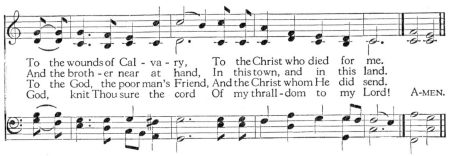

To the wounds of Cal - va - ry, To the Christ who died for me.
And the broth - er near at hand, In this town, and in this land.
To the God, the poor man's Friend, And the Christ whom He did send.
God, knit Thou sure the cord Of my thrall - dom to my Lord! A-MEN.

252

WILLIAM H. FOULKES, 1918   10. 10. 10. 10.   HALL
CALVIN W. LAUFER, 1918

In moderate time

1. Take Thou our minds, dear Lord, we hum - bly pray; Give us the
2. Take Thou our hearts, O Christ, they are Thine own; Come Thou with -
3. Take Thou our wills, Most High! Hold Thou full sway; Have in our
4. Take Thou our-selves, O Lord, heart, mind, and will; Through our sur -

mind of Christ each pass - ing day; Teach us to know the truth
in our souls and claim Thy throne; Help us to shed a - broad
in - most souls Thy per - fect way; Guard Thou each sa - cred hour
ren - dered souls Thy plans ful - fill. We yield our - selves to Thee—

that sets us free; Grant us in all our thoughts to hon - or Thee.
Thy death-less love; Use us to make the earth like heaven a - bove.
from self - ish ease; Guide Thou our or - dered lives as Thou dost please.
time, tal - ents, all; We hear, and hence-forth heed, Thy sov-ereign call. A-MEN.

The Christian Life

253

Frances Ridley Havergal, 1874   7.7.7.7.   ST. BEES
John B. Dykes, 1862

In moderate time; solemnly

1. Take my life, and let it be Con-se-cra-ted, Lord, to Thee.
2. Take my hands, and let them move At the im-pulse of Thy love.
3. Take my voice, and let me sing, Al-ways, on-ly, for my King.
4. Take my sil-ver and my gold; Not a mite would I with-hold.
5. Take my will, and make it Thine; It shall be no lon-ger mine.
6. Take my love; my Lord, I pour At Thy feet its treas-ure-store.

Take my mo-ments and my days; Let them flow in cease-less praise.
Take my feet, and let them be Swift and beau-ti-ful for Thee.
Take my lips, and let them be Filled with mes-sag-es from Thee.
Take my in-tel-lect, and use Ev-ery power as Thou shalt choose.
Take my heart, it is Thine own; It shall be Thy roy-al throne.
Take my-self, and I will be Ev-er, on-ly, all for Thee. A-men.

254

Henry Harbaugh, 1850   S. M.   LAKE ENON
Isaac B. Woodbury, 1856

Not too fast

1. Je-sus, I live to Thee, The love-li-est and best;
2. Je-sus, I die to Thee, When-ev-er death shall come;
3. Wheth-er to live or die, I know not which is best;
4. Liv-ing or dy-ing, Lord, I ask but to be Thine;

My life in Thee, Thy life in me, In Thy blest love I rest.
To die in Thee is life to me In my e-ter-nal home.
To live in Thee is bliss to me, To die is end-less rest.
My life in Thee, Thy life in me, Makes heaven for-ev-er mine. A-men.

Consecration and Stewardship

255

JOHN OXENHAM, 1925   8.8.8.4.   Church of Scotland Hymn Tune Book, 1862

AMBERG

In moderate time; Joyfully

1. All la - bor gained new dig - ni - ty Since He who all cre - a - tion made
2. No work is com-mon-place, if all Be done as un - to Him a - lone;
3. Each small-est com-mon thing He makes, Serves Him with its min - u - test part;
4. His ser - vice is life's high-est joy, It yields fair fruit a hun - dred fold,

Toiled with His hands for dai - ly bread Right man - ful - ly.
Life's sim-plest toil to Him is known, Who know - eth all.
Man on - ly, with his wan - dering heart, His way for - sakes.
Be this our prayer—'Not fame, nor gold, But—Thine em - ploy!' A-MEN.

Words used by permission of the author.

Alternative tune, *Almsgiving*.

256

FRANCES R. HAVERGAL, 1872   L.M.   ROBERT SCHUMANN, 1839

CANONBURY

In moderate time

1. Lord, speak to me, that I may speak In liv - ing ech - oes of Thy tone;
2. O lead me, Lord, that I may lead The wan-dering and the wa-vering feet;
3. O teach me, Lord, that I may teach The pre-cious things Thou dost im-part;
4. O fill me with Thy full - ness, Lord, Un - til my ver - y heart o'er-flow
5. O use me, Lord, use e - ven me, Just as Thou wilt, and when, and where;

As Thou hast sought, so let me seek Thy err - ing chil-dren lost and lone.
O feed me, Lord, that I may feed Thy hun-gering ones with man-na sweet!
And wing my words, that they may reach The hid-den depths of many a heart.
In kin-dling thought and glow-ing word, Thy love to tell, Thy praise to show.
Un - til Thy bless-ed face I see, Thy rest, Thy joy, Thy glo - ry share. A-MEN.

The Christian Life

257

Christopher Wordsworth, 1863
Revised, 1872

ALMSGIVING

John B. Dykes, 1865

8.8.8.4.

Joyfully

1. O Lord of heaven and earth and sea, To Thee all praise and
2. Thou didst not spare Thine on - ly Son, But gavest Him for a
3. We lose what on our-selves we spend; We have as treas - ure
4. To Thee, from whom we all de - rive— Our life, our gifts, our

glo - ry be; How shall we show our love to Thee, Who giv-est all?
world un-done, And free - ly with that bless - ed One Thou giv-est all.
with-out end What-ev - er, Lord, to Thee we lend, Who giv-est all.
power to give; O may we ev - er with Thee live, Who giv-est all! A-men.

258

William Walsham How, 1864

SCHUMANN
Mason and Webb's *Cantica Laudis*, Boston, 1850

S.M.

In moderate time

1. We give Thee but Thine own, What - e'er the gift may be:
2. May we Thy boun - ties thus As stew-ards true re - ceive,
3. To com - fort and to bless, To find a balm for woe,
4. The cap - tive to re - lease, To God the lost to bring,
5. And we be - lieve Thy word, Though dim our faith may be:

All that we have is Thine a - lone, A trust, O Lord, from Thee.
And glad - ly, as Thou bless-est us, To Thee our first fruits give.
To tend the lone and fa - ther-less, Is an - gels' work be - low.
To teach the way of life and peace—It is a Christ-like thing.
What-e'er for Thine we do, O Lord, We do it un - to Thee. A-men.

Alternative tune, Boylston.

Consecration and Stewardship

259

Grace Noll Crowell, 1936   8.4.8.4.8.8.8.   THY GREAT BOUNTY
Blanche Douglas Byles, 1925

In moderate time

1. Be - cause I have been giv - en much, I, too, must give:
   Be - cause of Thy great boun - ty, Lord, Each day I live,
   I shall di - vide my gifts from Thee With ev - ery broth - er
   that I see Who has the need of help from me.

2. Be - cause I have been shel - tered, fed, By Thy good care,
   I can - not see an - oth - er's lack And I not share
   My glow - ing fire, my loaf of bread, My roof's safe shel - ter
   o - ver - head, That he, too, may be com - fort - ed.

3. Be - cause love has been lav - ished so Up - on me, Lord,
   A wealth I know that was not meant For me to hoard,
   I shall give love to those in need, Shall show that love by
   word and deed; Thus shall my thanks be thanks in - deed. A-MEN.

Words from *Light of the Years*, by Grace Noll Crowell, copyright by Harper and Brothers.
Music copyright by Blanche Douglas Byles.

260

ROBERT D. MURRAY, 1880

8. 7. 8. 7. D.

PLEADING SAVIOUR
Plymouth Collection, 1855

In moderate time; joyfully

1. Lord, Thou lovest the cheer-ful giv - er, Who with o - pen heart and hand
2. Thine own life Thou free - ly gav - est As an of - fering on the cross
3. Sav - iour, Thou hast free - ly giv - en All the bless - ings we en - joy,

Bless - es free - ly, as a riv - er That re - fresh - es all the land;
For all sin - ners whom Thou sav - est From e - ter - nal shame and loss.
Earth - ly store and bread of heav - en, Love and peace with - out al - loy;

Grant us, then, the grace of giv - ing With a spir - it large and free,
Blest by Thee with gifts and grac - es, May we heed Thy Church-'s call,
Hum - bly now we bow be - fore Thee, And our all to Thee re - sign;

That our life and all our liv - ing We may con - se - crate to Thee.
Glad - ly in all times and pla - ces Give to Thee, who giv - est all.
For the king - dom, power, and glo - ry Are, O Lord, for - ev - er Thine. A-MEN.

Obedience and Service

261

FERDINAND Q. BLANCHARD, 1929

7.6.8.6.D.

ST. CHRISTOPHER
FREDERICK C. MAKER, 1881

Solemnly

1. Be - fore the cross of Je - sus Our lives are judged to - day;
2. The hopes that lead us on - ward, The fears that hold us back,
3. Yet hum - bly, in our striv - ing, O God, we face its test;

The mean - ing of our ea - ger strife Is test - ed by His Way.
Our will to dare great things for God, The cour - age that we lack,
We crave the power to do Thy will, With Him who did it best;

A - cross our rest - less liv - ing The light streams from His cross,
The faith we keep in good - ness, Our love, as low or pure—
On us let now the heal - ing Of His great Spi - rit fall,

And by its clear, re - veal - ing beams We meas - ure gain and loss.
On all, the judg - ment of the cross Falls stead - y, clear, and sure.
And make us brave and full of joy To an - swer to His call. A-MEN.

Words used by permission of the author.

The Christian Life

262

William Matson, 1833

L.M.

ROCKINGHAM OLD
Edward Miller, 1790

In moderate time

1. Teach me, O Lord, Thy holy way, And give me
2. Help me, O Saviour, here to trace The sacred
3. Guard me, O Lord, that I may ne'er Forsake the
4. Bless me in every task, O Lord, Begun, con-

an obedient mind, That in Thy service I may
footsteps Thou hast trod; And, meekly walking with my
right, or do the wrong; Against temptation make me
tinued, done for Thee; Fulfill Thy perfect work in

find My soul's delight from day to day.
God, To grow in goodness, truth, and grace.
strong, And round me spread Thy sheltering care.
me, And Thine abounding grace afford.   A-MEN.

263

Psalm xv
John Scrimger, 1849–1915

S.M.

MARIA JUNG UND ZART
Psalteriolum Harmonicum, 1642

With well defined rhythm

1. Lord, who shall come to Thee, And stand before Thy face?
2. The man of upright life, Sincere in word and deed,
3. Who honors godly men, But scorns the false and vile,
4. Who loves not usury, Nor takes a base reward;

Obedience and Service

Who shall a - bide, a wel-come guest, With - in Thy ho - ly place?
Who slan-ders neith-er friend nor foe, Nor i - dle tales will heed;
Who keeps his prom-ised word to all, Though loss be his the while;
Un-moved for - ev - er he shall be, And stand be - fore the Lord. A-MEN.

264

JOHN DRINKWATER, 1882-1937 10. 10. 10. 4. OVERLOOK PARK
CARL F. MUELLER, 1939

Rather slowly

1. We know the paths where - in our feet should press,
2. Grant us the will to fash - ion as we feel,
3. Knowl-edge we ask not— knowl - edge Thou hast lent,

A - cross our hearts are writ - ten Thy de - crees, Yet now, O Lord, be
Grant us the strength to la - bor as we know, Grant us the pur - pose,
But Lord, the will—there lies our bit - ter need; Give us to build a -

mer - ci - ful to bless With more than these.
ribbed and edged with steel, To strike the blow.
bove the deep in - tent The deed, the deed! A-MEN.

The Christian Life

265

CALVIN W. LAUFER, 1919

10. 10. 10. 10.

FIELD
CALVIN W. LAUFER, 1919

In moderate time

1. We thank Thee, Lord, Thy paths of serv - ice lead
2. We've sought and found Thee in the se - cret place
3. We've felt Thy touch in sor - row's dark - ened way
4. We've seen Thy glo - ry like a man - tle spread

To bla - zoned heights and down the slopes of need;
And mar - veled at the ra - diance of Thy face;
A - bound with love and sol - ace for the day;
O'er hill and dale in saf - fron flame and red;

They reach Thy throne, en - com - pass land and sea,
But of - ten in some far - off Gal - i - lee
And, 'neath the bur - dens there, Thy sov - reign - ty
But in the eyes of men, re - deemed and free,

And he who jour - neys in them walks with Thee.
Be - held Thee fair - er yet while serv - ing Thee.
Has held our hearts en - thralled while serv - ing Thee.
A splen - dor great - er yet while serv - ing Thee. A - MEN.

Obedience and Service

266

SHEPHERD KNAPP, 1907   11. 10. 11. 10.   WELWYN
ALFRED SCOTT-GATTY, 1902

With marked rhythm. May be sung in unison

1. Lord God of Hosts, whose pur-pose, nev-er swerv-ing,
2. Strong Son of God, whose work was His that sent Thee,
3. O Prince of Peace, Thou bring-er of good ti-dings,
4. Lord God, whose grace has called us to Thy serv-ice,

Leads toward the day of Je-sus Christ Thy Son,
One with the Fa-ther, thought and deed and word,
Teach us to speak Thy word of hope and cheer—
How good Thy thoughts toward us, how great their sum!

Grant us to march a-mong Thy faith-ful le-gions,
One make us all, true com-rades in Thy serv-ice,
Rest for the soul, and strength for all man's striv-ing,
We work with Thee, we go where Thou wilt lead us,

Armed with Thy cour-age, till the world is won.
And make us one in Thee with God the Lord.
Light for the path of life, and God brought near.
Un-til in all the earth Thy King-dom come.   A-MEN.

267

H. H. BARSTOW

C. M. D.

ST. LEONARD
HENRY HILES, 1867

In moderate time, with flowing rhythm

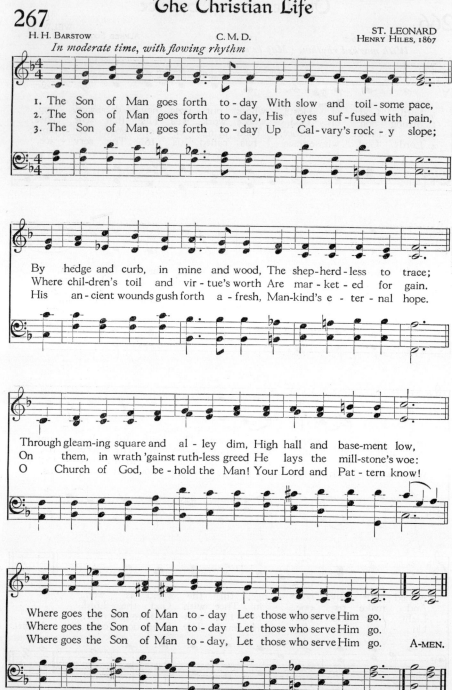

1. The Son of Man goes forth to-day With slow and toil-some pace,
2. The Son of Man goes forth to-day, His eyes suf-fused with pain,
3. The Son of Man goes forth to-day Up Cal-vary's rock-y slope;

By hedge and curb, in mine and wood, The shep-herd-less to trace;
Where chil-dren's toil and vir-tue's worth Are mar-ket-ed for gain.
His an-cient wounds gush forth a-fresh, Man-kind's e-ter-nal hope.

Through gleam-ing square and al-ley dim, High hall and base-ment low,
On them, in wrath 'gainst ruth-less greed He lays the mill-stone's woe:
O Church of God, be-hold the Man! Your Lord and Pat-tern know!

Where goes the Son of Man to-day Let those who serve Him go.
Where goes the Son of Man to-day Let those who serve Him go.
Where goes the Son of Man to-day, Let those who serve Him go. A-MEN.

Obedience and Service

268

HOWELL E. LEWIS, 1922

8.7.8.7.D.

ST. ASAPH

WILLIAM S. BAMBRIDGE, 1872

In march time

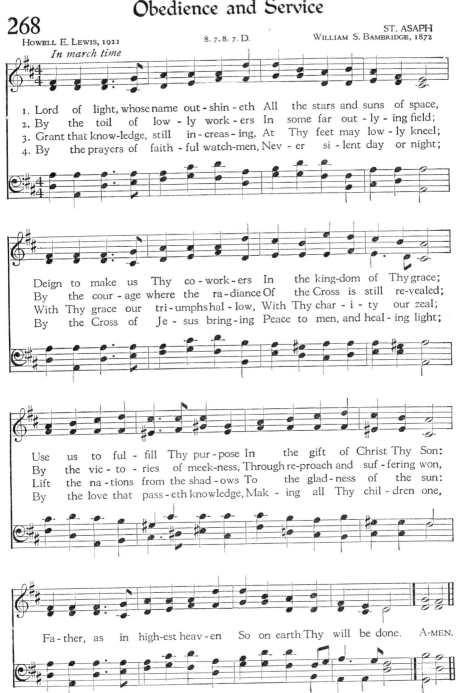

1. Lord of light, whose name out-shin-eth All the stars and suns of space,
2. By the toil of low-ly work-ers In some far out-ly-ing field;
3. Grant that know-ledge, still in-creas-ing, At Thy feet may low-ly kneel;
4. By the prayers of faith-ful watch-men, Nev-er si-lent day or night;

Deign to make us Thy co-work-ers In the king-dom of Thy grace;
By the cour-age where the ra-diance Of the Cross is still re-vealed;
With Thy grace our tri-umphs hal-low, With Thy char-i-ty our zeal;
By the Cross of Je-sus bring-ing Peace to men, and heal-ing light;

Use us to ful-fill Thy pur-pose In the gift of Christ Thy Son:
By the vic-to-ries of meek-ness, Through re-proach and suf-fering won,
Lift the na-tions from the shad-ows To the glad-ness of the sun:
By the love that pass-eth knowledge, Mak-ing all Thy chil-dren one,

Fa-ther, as in high-est heav-en So on earth Thy will be done. A-MEN.

Words used by permission of the author.

The Christian Life

269

Samuel Preiswerk, 1850
Tr. J. H. Horstmann, 1908

8. 6. 8. 6. 8. 8. 8. 8. 4. 6.

DIE SACH' IST DEIN

J. Michael Haydn, 1737-1806

In moderate time

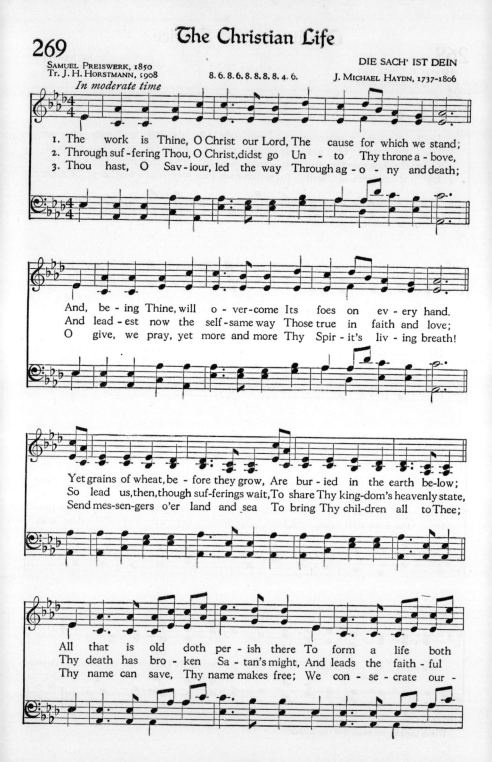

1. The work is Thine, O Christ our Lord, The cause for which we stand;
2. Through suf-fering Thou, O Christ, didst go Un - to Thy throne a - bove,
3. Thou hast, O Sav-iour, led the way Through ag - o - ny and death;

And, be - ing Thine, will o - ver-come Its foes on ev - ery hand.
And lead - est now the self-same way Those true in faith and love;
O give, we pray, yet more and more Thy Spir - it's liv - ing breath!

Yet grains of wheat, be - fore they grow, Are bur - ied in the earth be-low;
So lead us, then, though suf-ferings wait, To share Thy king-dom's heavenly state,
Send mes-sen-gers o'er land and sea To bring Thy chil-dren all to Thee;

All that is old doth per - ish there To form a life both
Thy death has bro - ken Sa - tan's might, And leads the faith - ful
Thy name can save, Thy name makes free; We con - se - crate our -

Obedience and Service

new and fair: So too are we From self and sin made free.
to the light; E - ter - nal light, From dark-ness in - to light.
selves to Thee As serv-ants true, As war-riors brave and true. A-MEN.

270

MILTON S. LITTLEFIELD, 1916   L. M.   BROOKFIELD
                                                         THOMAS B. SOUTHGATE, 1855

Not too fast

1. O   Son   of   Man, Thou mad - est known, Through qui - et
2. O   Work - man   true, may   we   ful - fill   In   dai - ly
3. Thou Mas - ter Work - man grant us   grace The   chal - lenge
4. And thus we   pray in   deed and   word, Thy   king - dom

work   in   shop and   home, The   sa - cred - ness of   com - mon
life   Thy   Fa - ther's will; In   du - ty's call   Thy   call we
of   our   tasks to   face; By   loy - al   scorn of   sec - ond
come   on   earth, O   Lord; In   work that gives ef - fect to

things, The   chance of   life   that each day   brings.
hear   To   full - er   life, through work sin - cere.
best, By   ef - fort true, to   meet each test.
prayer, Thy pur - pose for   Thy   world we   share.   A - MEN.

The Christian Life

JOHN E. BODE, 1868   7.6.7.6.D.   ANGEL'S STORY
ARTHUR H. MANN, 1883

In moderate time

1. O Je - sus, I have prom - ised To serve Thee to the end;
2. O let me feel Thee near me! The world is ev - er near;
3. O let me hear Thee speak - ing In ac - cents clear and still,
4. O Je - sus, Thou hast prom - ised To all who fol - low Thee

Be Thou for - ev - er near me, My Mas - ter and my Friend:
I see the sights that daz - zle, The tempt - ing sounds I hear;
A - bove the storms of pas - sion, The mur - murs of self - will!
That where Thou art in glo - ry There shall Thy serv - ant be;

I shall not fear the bat - tle If Thou art by my side,
My foes are ev - er near me, A - round me and with - in;
O speak to re - as - sure me, To has - ten or con - trol!
And, Je - sus, I have prom] - ised To serve Thee to the end;

Nor wan - der from the path - way If Thou wilt be my Guide.
But, Je - sus, draw Thou near - er, And shield my soul from sin.
O speak, and make me lis - ten, Thou Guard - ian of my soul!
O give me grace to fol - low My Mas - ter and my Friend! A-MEN.

Love and Fellowship

272

CHARLES WESLEY, 1747　　　　8.7.8.7.D.　　　　BEECHER
JOHN ZUNDEL, 1870

In moderate time

1. Love di - vine, all loves ex - cell - ing, Joy of heaven, to earth come down,
2. Breathe, O breathe Thy lov - ing Spir - it In - to ev - ery trou - bled breast;
3. Come, Al - might - y to de - liv - er, Let us all Thy life re - ceive;
4. Fin - ish, then, Thy new cre - a - tion; Pure and spot - less let us be;

Fix in us Thy hum - ble dwell - ing, All Thy faith - ful mer - cies crown:
Let us all in Thee in - her - it, Let us find the prom - ised rest;
Gra - cious - ly re - turn, and nev - er, Nev - er - more Thy tem - ples leave.
Let us see Thy great sal - va - tion Per - fect - ly re - stored in Thee;

Je - sus, Thou art all com - pas - sion, Pure, un - bound - ed love Thou art;
Take a - way the love of sin - ning; Al - pha and O - me - ga be;
Thee we would be al - ways bless - ing, Serve Thee as Thy hosts a - bove,
Changed from glo - ry in - to glo - ry, Till in heaven we take our place,

Vis - it us with Thy sal - va - tion, En - ter ev - ery trem - bling heart.
End of faith, as its be - gin - ning, Set our hearts at lib - er - ty.
Pray, and praise Thee with - out ceas - ing, Glo - ry in Thy per - fect love.
Till we cast our crowns be - fore Thee, Lost in won - der, love, and praise. A-MEN.

The Christian Life

273

Paul Gerhardt, 1653
Tr. John Wesley, 1739
Altered and revised, 1931

STELLA

8. 8. 8. 8. 8. 8.

Old English Melody

Moderately fast

1. Je - sus, Thy bound-less love to me No thought can reach, no tongue de-clare; O knit my thank-ful heart to Thee, And reign with-out a ri-val there! Thine whol - ly, Thine a - lone, I'd live, My-self to Thee en - tire - ly give.

2. O grant that noth-ing in my soul May dwell but Thy pure love a - lone; O may Thy love pos - sess me whole, My joy, my treas - ure, and my crown! All cold-ness from my heart re-move; May ev - ery act, word, thought, be love.

3. O Love, how gra - cious is Thy way! All fear be - fore Thy pres - ence flies; Care, an - guish, sor - row, melt a - way, Wher - e'er Thy heal - ing beams a - rise. O Je - sus, noth - ing may I see, Noth - ing de - sire, or seek, but Thee! A-men.

Love and Fellowship

274

Attributed to BERNARD OF CLAIRVAUX, 1091–1153
Tr. EDWARD CASWALL, 1849

C. M.

ST. AGNES

JOHN B. DYKES, 1866

In moderate time

1. Je - sus, the ver - y thought of Thee With sweet-ness fills my breast;
2. Nor voice can sing, nor heart can frame, Nor can the mem - ory find
3. O hope of ev - ery con - trite heart, O joy of all the meek,
4. But what to those who find? Ah, this Nor tongue nor pen can show:
5. Je - sus, our on - ly joy be Thou, As Thou our prize wilt be;

But sweet-er far Thy face to see, And in Thy pres-ence rest.
A sweet-er sound than Thy blest name, O Sav-iour of man-kind!
To those who fall, how kind Thou art! How good to those who seek!
The love of Je - sus, what it is None but His loved ones know.
Je - sus, be Thou our glo - ry now, And through e - ter - ni - ty. A - MEN.

275

OSCAR CLUTE, 1837–1901

S. M.

TRENTHAM

ROBERT JACKSON, 1894

In moderate time; reverently

1. O Love of God most full, O Love of God most free, Come warm my
2. Warm as the glow - ing sun, So shines Thy love on me; It wraps me
3. The wild - est sea is calm, The tem - pest brings no fear, The dark - est
4. O Love of God most full, O Love of God most free, Thou warmest my

heart, come fill my soul, Come lead me un - to Thee!
'round with kind - ly care, It draws me un - to Thee.
night is full of light, Be - cause Thy love is near.
heart, Thou fillest my soul, With might Thou strength-enest me. A - MEN.

Music used by permission of Mrs. Ethel Taylor.

The Christian Life

276

Johann Scheffler, 1657
Tr. Catherine Winkworth, 1759

DU MEINER SEELEN

8. 8. 8. 8. 8. 8. 8.

Arr. Henry Schwing

Joyfully

1. Thee will I love, . my strength, my tower; . . Thee will I love, my joy, my crown; Thee will I love with all my power, In all Thy works, and Thee a - lone; Thee will I love, till sa - cred fire Fill my whole soul with pure de - sire.

2. I thank Thee, O . . e - ter - nal Sun, . . . That Thy bright beams on me have shined; I thank Thee, who hast o - ver - thrown My foes and healed my wound-ed mind; I thank Thee whose en - liv - ening voice Bids my freed heart in Thee re - joice.

3. Thee will I love, . my joy, my crown; . . Thee will I love, my Lord, my God; Thee will I love, be-neath Thy frown Or smile, Thy scep - tre or Thy rod; What though my flesh and heart de - cay, Thee shall I love in end - less day.

A - MEN.

Love and Fellowship

277

JOHN CALVIN, 1509–1564   10. 10. 10. 10.   TOULON
Genevan Psalter, 1551

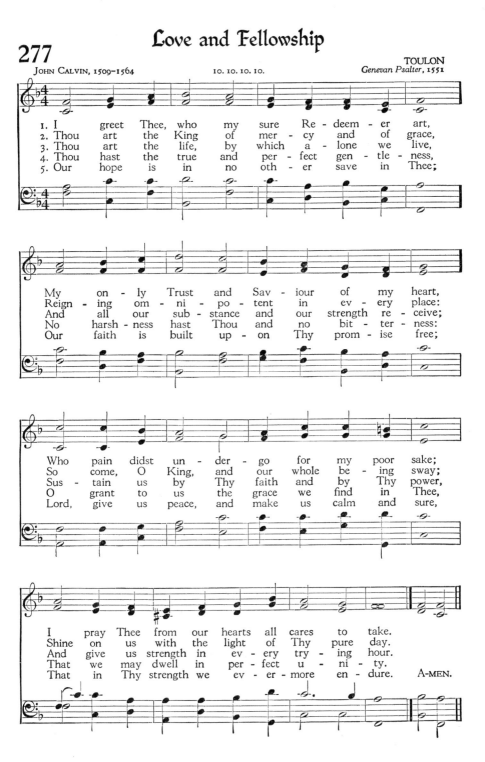

1. I greet Thee, who my sure Re - deem - er art,
2. Thou art the King of mer - cy and of grace,
3. Thou art the life, by which a - lone we live,
4. Thou hast the true and per - fect gen - tle - ness,
5. Our hope is in no oth - er save in Thee;

My on - ly Trust and Sav - iour of my heart,
Reign - ing om - ni - po - tent in ev - ery place:
And all our sub - stance and our strength re - ceive;
No harsh - ness hast Thou and no bit - ter - ness:
Our faith is built up - on Thy prom - ise free;

Who pain didst un - der - go for my poor sake;
So come, O King, and our whole be - ing sway;
Sus - tain us by Thy faith and by Thy power,
O grant to us the grace we find in Thee,
Lord, give us peace, and make us calm and sure,

I pray Thee from our hearts all cares to take.
Shine on us with the light of Thy pure day.
And give us strength in ev - ery try - ing hour.
That we may dwell in per - fect u - ni - ty.
That in Thy strength we ev - er - more en - dure. A-MEN.

The Christian Life

278

GEORGE MATHESON, 1882

8. 8. 8. 8. 6.

ST. MARGARET
ALBERT L. PEACE, 1885

Moderately slow. With exaltation

1. O Love that wilt not let me go, . .
   I rest my weary soul in Thee;
   I give Thee back the life I owe,
   That in Thine ocean depths its flow
   May rich - er, full - er be.

2. O Light that fol - lowest all my way, . .
   I yield my flick - ering torch to Thee;
   My heart re - stores its bor - rowed ray,
   That in Thy sun - shine's blaze its day
   May bright - er, fair - er be.

3. O Joy that seek - est me through pain, . .
   I can - not close my heart to Thee;
   I trace the rain - bow through the rain,
   And feel the prom - ise is not vain
   That morn shall tear - less be.

4. O Cross that lift - est up my head, . .
   I dare not ask to fly from Thee;
   I lay in dust life's glo - ry dead,
   And from the ground there blos - soms red
   Life that shall end - less be.

A-MEN.

Love and Fellowship

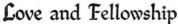

279

OZORA STEARNS DAVIS, 1909   C. M.   TALLIS' ORDINAL
THOMAS TALLIS, c. 1520-1585

Moderately slow

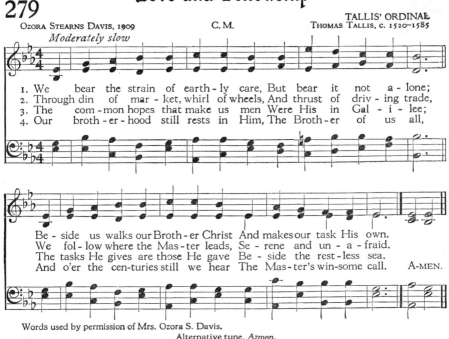

1. We bear the strain of earth-ly care, But bear it not a-lone;
2. Through din of mar-ket, whirl of wheels, And thrust of driv-ing trade,
3. The com-mon hopes that make us men Were His in Gal-i-lee;
4. Our broth-er-hood still rests in Him, The Broth-er of us all,

Be-side us walks our Broth-er Christ And makes our task His own.
We fol-low where the Mas-ter leads, Se-rene and un-a-fraid.
The tasks He gives are those He gave Be-side the rest-less sea.
And o'er the cen-turies still we hear The Mas-ter's win-some call. A-MEN.

Words used by permission of Mrs. Ozora S. Davis.
Alternative tune, *Azmon*.

280

JOHN FAWCETT, 1782   S. M.   BOYLSTON
LOWELL MASON, 1832

In moderate time

1. Blest be the tie that binds Our hearts in Chris-tian love:
2. Be-fore our Fa-ther's throne We pour our ar-dent prayers;
3. We share our mu-tual woes, Our mu-tual bur-dens bear,
4. From sor-row, toil, and pain, And sin, we shall be free;

The fel-low-ship of kin-dred minds Is like to that a-bove.
Our fears, our hopes, our aims, are one, Our com-forts and our cares.
And of-ten for each oth-er flows The sym-pa-thiz-ing tear.
And per-fect love and friend-ship reign Through all e-ter-ni-ty. A-MEN.

The Christian Life

281

MARTIN LUTHER, 1529
Tr. FREDERICK H. HEDGE, 1853   8. 7. 8. 7. 6. 6. 6. 6. 7.

EIN' FESTE BURG
MARTIN LUTHER, 1529

May be sung in unison. In majestic style

1. A might-y fort-ress is   our God, A bul-wark nev-er fail - ing;
2. Did we   in our own strength con-fide, Our striv-ing would be los - ing;
3. And though this world, with dev - ils filled, Should threaten to un-do   us;
4. That word a - bove all   earth - ly powers, No thanks to them, a - bid - eth;

Our help-er He a - mid the flood Of   mor-tal ills pre-vail - ing.
Were not the right man on   our side, The   man of God's own choos - ing.
We will not fear, for God hath willed His   truth to tri-umph through us.
The Spir - it and the gifts are ours Through Him who with us sid - eth.

For still our an-cient foe Doth seek to work us woe; His craft and power are
Dost ask who that may be? Christ Je - sus, it   is He, Lord Sab - a - oth His
The Prince of dark-ness grim, We trem-ble not for Him; His rage we can en -
Let goods and kin-dred go, This mor-tal life al - so; The bod - y they may

great; And, armed with cru - el hate, On earth is not his e - qual.
name, From age to age the same, And He must win the bat - tle.
dure, For lo! his doom is sure, One lit - tle word shall fell   him.
kill; God's truth a - bid-eth still, His king-dom is for - ev - er.   A-MEN.

Conflict and Victory

282

FREDERICK W. FABER, 1849
Stanzas 2, 3, alt.

8. 8. 8. 8. 8. 8.

ST. CATHERINE
HENRI F. HEMY, 1865
Alt. JAMES G. WALTON, 1871

With dignity and conviction

1. Faith of our fa - thers! liv - ing still In spite of dun - geon, fire, and sword, O how our hearts beat high with joy When-e'er we hear that glo - rious word: Faith of our fa - thers, ho - ly faith! We will be true to thee till death.

2. Faith of our fa - thers! we will strive To win all na - tions un - to thee; And through the truth that comes from God Man - kind shall then be tru - ly free: Faith of our fa - thers, ho - ly faith! We will be true to thee till death.

3. Faith of our fa - thers! we will love Both friend and foe in all our strife, And preach thee, too, as love knows how, By kind - ly words and vir - tuous life: Faith of our fa - thers, ho - ly faith! We will be true to thee till death. A - MEN.

The Christian Life

283

Psalm xlvi. *Scottish Psalter*, 1650   C.M.

WINCHESTER OLD
Este's Psalter, 1592
Arr. from CHRISTOPHER TYE

In moderate time

1. God is our Ref-uge and our Strength, In straits a pres-ent aid;
2. Though hills a-midst the seas be cast; Though wa-ters roar-ing make
3. A riv-er is, whose streams make glad The Cit-y of our God;
4. God in the midst of her doth dwell, And noth-ing shall her move;

There-fore, al-though the earth re-move, We will not be a-fraid;
And trou-bled be; yea though the hills By swell-ing seas do shake.
The ho-ly place, where-in the Lord Most High hath His a-bode.
The Lord to her an help-er will, And that right ear-ly, prove. A-MEN.

284

NICHOLAS VON ZINZENDORF, 1721
Tr. JANE BORTHWICK, 1853   5. 5. 8. 8. 5. 5.

SEELENBRÄUTIGAM
ADAM DRESE, 1698

Moderately slow

1. Je-sus, still lead on, Till our rest be won, And, al-
2. If the way be drear, If the foe be near, Let no
3. When we seek re-lief From a long-felt grief; When temp-
4. Je-sus, still lead on, Till our rest be won; Heaven-ly

though the way be cheer-less, We will fol-low calm and fear-less;
faith-less fears o'er-take us, Let not faith and hope for-sake us,
ta-tions come al-lur-ing, Make us pa-tient and en-dur-ing;
Lead-er, still di-rect us, Still sup-port, con-trol, pro-tect us,

Conflict and Victory

Guide us by Thy hand To our fa - ther - land.
For through man - y a woe To our home we go.
Show us that bright shore Where we weep no more.
Till we safe - ly stand In our fa - ther - land. A-MEN.

285

PHILIP DODDRIDGE, 1702–1751   C.M.   CHRISTMAS   GEORGE F. HANDEL, 1728

With spirit

1. A - wake, my soul, stretch ev - ery nerve, And
2. A cloud of wit - ness - es a - round Hold
3. 'Tis God's all - an - i - mat - ing voice That
4. Blest Sav - iour, in - tro - duced by Thee, Have

press with vig - or on; A heaven - ly race de-mands Thy zeal,
Thee in full sur - vey: For - get the steps al - read - y trod,
calls Thee from on high; 'Tis His own hand pre - sents the prize
I my race be - gun; And, crowned with vic - tory, at Thy feet

And an im - mor - tal crown, And an im - mor - tal crown.
And on - ward urge thy way, And on - ward urge thy way.
To thine as - pir - ing eye, To thine as - pir - ing eye.
I'll lay my hon - ors down, I'll lay my hon - ors down. A-MEN.

The Christian Life

286
FRANCES RIDLEY HAVERGAL, 1877   6. 5. 6. 5. 6. 5. D.   ARMAGEDDON
Arr. JOHN GOSS, 1871

In stately rhythm

1. Who is on the Lord's side? Who will serve the King? Who will be His
2. Not for weight of glo - ry, Not for crown or palm En - ter we the
3. Fierce may be the con - flict, Strong may be the foe, But the King's own

help - ers Oth - er lives to bring? Who will leave the world's side?
ar - my, Raise the war - rior psalm; But for love that claim - eth
ar - my None can o - ver throw: Round His stand-ards rang - ing,

Who will face the foe? Who is on the Lord's side? Who for
Lives for whom He died: He whom Je - sus nam - eth Must be
Vic - tory is se - cure, For His truth un - chang - ing Makes the

Him will go? By Thy call of mer - cy, By Thy grace di - vine
on His side. By Thy love con-strain - ing, By Thy grace di - vine
tri - umph sure. Joy - ful - ly en - list - ing, By Thy grace di - vine

Conflict and Victory

We are on the Lord's side, Sav-iour, we are Thine. A-MEN.

287

HARRY EMERSON FOSDICK, 1930   8. 7. 8. 7. 8. 7.   REGENT SQUARE
HENRY SMART, 1867

In moderate time, with dignity

1. God of grace and God of glo-ry, On Thy peo-ple pour Thy power;
2. Lo! the hosts of e-vil round us Scorn Thy Christ, as-sail His ways!
3. Cure Thy chil-dren's war-ring mad-ness, Bend our pride to Thy con-trol;
4. Set our feet on loft-y pla-ces; Gird our lives that they may be

Crown Thine an-cient church-'s sto-ry; Bring her bud to glo-rious flower.
From the fears that long have bound us Free our hearts to faith and praise:
Shame our wan-ton, sel-fish glad-ness, Rich in things and poor in soul.
Ar-mored with all Christ-like gra-ces In the fight to set men free.

Grant us wis-dom, Grant us cour-age, For the fac-ing of this hour.
Grant us wis-dom, Grant us cour-age, For the liv-ing of these days.
Grant us wis-dom, Grant us cour-age, Lest we miss Thy king-dom's goal.
Grant us wis-dom, Grant us cour-age, That we fail not man nor Thee! A-MEN.

Words used by permission of the author.

The Christian Life

288

Reginald Heber, 1827   C. M. D.   ALL SAINTS NEW
Henry S. Cutler, 1872

In martial rhythm

1. The Son of God goes forth to war, A king-ly crown to gain;
2. The mar-tyr first, whose ea-gle eye Could pierce be-yond the grave,
3. A glo-rious band, the cho-sen few On whom the Spir-it came,
4. A no-ble ar-my, men and boys, The ma-tron and the maid,

His blood-red ban-ner streams a-far: Who fol-lows in His train?
Who saw his Mas-ter in the sky, And called on Him to save;
Twelve val-iant saints, their hope they knew, And mocked the cross and flame;
A-round the Sav-iour's throne re-joice In robes of light ar-rayed;

Who best can drink his cup of woe, Tri-um-phant o-ver pain,
Like Him, with par-don on his tongue In midst of mor-tal pain,
They met the ty-rant's bran-dished steel, The li-on's gor-y mane,
They climbed the steep as-cent of heaven Through per-il, toil, and pain;

Who pa-tient bears his cross be-low, He fol-lows in His train.
He prayed for them that did the wrong: Who fol-lows in His train?
They bowed their necks the death to feel: Who fol-lows in their train?
O God, to us may grace be given To fol-low in their train!

A-MEN.

Conflict and Victory

289

Charles Wesley, 1749

S. M. D.

DIADEMATA
George J. Elvey, 1868

In martial rhythm

1. Sol - diers of Christ, a - rise, And put your ar - mor on;
2. Stand, then, in His great might, With all His strength en - dued;
3. That, hav - ing all things done, And all your con - flicts past,

Strong in the strength which God sup-plies Through His e - ter - nal Son;
And take, to arm you for the fight, The pan - o - ply of God!
Ye may o'er - come through Christ a - lone, And stand com-plete at last.

Strong in the Lord of Hosts, And in His might - y power;
From strength to strength go on, Wres - tle, and fight, and pray;
To God, the Fa - ther, Son, And Spir - it ev - er blest,

Who in the strength of Je - sus trusts Is more than con - quer - or.
Tread all the powers of dark-ness down, And win the well-fought day;
The One in Three, the Three in One Be end-less praise ad - dressed! A-men.

The Christian Life

GEORGE DUFFIELD, 1858   7.6.7.6.D.   WEBB
GEORGE J. WEBB, 1837

In moderate rhythm

1. Stand up, stand up for Je - sus, Ye sol - diers of the cross;
2. Stand up, stand up for Je - sus, The trump - et call o - bey;
3. Stand up, stand up for Je - sus, Stand in His strength a - lone;
4. Stand up, stand up for Je - sus, The strife will not be long;

Lift high His roy - al ban - ner, It must not suf - fer loss:
Forth to the might - y con - flict, In this His glo - rious day:
The arm of flesh will fail you, Ye dare not trust your own:
This day the noise of bat - tle, The next the vic - tor's song:

From vic - tory un - to vic - tory His ar - my He shall lead,
Ye that are men now serve Him A - gainst un - num - bered foes;
Put on the gos - pel ar - mor, Each piece put on with prayer;
To Him that o - ver - com - eth A crown of life shall be;

Till ev - ery foe is van - quished, And Christ is Lord in - deed.
Let cour - age rise with dan - ger, And strength to strength op - pose.
Where du - ty calls, or dan - ger, Be nev - er want - ing there.
He with the King of Glo - ry Shall reign e - ter - nal - ly.

A-MEN.

Conflict and Victory

291
GEORGE T. COSTER, 1900
6. 6. 6. 6. 8. 8.
ARTHUR'S SEAT
JOHN GOSS, 1874

In march rhythm

1. March on, O soul, with strength! Like those strong men of old
2. The sons of fa - thers we By whom our faith is taught
3. March on, O soul, with strength, As strong the bat - tle rolls!
4. Not long the con - flict: soon The ho - ly war shall cease,

Who 'gainst en - thron - ed wrong Stood con - fi - dent and bold;
To fear no ill, to fight The ho - ly fight they fought:
'Gainst lies and lusts and wrongs, Let cour - age rule our souls:
Faith's war - fare end - ed, won The home of end - less peace!

Who, thrust in prison or cast to flame,
He - ro - ic war - riors, ne'er from Christ
In keen - est strife, Lord, may we stand,
Look up! the vic - tor's crown at length!

Still made their glo - ry in Christ's Name.
By an - y lure or guile en - ticed.
Up - held and strength - ened by Thy hand.
March on, O soul, march on, with strength! A-MEN.

The Christian Life

Sabine Baring-Gould, 1865   6. 5. 6. 5. D. with Refrain   ST. GERTRUDE
                 In march rhythm   Arthur S. Sullivan, 1871

1. On - ward, Chris-tian sol - diers, March-ing as to war, With the cross of
2. Like a might - y ar - my Moves the Church of God; Broth-ers, we are
3. Crowns and thrones may per - ish, King-doms rise and wane, But the Church of
4. On - ward, then, ye peo - ple, Join our hap - py throng, Blend with ours your

Je - sus Go - ing on be - fore: Christ the roy - al Mas - ter
tread - ing Where the saints have trod; We are not di - vid - ed,
Je - sus Con - stant will re - main; Gates of hell can nev - er
voic - es In the tri - umph song; Glo - ry, laud, and hon - or

Leads a - gainst the foe; For - ward in - to bat - tle,
All one bod - y we, One in hope and doc - trine,
'Gainst that Church pre - vail; We have Christ's own prom - ise,
Un - to Christ the King; This through count - less a - ges

Refrain

See, His ban - ners go. On - ward, Chris - tian sol - diers,
One in char - i - ty.
And that can - not fail.
Men and an - gels sing.

Conflict and Victory

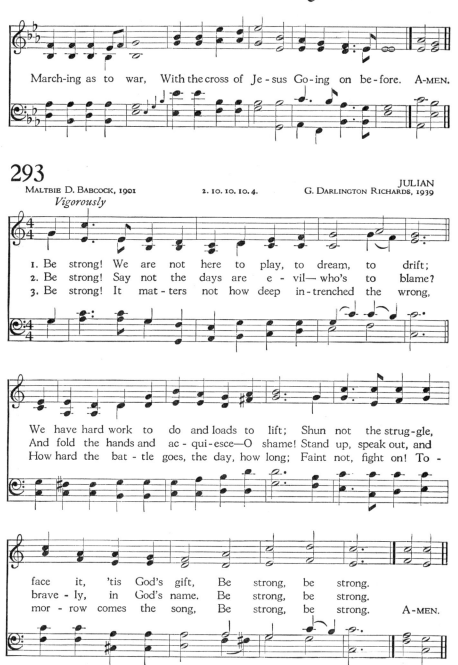

Marching as to war, With the cross of Jesus Going on before. A-MEN.

293

MALTBIE D. BABCOCK, 1901   2. 10. 10. 10. 4.   G. DARLINGTON RICHARDS, 1939

JULIAN

Vigorously

1. Be strong! We are not here to play, to dream, to drift;
2. Be strong! Say not the days are e - vil— who's to blame?
3. Be strong! It mat - ters not how deep in - trenched the wrong,

We have hard work to do and loads to lift; Shun not the strug-gle,
And fold the hands and ac - qui-esce—O shame! Stand up, speak out, and
How hard the bat - tle goes, the day, how long; Faint not, fight on! To -

face it, 'tis God's gift, Be strong, be strong.
brave - ly, in God's name. Be strong, be strong.
mor - row comes the song, Be strong, be strong. A -MEN.

The Christian Life

294

ST. ANDREW OF CRETE, 660–732
Tr. JOHN MASON NEALE, 1862
Alt. in *The Parish Hymn Book*, 1863

ST. ANDREW OF CRETE
JOHN B. DYKES, 1868

6.5.6.5.D.
First Tune

In moderate time

1. Chris - tian, dost thou see them, On the ho - ly ground,
2. Chris - tian, dost thou feel them, How they work with - in,
3. Chris - tian, dost thou hear them, How they speak thee fair?
4. "Well I know thy trou - ble, O My serv - ant true,

How the powers of dark - ness Rage thy steps a - round?
Striv - ing, tempt - ing, lur - ing, Goad - ing in - to sin?
"Al - ways fast and vig - il? Al - ways watch and prayer?"
Thou art ver - y wea - ry— I was wea - ry too;

Chris - tian, up and smite them, Count - ing gain but loss,
Chris - tian, nev - er trem - ble; Nev - er be down - cast;
Chris - tian, an - swer bold - ly, "While I breathe I pray!"
But that toil shall make thee Some day all Mine own,

In the strength that com - eth By the ho - ly cross.
Gird thee for the bat - tle; Thou shalt win at last.
Peace shall fol - low bat - tle, Night shall end in day.
And the end of sor - row Shall be near My throne." A-MEN.

Conflict and Victory

295

St. Andrew of Crete, 700
Tr. John Mason Neale, 1862
Alt. in *Parish Hymn Book*, 1863

6.5.6.5. D.
Second Tune

HOLY WAR

Josiah Booth, 1877

Unison. In moderate time

1. Chris-tian, dost thou see them On the ho-ly ground,
2. Chris-tian, dost thou feel them, How they work with-in,
3. Chris-tian, dost thou hear them, How they speak thee fair?
4. "Well I know thy trou-ble, O My serv-ant true;

How the powers of dark - ness Com-pass thee a-round?
Striv-ing, tempt-ing, lur - ing, Goad-ing in-to sin?
"Al-ways fast and vig - il? Al-ways watch and prayer?"
Thou art ver-y wea - ry, I was wea-ry too;

Harmony

Chris - tian, up and smite them, Count - ing gain but loss;
Chris - tian, nev - er trem - ble; Nev - er be down - cast;
Chris - tian, an - swer bold - ly, "While I breathe I pray,"
But that toil shall make thee Some day all Mine own,

Org.

In the strength that com - eth By the ho - ly Cross.
Gird thee for the bat - tle, Thou shalt win at last.
Peace shall fol - low bat - tle, Night shall end in day.
And the end of sor - row Shall be near My throne." A-MEN.

The Christian Life

JOHN BUNYAN, 1684; alt.

6. 5. 6. 5. 6. 6. 6. 5.

ST. DUNSTAN'S
WINFRED DOUGLAS, 1917

In stately rhythm

1. He who would val - iant be 'Gainst all dis - as - ter,
2. Who so be - set him round With dis - mal sto - ries,
3. Since, Lord, Thou dost de - fend Us with Thy Spir - it,

Let Him in con - stan - cy Fol - low the Mas - ter.
Do but them - selves con - found— His strength the more is.
We know we at the end Shall life in - her - it.

There's no dis - cour - age - ment Shall make him once re - lent
No foes shall stay his might, Though he with gi - ants fight:
Then, fan - cies, flee a - way! I'll fear not what men say,

His first a - vowed in - tent To be a pil - grim.
He will make good his right To be a pil - grim.
I'll la - bor night and day To be a pil - grim. A-MEN.

Conflict and Victory

297

Arthur Cleveland Coxe, 1840; alt.

May be sung in unison. *With dignity*

8. 7. 8. 7. D.

IN BABILONE
Dutch traditional melody

1. We are liv - ing, we are dwell-ing In a grand and aw - ful time,
2. Will ye play, then? will ye dal - ly Far be - hind the bat - tle line?
3. Sworn to yield, to wa - ver, nev - er; Con - se - crat - ed, born a - gain;

In an age on a - ges tell-ing; To be liv - ing is sub-lime.
Up! it is Je - ho - vah's ral - ly; God's own arm hath need of thine.
Sworn to be Christ's sol - diers ev - er, O for Christ at least be men!

Hark! the wak - ing up of na - tions, Hosts ad - van - cing to the fray;
Worlds are char - ging, heaven be - hold - ing; Thou hast but an hour to fight;
O let all the soul with - in you For the truth's sake go a - broad!

Hark! what soundeth is cre - a - tion's Groan-ing for the lat - ter day.
Now, the bla - zoned cross un - fold-ing, On, right on - ward for the right!
Strike! let ev - ery nerve and sin - ew Tell on a - ges, tell for God. A-MEN.

Music used by permission of Mrs. Julius Röntgen.

The Christian Life

298

JOHN S. B. MONSELL, 1863   L. M. with Refrain   COURAGE
HORATIO W. PARKER, 1903

With spirit

1. Fight the good fight with all thy might; Christ is thy strength, and
2. Run the straight race through God's good grace, Lift up thine eyes, and
3. Cast care a-side, up-on thy Guide Lean, and His mer-cy
4. Faint not nor fear, His arms are near; He chang-eth not and

Christ thy right. Lay hold on life, and it shall be Thy joy and
seek His face; Life with its way be-fore us lies, Christ is the
will pro-vide;—Trust, and thy trust-ing soul shall prove Christ is its
thou art dear; On-ly be-lieve, and thou shalt see That Christ is

crown e-ter-nal-ly; Lay hold on life, and it shall
path, and Christ the prize; Life with its way be-fore us
life, and Christ its love; Trust, and thy trust-ing soul shall
all in all to thee; On-ly be-lieve, and thou shalt

be Thy joy and crown e-ter-nal-ly.
lies, Christ is the path, and Christ the prize.
prove Christ is its life, and Christ its love.
see That Christ is all in all to thee. A-MEN.

Conflict and Victory

299

ERNEST W. SHURTLEFF, 1888   7. 6. 7. 6. D.   LANCASHIRE
HENRY SMART, 1836

With spirit

1. Lead on, O King e - ter - nal! The day of march has come;
2. Lead on, O King e - ter - nal, Till sin's fierce war shall cease,
3. Lead on, O King e - ter - nal, We fol - low, not with fears;

Hence-forth in fields of con - quest Thy tents shall be our home.
And ho - li - ness shall whis - per The sweet A - men of peace;
For glad - ness breaks like morn - ing Wher - e'er Thy face ap - pears;

Through days of prep - a - ra - tion Thy grace has made us strong,
For not with swords, loud clash - ing, Nor roll of stir - ring drums;
Thy cross is lift - ed o'er us; We jour - ney in its light;

And now, O King e - ter - nal, We lift our bat - tle song.
But deeds of love and mer - cy The heaven-ly king - dom comes.
The crown a - waits the con - quest; Lead on, O God of might! A-MEN.

The Christian Life

WER NUR DEN LIEBEN GOTT LÄSST WALTEN

GEORG NEUMARK, 1641
Tr. CATHERINE WINKWORTH, 1855   9. 8. 9. 8. 8. 8.   GEORG NEUMARK, 1657

300

Confidently, but in moderate time

1. If thou but suf-fer God to guide thee, And hope in
2. On-ly be still, and wait His lei-sure In cheer-ful
3. Sing, pray, and swerve not from His ways, ... But do thine

Him through all thy ways, He'll give thee strength, what-e'er be-tide thee,
hope, with heart con-tent To take what-e'er thy Fa-ther's pleas-ure
own part faith-ful-ly; Trust His rich prom-is-es of grace, . .

And bear thee through the e-vil days; Who trusts in God's un-
And all-dis-cern-ing love hath sent; Nor doubt our in-most
So shall they be ful-filled in thee; God nev-er yet for-

chang-ing love Builds on the rock that naught can move.
wants are known To Him who chose us for His own.
sook at need The soul that trust-ed Him in-deed. A-MEN.

Comfort and Trust

301

NYLAND
Finnish Hymn Melody
Har. DAVID EVANS

ANNA LAETITIA WARING, 1820–1910   7.6.7.6. D.

Not too slowly, with flowing rhythm

1. In heaven-ly love a - bid - ing, No change my heart shall fear;
2. Wher - ev - er He may guide me, No want shall turn me back;
3. Green pas - tures are be - fore me, Which yet I have not seen;

And safe is such con - fid - ing, For noth - ing chan - ges here.
My Shep - herd is be - side me, And noth - ing can I lack.
Bright skies will soon be o'er me, Where dark - est clouds have been.

The storm may roar with - out me, My heart may low be laid;
His wis - dom ev - er wak - eth, His sight is nev - er dim;
My hope I can - not meas - ure, My path to life is free;

But God is round a - bout me, And can I be dis-mayed?
He knows the way He tak - eth, And I will walk with Him.
My Sav - iour has my treas - ure, And He will walk with me.   A-MEN.

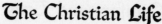

The Christian Life

302

JOHN MASON NEALE, 1862
Stanza 1, line 1; stanza 5, line 3, alt.

STEPHANOS

8. 5. 8. 3.

HENRY W. BAKER, 1868

In moderate time

1. Art thou wea - ry, heav - y - lad - en, Art thou sore dis - trest?
2. Hath He marks to lead me to Him, If He be my Guide?
3. Is there di - a - dem, as Mon - arch, That His brow a - dorns?
4. If I ask Him to re - ceive me, Will He say me nay?
5. Find - ing, follow - ing, keep - ing, strug - gling Is He sure to bless?

"Come to Me," saith One, "and, com - ing, Be at rest."
"In His feet and hands are wound prints, And His side."
"Yea, a crown, in ver - y sure - ty, But of thorns."
"Not till earth and not till heav - en Pass a - way."
"Saints, a - pos - tles, proph - ets, mar - tyrs, An - swer, 'Yes.'" A-MEN.

303

THOMAS MOORE, 1816
and THOMAS HASTINGS, 1832

CONSOLATOR

11. 10. 11. 10.

SAMUEL WEBBE, 1792

Moderately fast

1. Come, ye dis - con - so - late, wher - e'er ye lan - guish, Come to the
2. Joy of the des - o - late, Light of the stray - ing, Hope of the
3. Here see the Bread of life, see wa - ters flow - ing Forth from the

mer - cy - seat, fer - vent - ly kneel; Here bring your wound - ed hearts,
pen - i - tent, fade - less and pure; Here speaks the Com - fort - er,
throne of God, pure from a - bove; Come to the feast of love,

Comfort and Trust

here tell your an - guish; Earth has no sor-row that heaven can-not heal.
ten - der - ly say - ing, "Earth has no sor-row that heaven can-not cure."
come, ev - er know-ing, Earth has no sor-row but heaven can re-move. A-MEN.

304

Psalm xxiii
HENRY W. BAKER, 1868

8. 7. 8. 7.

DOMINUS REGIT ME

JOHN B. DYKES, 1868

In moderate time

1. The   King   of   love   my   Shep - herd   is,
2. Where   streams   of   liv - ing   wa - ter   flow
3. Per - verse   and   fool - ish   oft   I   strayed,
4. In   death's   dark   vale   I   fear   no   ill
5. And   so   through   all   the   length   of   days

Whose good - ness fail - eth nev - er; I noth - ing lack if
My ran - somed soul He lead - eth, And where the ver - dant
But yet in love He sought me, And on His shoul - der
With Thee, dear Lord, be - side me; Thy rod and staff my
Thy good - ness fail - eth nev - er: Good Shep - herd, may I

I   am His   And He   is mine for - ev - er.
pas - tures grow, With food   ce - les - tial   feed - eth.
gen - tly laid,   And home,   re - joi - cing,   brought me.
com - fort still,   Thy cross   be - fore   to   guide me.
sing Thy praise   With - in   Thy house   for - ev - er. A-MEN.

The Christian Life

WILLIAM C. DIX, 1867   7.6.7.6.D.   MEIRIONYDD
Welsh Hymn Melody
Arr. W. LLOYD, 1785–1852

Not too fast

1. "Come un-to me, ye wea-ry, And I will give you rest."
2. "Come un-to me, ye wan-derers, And I will give you light."
3. "Come un-to me, ye faint-ing, And I will give you life."
4. "And who-so-ev-er com-eth, I will not cast him out."

O bless-ed voice of Je-sus, Which comes to hearts op-pressed!
O lov-ing voice of Je-sus, Which comes to cheer the night!
O cheer-ing voice of Je-sus, Which comes to aid our strife!
O wel-come voice of Je-sus, Which drives a-way our doubt!

It tells of ben-e-dic-tion, Of par-don, grace, and peace,
Our hearts were filled with sad-ness, And we had lost our way;
The foe is stern and ea-ger, The fight is fierce and long;
Which calls us, ver-y sin-ners, Un-wor-thy though we be

Of joy that hath no end-ing, Of love which can-not cease.
But morn-ing brings us glad-ness, And songs, the break of day.
But Thou hast made us might-y, And strong-er than the strong.
Of love so free and bound-less, To come, dear Lord, to Thee! A-MEN.

Music used by permission of Dr. Basil Harwood.

Comfort and Trust

306

Hymn of the Hungarian Galley Slaves
Tr. William Toth, 1938
Metrical version, G. J. Neumann, 1938   8. 7. 8. 7. 7. 8. 8.

MAGYAR
Gályarabok Éneke, 1674

In moderate time, with confidence

1. Lift   thy head, O   Zi - on,   weep - ing,   Still   the Lord thy Fa - ther is;
2. Though the sea his waves as - sem - ble   And   in   fur - y   fall   on thee,
3. Though the hills and vales be   riv - en   God cre - a - ted with His hand,
4. Though in chains thou now art   griev - ing,   Though a   tor-tured slave thou die,

Thou   art dai - ly in His   keep - ing,   And thine ev - ery care is   His.
Though thou cry, with heart a - trem - ble,   "O,   my Sav-iour, suc - cor   me!"
Though the mov-ing signs of   heav - en   Wars pres - age in   ev - ery   land,
Zi - on, if thou die be - liev - ing,   Heav-en's path shall o - pen   lie.

Rise   and be of   glad - some heart,   And with cour - age play thy   part;
Though un - trou-bled   still He   sleep   Who thy hope   is   on the   deep,
Yet,   O   Zi - on, have   no   fear: Ev - er   is   thy Help - er   near;
Up - ward gaze and hap - py   be,   God hath not for - sak - en   thee;

Soon   a - gain His arms will fold thee   To His lov-ing heart and hold   thee.
Zi - on, calm the breast that quaketh; Nev-er God His own for - sak - eth.
He hath sought thee, He hath found thee; Lo! His wings are walls a - round thee.
Thou His peo-ple art, and sure - ly   He will fold His own se - cure - ly.   A-MEN.

The Christian Life

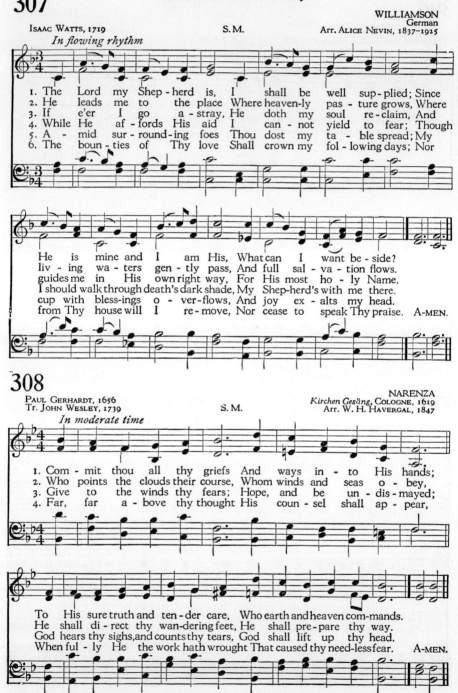

307

Isaac Watts, 1719

S. M.

WILLIAMSON
German
Arr. Alice Nevin, 1837–1925

In flowing rhythm

1. The Lord my Shep-herd is, I shall be well sup-plied; Since
2. He leads me to the place Where heaven-ly pas-ture grows, Where
3. If e'er I go a-stray, He doth my soul re-claim, And
4. While He af-fords His aid I can-not yield to fear; Though
5. A-mid sur-round-ing foes Thou dost my ta-ble spread; My
6. The boun-ties of Thy love Shall crown my fol-low-ing days; Nor

He is mine and I am His, What can I want be-side?
liv-ing wa-ters gen-tly pass, And full sal-va-tion flows.
guides me in His own right way, For His most ho-ly Name.
I should walk through death's dark shade, My Shep-herd's with me there.
cup with bless-ings o-ver-flows, And joy ex-alts my head.
from Thy house will I re-move, Nor cease to speak Thy praise. A-men.

308

Paul Gerhardt, 1656
Tr. John Wesley, 1739

S. M.

NARENZA
Kirchen Gesäng, Cologne, 1619
Arr. W. H. Havergal, 1847

In moderate time

1. Com-mit thou all thy griefs And ways in-to His hands;
2. Who points the clouds their course, Whom winds and seas o-bey,
3. Give to the winds thy fears; Hope, and be un-dis-mayed;
4. Far, far a-bove thy thought His coun-sel shall ap-pear,

To His sure truth and ten-der care, Who earth and heaven com-mands.
He shall di-rect thy wan-der-ing feet, He shall pre-pare thy way.
God hears thy sighs, and counts thy tears, God shall lift up thy head.
When ful-ly He the work hath wrought That caused thy need-less fear. A-men.

Comfort and Trust

309

SAMUEL RODIGAST, 1676
Tr. CATHERINE WINKWORTH, 1863

WAS GOTT TUT DAS IST WOHLGETAN
Weimar Gesangbuch, 1681
SEVERUS GASTORIUS, fl. 1675

8. 7. 8. 7. 4. 4. 8. 8.

In well-defined rhythm

1. What-e'er my God or-dains is right; His ho-ly will a - bid - eth;
2. What-e'er my God or-dains is right; He nev-er will de - ceive me;
3. What-e'er my God or-dains is right; Here shall my stand be tak - en;

I will be still, what-e'er He doth, And fol-low where He guid - eth.
He leads me by the prop-er path; I know He will not leave me.
Though sor-row, need, or death be mine, Yet am I not for - sak - en;

He is my God; Though dark my road, He holds me that I
I take, con - tent, What He hath sent; His hand can turn my
My Fa-ther's care Is round me there; He holds me that I

shall not fall; Where-fore to Him I leave it all.
griefs a - way, And pa - tient-ly I wait His day.
shall not fall, And so to Him I leave it all. A-MEN.

The Christian Life

310

John Greenleaf Whittier, 1867   C. M. D.   ST. LEONARD
Henry Hiles, 1867

With quiet confidence

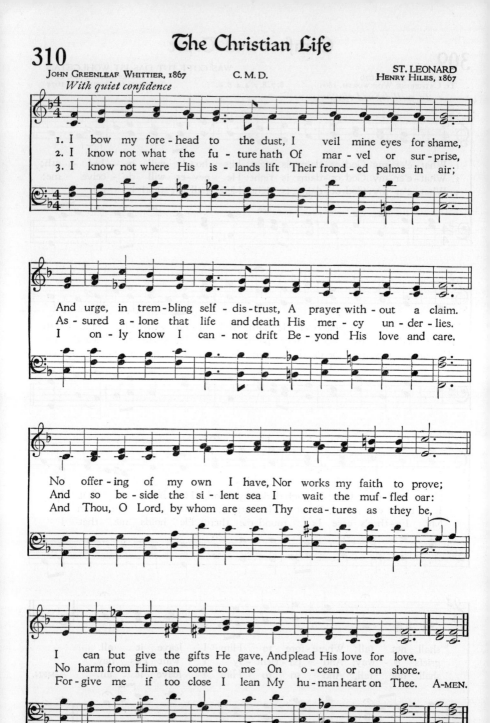

1. I bow my fore-head to the dust, I veil mine eyes for shame,
2. I know not what the fu-ture hath Of mar-vel or sur-prise,
3. I know not where His is-lands lift Their frond-ed palms in air;

And urge, in trem-bling self-dis-trust, A prayer with-out a claim.
As-sured a-lone that life and death His mer-cy un-der-lies.
I on-ly know I can-not drift Be-yond His love and care.

No offer-ing of my own I have, Nor works my faith to prove;
And so be-side the si-lent sea I wait the muf-fled oar;
And Thou, O Lord, by whom are seen Thy crea-tures as they be,

I can but give the gifts He gave, And plead His love for love.
No harm from Him can come to me On o-cean or on shore.
For-give me if too close I lean My hu-man heart on Thee. A-MEN.

Comfort and Trust

311

WELWYN

MILDRED WHITNEY STILLMAN, 1934   11.10.11.10.   ALFRED SCOTT-GATTY, 1847-1918

In moderate time; with joyous reverence

1. Now once a - gain for help that nev - er fail - eth
2. That we may rise and go forth from Thine al - tar
3. Know - ing there will not be so dark a val - ley
4. O Light that led the saints through all the a - ges,

We bring our griev - ous bur - den un - to Thee; . .
To bear the load we could not bear be - fore, . .
But those who watch may find Thy guid - ing ray, . .
O Hope that lift - ed up the mar - tyr's head, . .

Pour down Thy strength, for noth - ing else a - vail - eth;
With mind se - rene, with step that does not fal - ter,
Know - ing there will not be so blind an al - ley
O Com - fort - er of chil - dren and of sa - ges,

Bless Thou the bow - ing head, the bend - ing knee:
Know - ing Thy hand will o - pen ev - ery door.
But it will o - pen on Thy broad high - way.
With us a - bide through all the years a - head! A-MEN.

The Christian Life

Julie von Hausmann, 1867
Tr. R. A. John, 1912

7. 4. 7. 4. D.

SO NIMM DENN

Fr. Silcher, 1842

In moderate time

1. Take Thou my hand and lead me Un - to the end;
2. Thou might - y God of a - ges, O be Thou near;
3. When eve - ning's shad - ows length - en, The night is come,

In life and death I need Thee, O bless - ed Friend;
When an - gry tem - pest ra - ges I need not fear;
My faint heart, Fa - ther, strength - en And bring me home.

I can - not live with - out Thee For one brief day;
Close by Thy side a - bid - ing I fear no foe,
Take Thou my hand and lead me Un - to the end,

Lord, be Thou ev - er near me, And lead the way.
While Thy strong hand is guid - ing Life hath no woe.
In life and death I need Thee, O bless - ed Friend! A-MEN.

Comfort and Trust

JEWETT

Benjamin Schmolck, c. 1704
Tr. Jane Laurie Borthwick, 1854

6. 6. 6. 6. D.

Carl Maria von Weber
Arr. Joseph P. Holbrook, 1862

313

In moderate time

1. My Je - sus, as Thou wilt! O may Thy will be mine!
2. My Je - sus, as Thou wilt! Though seen through many a tear
3. My Je - sus, as Thou wilt! All shall be well for me;

In - to Thy hand of love I would my all re - sign.
Let not my star of hope Grow dim or dis - ap - pear.
Each chan - ging fu - ture scene I glad - ly trust with Thee.

Through sor - row or through joy, Con - duct me as Thine own;
Since Thou on earth hast wept, And sor - rowed oft a - lone,
Straight to my home a - bove I trav - el calm - ly on,

And help me still to say, "My Lord, Thy will be done."
If I must weep with Thee, My Lord, Thy will be done.
And sing, in life or death, "My Lord, Thy will be done." A-MEN.

The Christian Life

"K," in Rippon's *Selection*, 1787   11.11.11.11.   From J. F. Wade's *Cantus Diversi*, 1751

ADESTE FIDELES

With spirit

1. How firm a foun-da-tion, ye saints of the Lord, Is laid for your
2. "Fear not, I am with thee, O be not dis-mayed; For I am thy
3. "When through the deep wa-ters I call thee to go, The riv-ers of
4. "The soul that on Je-sus hath leaned for re-pose, I will not, I

faith in His ex-cel-lent Word! What more can He say than to
God, and will still give thee aid; I'll strength-en thee, help thee, and
woe shall not thee o-ver-flow; For I will be with thee thy
will not de-sert to his foes; That soul, though all hell should en-

you He hath said, Who un-to the Sav-iour for ref-uge have fled,
cause thee to stand, Up-held by My right-eous, om-nip-o-tent hand,
trou-bles to bless, And sanc-ti-fy to thee thy deep-est dis-tress,
deav-or to shake, I'll nev-er, no, nev-er, no, nev-er for-sake,

Who un-to the Sav-iour for ref-uge have fled?
Up-held by My right-eous, om-nip-o-tent hand.
And sanc-ti-fy to thee thy deep-est dis-tress.
I'll nev-er, no, nev-er, no, nev-er for-sake." A-men.

Comfort and Trust

315

John Henry Newman, 1833   10. 4. 10. 4. 10. 10.

LUX BENIGNA
John B. Dykes, 1865

In moderate time

1. Lead, kind-ly Light, a-mid the en-cir-cling gloom, Lead Thou me on;
2. I was not ev-er thus, nor prayed that Thou Shouldst lead me on;
3. So long Thy power hath blest me, sure it still Will lead me on

The night is dark, and I am far from home, Lead Thou me on.
I loved to choose and see my path; but now Lead Thou me on.
O'er moor and fen, o'er crag and tor-rent, till The night is gone;

Keep Thou my feet; I do not ask to see . . .
I loved the gar-ish day, and, spite of fears, . .
And with the morn those an-[gel fa-ces smile, . .

The dis-tant scene; one step e-nough for me.
Pride ruled my will: re-mem-ber not past years.
Which I have loved long since, and lost a-while. A-MEN.

The Christian Life

316

CHARLES WESLEY, 1740

7.7.7.7. D.
First Tune

MARTYN
SIMEON B. MARSH, 1834

In moderate time

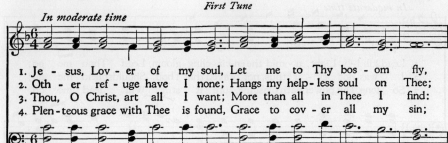

1. Je - sus, Lov - er of my soul, Let me to Thy bos - om fly,
2. Oth - er ref - uge have I none; Hangs my help - less soul on Thee;
3. Thou, O Christ, art all I want; More than all in Thee I find;
4. Plen - teous grace with Thee is found, Grace to cov - er all my sin;

While the near - er wa - ters roll, While the tem - pest still is high:
Leave, ah! leave me not a - lone, Still sup - port and com - fort me.
Raise the fall - en, cheer the faint, Heal the sick, and lead the blind.
Let the heal - ing streams a - bound; Make and keep me pure with - in.

Hide me, O my Sav - iour, hide, Till the storm of life is past;
All my trust on Thee is stayed, All my help from Thee I bring;
Just and ho - ly is Thy Name; I am all un - right - eous - ness;
Thou of life the foun - tain art, Free - ly let me take of Thee;

Safe in - to the ha - ven guide; O re - ceive my soul at last!
Cov - er my de - fense - less head With the shad - ow of Thy wing.
False and full of sin I am, Thou art full of truth and grace.
Spring Thou up with - in my heart, Rise to all e - ter - ni - ty. A - MEN.

Hope and Confidence

317

Charles Wesley, 1740

7.7.7.7.D.
Second Tune

ABERYSTWYTH
Joseph Parry, 1879

In moderate time

1. Je - sus, Lov - er of my soul, Let me to Thy bos - om fly,
2. Oth - er ref - uge have I none; Hangs my help - less soul on Thee;
3. Thou, O Christ, art all I want; More than all in Thee I find:
4. Plen - teous grace with Thee is found, Grace to cov - er all my sin;

While the near - er wa - ters roll, While the tem - pest still is high:
Leave, ah! leave me not a - lone, Still sup - port and com - fort me.
Raise the fall - en, cheer the faint, Heal the sick, and lead the blind.
Let the heal - ing streams a - bound; Make and keep me pure with - in.

Hide me, O my Sav - iour, hide, Till the storm of life is past;
All my trust on Thee is stayed, All my help from Thee I bring;
Just and ho - ly is Thy Name; I am all un - right - eous-ness;
Thou of life the Foun - tain art, Free-ly let me take of Thee;

Safe in - to the ha - ven guide; O re - ceive my soul at last!
Cov - er my de - fense-less head With the shad - ow of Thy wing.
False and full of sin I am, Thou art full of truth and grace.
Spring Thou up with-in my heart, Rise to all e - ter - ni - ty. A-MEN.

Music used by permission of Messrs. Hughes and Sons.

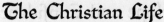

The Christian Life

318

SARAH F. ADAMS, 1841 · 6. 4. 6. 4. 6. 6. 6. 4. · BETHANY
LOWELL MASON, 1856

In moderate time

1. Near - er, my God, to Thee, Near - er to Thee! E'en though it
2. Though like the wan - der - er, The sun gone down; Dark - ness be
3. There let the way ap - pear Steps un - to heaven; All that Thou
4. Then, with my wak - ing thoughts Bright with Thy praise, Out of my
5. Or if on joy - ful wing Cleav - ing the sky, Sun, moon, and

be a cross That rais - eth me; Still all my song shall be,
o - ver me, My rest a stone; Yet in my dreams I'd be
send - est me In mer - cy given; An - gels to beck - on me
ston - y griefs Beth - el I'll raise; So by my woes to be
stars for - got, Up - wards I fly, Still all my song shall be,

Near - er, my God, to Thee, Near - er, my God, to Thee, Near - er to Thee! A-MEN.

319

WILLIAM COWPER, 1772 · C. M. · BEATITUDO
JOHN B. DYKES, 1875

In flowing rhythm

1. O for a clo - ser walk with God, A calm and heaven - ly frame,
2. Re - turn, O Ho - ly Dove, re - turn, Sweet mes - sen - ger of rest;
3. The dear - est i - dol I have known, What - e'er that i - dol be,
4. So shall my walk be close with God, Calm and se - rene my frame;

Hope and Confidence

A light to shine up-on the road That leads me to the Lamb.
I hate the sins that made Thee mourn, And drove Thee from my breast.
Help me to tear it from Thy throne, And wor-ship on-ly Thee.
So pu-rer light shall mark the road That leads me to the Lamb. A-MEN.

320

Anonymous
Tr. CATHERINE WINKWORTH, 1863, alt.   7. 8. 7. 8. 7. 7.

JESUS MEINE ZUVERSICHT (RATISBON)
JOHANN CRÜGER'S
Praxis Pietatis Melica, c. 1653

Not too slow

1. Je - sus Christ, my sure De-fense And my Sav-iour, ev-er liv - eth;
2. Je - sus, my Re-deem-er, lives! I, too, un-to life must wak - en;
3. Nay, too close-ly am I bound Un-to Him by hope for-ev - er;

Know - ing this, my con-fi-dence Rests up-on the hope it giv - eth,
End - less joy my Sav-iour gives; Shall my cour-age then be shak - en?
Faith's strong hand the rock hath found, Grasped it and will leave it nev - er:

Though the night of death be fraught Still with many an anx-ious thought.
Shall I fear? Or could the Head Rise and leave His mem-bers dead?
Death it-self can nev-er part From its Lord the trust-ing heart. A-MEN.

The Christian Life

321

GERHARD TERSTEEGEN, 1729
Tr. JOHN WESLEY, 1738

8.8.8.8.8.8.

ST. CHRYSOSTOM

JOSEPH BARNBY, 1871

In flowing rhythm

1. Thou hid-den Love of God, whose height, Whose depth un-fath-omed, no man knows, I see from far Thy beau-teous light, And on-ly sigh for Thy re-pose; My heart is pained, nor can it be At rest till it finds rest in Thee.

2. Is there a thing be-neath the sun That strives with Thee my heart to share? Ah, tear it thence, and reign a-lone, The Lord of ev-ery mo-tion there! Then shall my heart from earth be free, Where it hath found re-pose in Thee.

3. O Love, Thy sov-ereign aid im-part To save me from low thought-ed care; Chase this self-will from out my heart, From all its hid-den maz-es there; Make me Thy du-teous child, that I Cease-less may "Ab-ba, Fa-ther," cry.

4. Each mo-ment draw from earth a-way My heart, that low-ly waits Thy call; Speak to my in-most soul, and say, "I am thy Love, thy God, thy All!" To feel Thy power, to hear Thy voice, To taste Thy love, be all my choice.

A-MEN.

The Church

322

SAMUEL J. STONE, 1866   7.6.7.6.D.   AURELIA
SAMUEL S. WESLEY, 1864

In moderate time, with breadth and dignity

1. The Church's one Foun-da - tion Is Je - sus Christ her Lord;
2. E - lect from ev - ery na - tion, Yet one o'er all the earth,
3. 'Mid toil and trib - u - la - tion, And tu - mult of her war,
4. Yet she on earth hath un - ion With God the Three in One,

She is His new cre - a - tion By wa - ter and the word:
Her char - ter of sal - va - tion One Lord, one faith, one birth;
She waits the con - sum - ma - tion Of peace for - ev - er - more;
And mys - tic sweet com - mun - ion With those whose rest is won:

From heaven He came and sought her To be His ho - ly Bride;
One ho - ly Name she bless - es, Par - takes one ho - ly food,
Till with the vi - sion glo - rious Her long - ing eyes are blest,
O hap - py ones and ho - ly! Lord, give us grace that we,

With His own blood He bought her, And for her life He died.
And to one hope she press - es, With ev - ery grace en - dued.
And the great Church vic - to - rious Shall be the Church at rest.
Like them, the meek and low - ly, On high may dwell with Thee. A-MEN.

The Church of Christ

323

JOHN NEWTON, 1779
With exultation

8. 7. 8. 7. D.

AUSTRIAN HYMN
FRANZ JOSEPH HAYDN, 1797

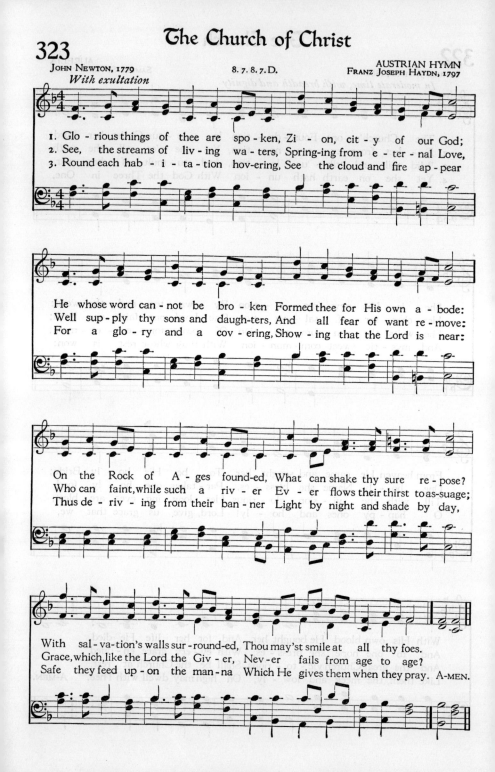

1. Glo - rious things of thee are spo - ken, Zi - on, cit - y of our God;
2. See, the streams of liv - ing wa - ters, Spring-ing from e - ter - nal Love,
3. Round each hab - i - ta - tion hov-ering, See the cloud and fire ap - pear

He whose word can - not be bro - ken Formed thee for His own a - bode:
Well sup - ply thy sons and daugh-ters, And all fear of want re - move:
For a glo - ry and a cov - ering, Show - ing that the Lord is near:

On the Rock of A - ges found-ed, What can shake thy sure re - pose?
Who can faint, while such a riv - er Ev - er flows their thirst to as-suage;
Thus de - riv - ing from their ban - ner Light by night and shade by day,

With sal - va - tion's walls sur - round-ed, Thou may'st smile at all thy foes.
Grace, which, like the Lord the Giv - er, Nev - er fails from age to age?
Safe they feed up - on the man - na Which He gives them when they pray. A-MEN.

The Church

324

Latin, 7th century
Tr. JOHN MASON NEALE, 1851

8.7.8.7.8.7.

REGENT SQUARE
HENRY SMART, 1867

In moderate time, with dignity

1. Christ is made the sure Foun-da-tion, Christ the Head and Cor-ner Stone, Cho-sen of the Lord and pre-cious, Bind-ing all the Church in one; Ho-ly Zi-on's help for-ev-er, And her con-fi-dence a-lone.

2. To this tem-ple, where we call Thee, Come, O Lord of hosts, to-day: With Thy wont-ed lov-ing-kind-ness Hear Thy peo-ple as they pray; And Thy full-est ben-e-dic-tion Shed with-in its walls al-way.

3. Here vouch-safe to all Thy serv-ants What they ask of Thee to gain, What they gain from Thee for-ev-er With the bless-ed to re-tain, And here-aft-er in Thy glo-ry Ev-er-more with Thee to reign.

4. Laud and hon-or to the Fa-ther, Laud and hon-or to the Son, Laud and hon-or to the Spir-it, Ev-er Three and ev-er One, One in might, and One in glo-ry, While un-end-ing a-ges run! A-MEN.

The Church of Christ

325

Samuel Longfellow, 1864 — C. M. — ST. JAMES — Raphael Courteville, d. 1772

In moderate time

1. One ho - ly Church of God ap - pears Through
2. From old - est time, on far - thest shores, Be -
3. The truth is her pro - phet - ic gift, The
4. O liv - ing Church, thine er - rand speed, Ful -

ev - ery age and race, Un - wast - ed by the
neath the pine or palm, One un - seen Pres - ence
soul her sa - cred page; And feet on mer - cy's
fill thy task sub - lime; With Bread of life earth's

lapse of years, Un - changed by chang - ing place.
she a - dores, With si - lence, or with psalm.
er - rands swift Do make her pil - grim - age.
hun - gers feed; Re - deem the e - vil time! A-MEN.

326

Arthur Cleveland Coxe, 1839 — C. M. — ST. ANNE — William Croft, 1708

Majestically

1. O where are kings and em - pires now Of old that went and came?
2. We mark her good - ly bat - tle - ments, And her foun - da - tions strong;
3. For not like king - doms of the world Thy ho - ly Church, O God,
4. Un - shak - en as e - ter - nal hills, Im - mov - a - ble she stands,

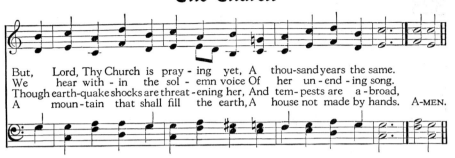

But, Lord, Thy Church is pray-ing yet, A thou-sand years the same.
We hear with-in the sol-emn voice Of her un-end-ing song.
Though earth-quake shocks are threat-ening her, And tem-pests are a-broad,
A moun-tain that shall fill the earth, A house not made by hands. A-MEN.

327

CHRISTUS DER IST MEIN LEBEN (BREMEN)

Psalm cxxxiv
United Presbyterian Book of Psalms,
U.S.A., 1871   7. 6. 7. 6.   MELCHIOR VULPIUS, 1609

Gracefully

1. Lord God of Hosts, how love-ly The
2. My soul is long-ing, faint-ing, Je-
3. Be-hold, the spar-row find-eth A
4. And where, se-cure-ly shel-tered, Her
5. Blest who Thy house in-hab-it! They

place where Thou dost dwell! Thy tab-er-na-cles
ho-vah's courts to see; My heart and flesh are
house in which to rest, The swal-low hath dis-
young she forth may bring; So, Lord of Hosts, Thy
ev-er give Thee praise; Blest all whom Thou dost

ho-ly In pleas-ant-ness ex-cel.
cry-ing, O liv-ing God, to Thee.
cov-ered Where she may build her nest,
al-tars I seek, my God, my King.
strength-en, Who love the sa-cred ways! A-MEN.

The Church of Christ

328

Robert Collyer, 1873   L. M.   MENDON / German Melody / Arr. Samuel Dyer, 1828

In moderate time

1. Un - to Thy tem - ple, Lord, we come With thank - ful
2. The com - mon home of rich and poor, Of bond and
3. And dwell Thou with us in this place, Thou and Thy
4. May Thy whole truth be spo - ken here; Thy gos - pel

hearts to wor - ship Thee; And pray that this may be our home
free, and great and small; Large as Thy love for - ev - er - more,
Christ, to guide and bless. Here make the well-springs of Thy grace
light for - ev - er shine; Thy per - fect love cast out all fear,

Un - til we touch e - ter - ni - ty;
And warm and bright and good to all.
Like foun - tains in the wil - der - ness.
And hu - man life be - come di - vine. A - MEN.

329

Psalm cxxxvii
Timothy Dwight, 1800   S. M.   ST. THOMAS / Williams' Psalmody, 1770

Joyously

1. I love Thy King - dom, Lord, The house of
2. I love Thy Church, O God: Her walls be -
3. For her my tears shall fall, For her my
4. Be - yond my high - est joy I prize her
5. Sure as Thy truth shall last, To Zi - on

The Church

Thine a - bode, The Church our blest Re -
fore Thee stand, Dear as the ap - ple
prayers as - cend; To her my cares and
heaven - ly ways, Her sweet com - mun - ion,
shall be given The bright - est glo - ries

deem - er saved With His own pre - cious blood.
of Thine eye, And grav - en on Thy hand.
toils be given, Till toils and cares shall end.
sol - emn vows, Her hymns of love and praise.
earth can yield, And bright - er bliss of heaven. A-MEN.

330

SAMUEL JOHNSON, 1864   C. M.   NUN DANKET ALL' (GRÄFENBERG)
JOHANN CRÜGER'S
Praxis Pietatis Melica, 1653

May be sung in unison. Majestically

1. Cit - y of God, how broad and far Out-spread thy walls sub - lime!
2. One ho - ly Church, one ar - my strong, One stead-fast high in - tent,
3. How pure - ly hath thy speech come down From man's pri - me - val youth;
4. How gleam thy watch-fires through the night, With nev - er - faint - ing ray;
5. In vain the surg - e's an - gry shock, In vain the drift - ing sands;

The true thy char-tered free-men are Of ev - ery age and clime.
One work - ing band, one har - vest-song, One King Om - nip - o - tent.
How grand-ly hath thine em - pire grown Of free-dom, love, and truth!
How rise thy towers, se - rene and bright, To meet the dawn - ing day!
Un-harmed up - on the E - ter - nal Rock The e-ter-nal cit - y stands. A-MEN.

The Church of Christ

331

From the German
Tr. SAMUEL GILMAN, 1791–1858, alt.

L. M.

FEDERAL STREET
HENRY K. OLIVER, 1833

In moderate time

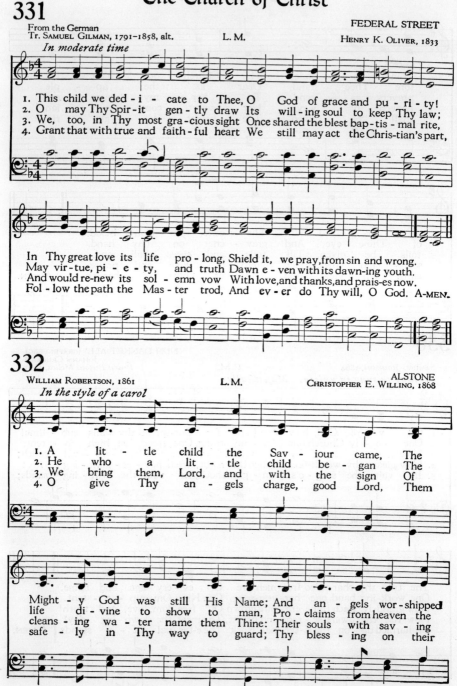

1. This child we ded - i - cate to Thee, O God of grace and pu - ri - ty!
2. O may Thy Spir - it gen - tly draw Its will - ing soul to keep Thy law;
3. We, too, in Thy most gra - cious sight Once shared the blest bap - tis - mal rite,
4. Grant that with true and faith - ful heart We still may act the Chris - tian's part,

In Thy great love its life pro - long, Shield it, we pray, from sin and wrong.
May vir - tue, pi - e - ty, and truth Dawn e - ven with its dawn - ing youth.
And would re-new its sol - emn vow With love, and thanks, and prais-es now.
Fol - low the path the Mas - ter trod, And ev - er do Thy will, O God. A-MEN.

332

WILLIAM ROBERTSON, 1861

L. M.

ALSTONE
CHRISTOPHER E. WILLING, 1868

In the style of a carol

1. A lit - tle child the Sav - iour came, The
2. He who a lit - tle child be - gan The
3. We bring them, Lord, and with the sign Of
4. O give Thy an - gels charge, good Lord, Them

Might - y God was still His Name; And an - gels wor - shipped
life di - vine to show to man, Pro - claims from heaven the
cleans - ing wa - ter name them Thine: Their souls with sav - ing
safe - ly in Thy way to guard; Thy bless - ing on their

The Sacraments
Holy Baptism

as He lay, The seem - ing in - fant of a day.
mes - sage free, "Let lit - tle chil - dren come to Me."
grace en - dow, Bap - tize them with Thy Spir - it now.
lives com - mand, And write their names up - on Thy hand. A-MEN.

333

HOWELL E. LEWIS, 1922   10. 10. 10. 10.   LANGRAN
                                                        JAMES LANGRAN, 1862

In moderate time

1. Friend of the home: as when in Gal - i - lee The moth-ers brought their
2. Thine are they, by Thy love's e - ter - nal claim, Thine we bap - tize them
3. Lord, may Thy Church, as with a moth-er's care, For Thee the lambs with -

lit - tle ones to Thee, So we, dear Lord, would now the chil - dren bring,
in the three-fold Name; Yet not the sign we trust, Lord, but the grace
in her bo - som bear; And grant, as morn - ing grows to noon, that they

And seek for them the shel - ter of Thy wing.
That in Thy fold pre - pared the lambs a place.
Still in her love and ho - ly serv - ice stay. A - MEN.

The Church of Christ

334

JOHANN FRANCK, c. 1649
Tr. CATHERINE WINKWORTH, 1863

SCHMÜCKE DICH O LIEBE SEELE (BERLIN)

L. M. D.

JOHANN CRÜGER, 1649

In moderate time

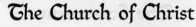

1. Deck thy-self, my soul, with glad - ness, Leave the gloom - y
2. Has - ten as a bride to meet Him, And with lov - ing
3. Now I sink be - fore Thee low - ly, Filled with joy most
4. Sun, who all my life dost bright - en, Light, who dost my

haunts of sad - ness; Come in - to the day-light's splen - dor,
rev - erence greet Him, For with words of life im - mor - tal
deep and ho - ly, As, with trem - bling awe and won - der,
soul en - light - en, Joy, the sweet - est man e'er know - eth,

There with joy thy prais - es ren - der Un - to Him whose grace un - bound - ed
Now He knock - eth at thy por - tal; O - pen thou the gates be - fore Him,
On Thy might - y works I pon - der; Now by mys - ter - y sur - round - ed,
Fount, whence all my be - ing flow - eth, At Thy feet I fall, my Mak - er,

Hath this won - drous ban - quet found - ed; High o'er all the heavens He
Say - ing, as thou dost a - dore Him: Suf - fer, Lord, that I re -
Depths no man has ev - er sound - ed, None may dare to pierce, un -
Let me be a fit par - tak - er Of this bless - ed food from

The Sacraments
The Lord's Supper

reign - eth, Yet to dwell with thee He deign - eth.
ceive Thee, And I nev - er - more will leave Thee.
bid - den, Se - crets that with Thee are hid - den.
heav - en, In Thy love to mor - tals giv - en. A-MEN.

335

SAXBY

Attributed to BERNARD OF CLAIRVAUX, c. 1150
Tr. RAY PALMER, 1858   L. M.   TIMOTHY R. MATTHEWS, 1883

In flowing rhythm

1. Je - sus, Thou Joy of lov - ing hearts, Thou Fount of
2. Thy truth un - changed hath ev - er stood; Thou sav - est
3. We taste Thee, O Thou liv - ing Bread, And long to
4. O Je - sus, ev - er with us stay, Make all our

life, Thou Light of men, From the best bliss that
those that on Thee call; To them that seek Thee
feast up - on Thee still; We drink of Thee, the
mo - ments calm and bright; Chase the dark night of

earth im - parts We turn un - filled to Thee a - gain.
Thou art good, To them that find Thee all in all.
Foun - tain - head, And thirst our souls from Thee to fill.
sin a - way, Shed o'er the world Thy ho - ly light. A - MEN.

The Church of Christ

336

From the Liturgy of St. James
Tr. Gerard Moultrie, 1868

8. 7. 8. 7. 8. 7.

PICARDY

French Traditional Carol

Slowly and with reverence

1. Let all mor-tal flesh keep si-lence, And with fear and trem-bling stand;
2. King of kings, yet born of Ma-ry, As of old on earth He stood,
3. Rank on rank the host of heav-en Spreads its van-guard on the way,
4. At His feet the six - winged ser-aph; Cher-u-bim, with sleep-less eye,

Pon-der noth-ing earth-ly - mind-ed, For with bless-ing in His hand,
Lord of lords, in hu-man ves-ture—In the bod-y and the blood—
As the Light of Light de-scend-eth From the realms of end-less day,
Veil their fa-ces to the pres-ence, As with cease-less voice they cry,

Christ our God to earth de-scend - eth, Our full hom-age to de - mand.
He will give to all the faith - ful His own self for heavenly food.
That the powers of hell may van - ish As the dark-ness clears a - way.
Al - le-lu-ia, Al-le-lu - ia, Al-le-lu-ia, Lord Most High! A-men.

The Sacraments
The Lord's Supper

337

REGINALD HEBER, 1827

9.8.9.8.D.

RENDEZ A DIEU
LOUIS BOURGEOIS, 1543
From *Genevan Psalter*

Rather slowly

Bread of the world in mer-cy bro-ken, Wine of the
soul in mer-cy shed, By whom the words of life were spo-ken,
And in whose death our sins are dead: Look on the heart by sor-row
bro-ken, Look on the tears by sin-ners shed, And be Thy
feast to us the to-ken That by Thy grace our souls are fed. A-MEN.

The Church of Christ

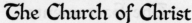

338

JAMES MONTGOMERY, 1825   C. M.   MARTYRDOM
HUGH WILSON, 1766-1824

Rather slowly, with dignity

1. Ac - cord - ing to Thy gra - cious word, In meek hu - mil - i - ty,
2. Thy bod - y, bro - ken for my sake, My bread from heaven shall be;
3. When to the cross I turn mine eyes, And rest on Cal - va - ry,
4. Re - mem - ber Thee, and all Thy pains, And all Thy love to me:

This will I do, my dy - ing Lord, I will re - mem - ber Thee.
Thy tes - ta - men - tal cup I take, And thus re - mem - ber Thee.
O Lamb of God, my Sac - ri - fice, I must re - mem - ber Thee;
Yea, while a breath, a pulse re - mains, Will I re - mem - ber Thee. A - MEN.

339

JAMES MONTGOMERY, 1825   C. M.   ST. FLAVIAN
Day's Psalter, 1563

Slowly, with deep reverence

1. Be known to us in break - ing bread, But do not then de - part;
2. There sup with us in love di - vine; Thy bod - y and Thy blood,

Sav - iour, a - bide with us, and spread Thy ta - ble in our heart.
That liv - ing bread, that heaven - ly wine, Be our im - mor - tal food. A-MEN.

The Sacraments
The Lord's Supper

WILLIAM BRIGHT, 1874

10. 10. 10. 10. 10. 10.

UNDE ET MEMORES
WILLIAM H. MONK, 1875

In moderate time

1. And now, O Fa-ther, mind-ful of the love That bought us, once for
2. Look, Fa-ther, look on His a-noint-ed face, And on-ly look on
3. And so we come; O draw us to Thy feet, Most pa-tient Sav-iour,

all, on Cal-vary's tree, And hav-ing with us Him that pleads a-bove,
us as found in Him; Look not on our mis-us-ings of Thy grace,
who canst love us still; And by this food, so full of awe, so sweet,

We here pre-sent, we here spread forth to Thee That on-ly of-fering
Our prayer so lan-guid, and our faith so dim; For lo! be-tween our
De-liv-er us from ev-ery touch of ill; In Thine own serv-ice

per-fect in Thine eyes, The one true, pure, im-mor-tal Sac-ri-fice.
sins and their re-ward We set the Pas-sion of Thy Son our Lord.
make us glad and free, And grant us nev-er-more to part with Thee. A-MEN.

The Church of Christ

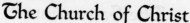

341

HORATIUS BONAR, 1855 · 10. 10. 10. 10. · MORECAMBE
FREDERICK C. ATKINSON, 1870

Rather slowly, with deep reverence

1. Here, O my Lord, I see Thee face to face; Here would I touch and
2. Here would I feed up-on the bread of God, Here drink with Thee the
3. This is the hour of ban-quet and of song; This is the heaven-ly
4. I have no help but Thine, nor do I need An-oth-er arm save

han-dle things un-seen, Here grasp with firm-er hand e-ter-nal grace,
roy-al wine of heaven; Here would I lay a-side each earth-ly load,
ta-ble spread for me: Here let me feast, and, feast-ing, still pro-long
Thine to lean up-on: It is e-nough, my Lord, e-nough in-deed;

And all my wea-ri-ness up-on Thee lean.
Here taste a-fresh the calm of sin for-given.
The brief, bright hour of fel-low-ship with Thee.
My strength is in Thy might, Thy might a-lone.   A-MEN.

342

From *Songs of Praise* · 11. 11. 11. 5. · CHRISTE FONS JUGIS
Rouen Church Melody

May be sung in unison

1. Where-fore, O Fa-ther, we Thy hum-ble serv-ants Of-fer our
2. So, Lord, we thank Thee, for that Thou dost feed us, Mem-bers u-

The Sacraments
The Lord's Supper

praises, with our glad thanksgiving, Offer ourselves, Lord,
united in that mystic body— Company blessed

souls and bodies to Thee, Christ's death proclaiming.
of all faithful people: Thus we would serve Thee. A-MEN.

343

AARON R. WOLFE, 1858 S. M. BOYLSTON
LOWELL MASON, 1832

Not too fast; with solemnity

1. A parting hymn we sing A-round Thy table, Lord;
2. Here have we seen Thy face, And felt Thy presence here;
3. The purchase of Thy blood, By sin no longer led,
4. In self-forgetting love Be our communion shown,

A-gain our grateful tribute bring, Our solemn vows record.
So may the savor of Thy grace In word and life appear.
The path our dear Redeemer trod May we rejoicing tread.
Un-til we join the Church above, And know as we are known. A-MEN.

The Church of Christ

344

George H. Bourne, 1840-1925

8. 7. 8. 7. 4. 7.

BRYN CALFARIA
William Owen, 1814-1893

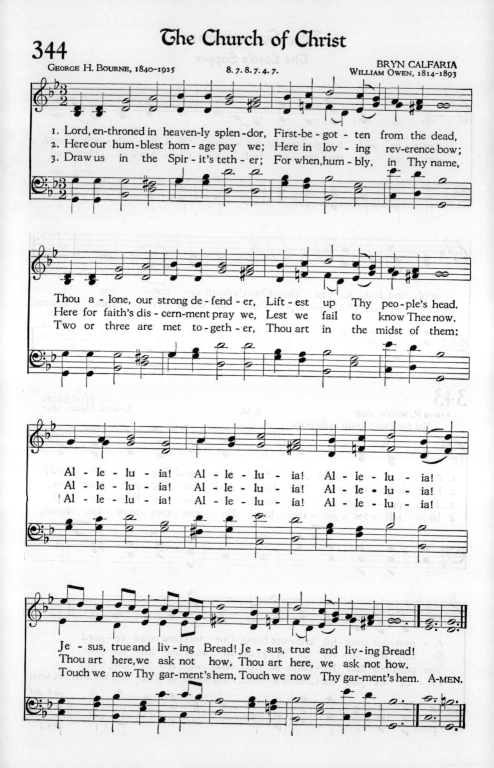

1. Lord, en-throned in heaven-ly splen-dor, First-be-got-ten from the dead,
2. Here our hum-blest hom-age pay we; Here in lov-ing rev-erence bow;
3. Draw us in the Spir-it's teth-er; For when, hum-bly, in Thy name,

Thou a-lone, our strong de-fend-er, Lift-est up Thy peo-ple's head.
Here for faith's dis-cern-ment pray we, Lest we fail to know Thee now.
Two or three are met to-geth-er, Thou art in the midst of them:

Al-le-lu-ia! Al-le-lu-ia! Al-le-lu-ia!
Al-le-lu-ia! Al-le-lu-ia! Al-le-lu-ia!
Al-le-lu-ia! Al-le-lu-ia! Al-le-lu-ia!

Je-sus, true and liv-ing Bread! Je-sus, true and liv-ing Bread!
Thou art here, we ask not how, Thou art here, we ask not how.
Touch we now Thy gar-ment's hem, Touch we now Thy gar-ment's hem. A-men.

The Rites

Confirmation

345

Frances M. Owen, 1872

7.7.7.7.7.7.

ILLUMINATIO
George J. Elvey, 1885

In moderate time

1. When Thy sol - diers take their swords, When they speak the sol - emn words, When they kneel be - fore Thee here, Feel - ing Thee, their Fa - ther, near; These Thy chil - dren, Lord, de - fend, To their help Thy Spir - it send.

2. When the world's sharp strife is nigh, When they hear the bat - tle - cry, When they rush in - to the fight, Know - ing not temp - ta - tion's might; These Thy chil - dren, Lord, de - fend, To their zeal Thy wis - dom lend.

3. When their hearts are lift - ed high With suc - cess or vic - to - ry, When they feel the con - queror's pride— Lest they grow self - sat - is - fied, These Thy chil - dren, Lord, de - fend, Teach their souls to Thee to bend.

4. When the vows that they have made, When the prayers that they have prayed Shall be fad - ing from their hearts, When their first warm faith de - parts, These Thy chil - dren, Lord, de - fend, Keep them faith - ful to the end. A - MEN.

The Church of Christ

346

MATTHEW BRIDGES, 1848   C. M.   ST. STEPHEN
WILLIAM JONES, 1789

In moderate time

1. My God, ac - cept my heart this day,
2. Be - fore the cross of Him who died,
3. A - noint me with Thy heaven - ly grace,
4. Let ev - ery thought, and work, and word,

And make it al - ways Thine, That I from Thee no
Be - hold, I pros - trate fall; Let ev - ery sin be
A - dopt me for Thine own, That I may see Thy
To Thee be ev - er given; Then life shall be Thy

more may stray, No more from Thee de - cline.
cru - ci - fied, Let Christ be all in all.
glo - rious face, And wor - ship at Thy throne.
serv - ice, Lord, And death the gate of heaven. A-MEN.

347

MARIANNE HEARN, 1887   8. 8. 8. 6.   JUST AS I AM
JOSEPH BARNBY, 1883

In rather slow time

1. Just as I am, Thine own to be, Friend of the
2. In the glad morn - ing of my day, My life to
3. I would live ev - er in the light, I would work
4. Just as I am, young, strong and free, To be the

The Rites
Confirmation

young, who lov - est me, To con - se - crate my -
give, my vows to pay, With no re - serve and
ev - er for the right, I would serve Thee with
best that I can be For truth, and right - eous -

Slower

self to Thee, O Je - sus Christ, I come.
no de - lay, With all my heart I come.
all my might; There - fore, to Thee I come.
ness, and Thee, Lord of my life, I come. A - MEN.

348

MARY F. MAUDE, 1847   7.7.7.7.   HORSHAM
                                                   English Traditional Melody

In rather slow time

1. Thine for - ev - er! God of love, Hear us from Thy throne a - bove;
2. Thine for - ev - er! O how blest They who find in Thee their rest!
3. Thine for - ev - er! Lord of life, Shield us through our earth - ly strife;
4. Thine for - ev - er! Thou our Guide, All our wants by Thee sup - plied,

Thine for - ev - er may we be Here and in e - ter - ni - ty!
Sav - iour, Guardian, heaven - ly Friend, O de - fend us to the end!
Thou the Life, the Truth, the Way, Guide us to the realms of day!
All our sins by Thee for - given, Led by Thee from earth to heaven! A - MEN.

The Church of Christ

DENIS WORTMAN, 1884, alt.   10. 10. 10. 10.   TOULON
                                                    Genevan Psalter, 1551

With dignity

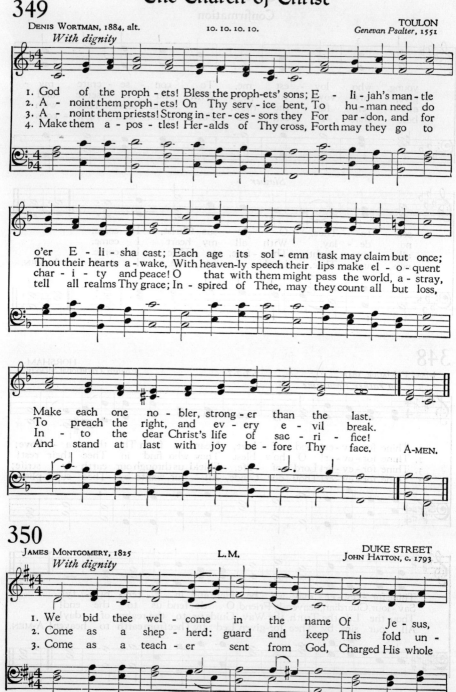

1. God of the proph-ets! Bless the proph-ets' sons; E - li-jah's man-tle
2. A - noint them proph-ets! On Thy serv-ice bent, To hu-man need do
3. A - noint them priests! Strong in-ter-ces-sors they For par-don, and for
4. Make them a - pos-tles! Her-alds of Thy cross, Forth may they go to

o'er E - li-sha cast; Each age its sol-emn task may claim but once;
Thou their hearts a - wake, With heaven-ly speech their lips make el - o - quent
char - i - ty and peace! O that with them might pass the world, a - stray,
tell all realms Thy grace; In - spired of Thee, may they count all but loss,

Make each one no - bler, strong-er than the last.
To preach the right, and ev - er-y e - vil break.
In - to the dear Christ's life of sac - ri - fice!
And stand at last with joy be - fore Thy face.   A-MEN.

350

JAMES MONTGOMERY, 1825   L. M.   DUKE STREET
                                        JOHN HATTON, c. 1793

With dignity

1. We bid thee wel - come in the name Of Je - sus,
2. Come as a shep - herd: guard and keep This fold un -
3. Come as a teach - er sent from God, Charged His whole

The Rites
Ordination and Installation

our ex- alt- ed Head; Come as a serv- ant:
harmed by earth and sin; Nour- ish the lambs and
coun- sel to de- clare; Lift o'er our ranks the

so He came, And we re- ceive thee in His stead.
feed the sheep, The wound- ed heal, the lost bring in.
proph- et's rod, While we up- hold thy hands with prayer. A-MEN.

351

JAMES MONTGOMERY, 1833, alt.   L. M.   FEDERAL STREET
HENRY K. OLIVER, 1832

In moderate time

1. Lord, pour Thy Spir- it from on high, And Thine or-dain- ed serv-ants bless;
2. With- in Thy tem- ple when they stand To teach the truth as taught by Thee,
3. Faith, wis-dom, zeal do Thou im- part, Give firm-ness and hu-mil- i- ty,
4. To watch and pray and nev- er faint, By day and night their guard to keep;

Thy promised power to each sup- ply, Thy shepherds clothe with righteousness.
Like stars, O Sav-iour, in Thy hand, May all Thy Church's pas-tors be.
To bear Thy peo-ple on their heart, Bring wan-dering souls safe home to Thee.
To warn the sin-ner, cheer the saint, Pro-tect Thy lambs and feed Thy sheep. A-MEN.

The Church of Christ

352

Samuel F. Smith, 1808–1895

L. M.

MISSIONARY CHANT
Heinrich Christopher Zeuner, 1832

With spirit, but broadly

1. Go, her-alds of sal-va-tion,forth; Go in your heaven-ly Mas-ter's name;
2. Go forth to sow the liv-ing seed; Seek not earth's praise,nor dread its blame;
3. Lo, I am with you,saith the Lord, My grace your spir-it shall sus-tain;
4. Go forth in hope; my bur-den take, Till God's great reap-ing day shall come;

From east to west,from south to north,The glo-rious gos-pel wide pro-claim.
Nor la-bors fear, nor tri-als heed; Go forth to con-quer in His Name.
Strong is my arm, and sure my word; My servants shall not toil in vain.
Then they who sowed in tears shall wake,And hail the joy-ful har-vest home. A-men.

353

John Armstrong, 1847

L. M.

MELCOMBE
Samuel Webbe, 1782

In moderate time

1. O Thou who mak-est souls to shine With light from bright-er worlds a-bove,
2. Do Thou Thy ben-e-dic-tion give On all who teach, on all who learn,
3. Give those that teach pure hearts and wise,Faith,hope,and love,all warmed by prayer;
4. O bless the shep-herd,bless the sheep,That guide and guid-ed both be one—

Now send Thy glis-ten-ing dew di-vine On all who seek a Sav-iour's love.
That all Thy Church may ho-lier live,And ev-ery lamp more bright-ly burn.
Them-selves first train-ing for the skies, They best will raise their peo-ple there.
One in the faithful watch they keep,Un-til this hur-ry-ing life be done. A-men.

354

THOMAS TIPLADY

WALTHAM
J. BAPTISTE CALKIN, 1872

Moderately fast, with dignity

1. O men of God, go forth to win The world for Je - sus Christ your Lord;
2. To North and South, to East and West, Go forth in Christ's most ho - ly Name;
3. Let noth - ing daunt your ar - dor pure, Nor turn you from your pur - pose great;
4. On Cal - va - ry the Sav - iour died For ev - ery man of ev - ery race;

With faith that glows, and love that burns, Proclaim to all His gra - cious Word.
On ev - ery hill a bea - con light, And set the world with truth a - flame.
To save a world Christ sends you out, And for your mes - sage mil - lions wait.
'Tis yours to make the good news known, And be the chan - nels of His grace. A-MEN.

Words used by permission of the author.

355

HORATIUS BONAR, 1843

L. M.

PENTECOST
WILLIAM BOYD, 1868

With spirit

1. Go, la - bor on: spend, and be spent, Thy joy to do the Fa - ther's will:
2. Go, la - bor on; 'tis not for nought; Thy earth - ly loss is heaven - ly gain:
3. Go, la - bor on while it is day: The world's dark night is hasten - ing on;
4. Toil on, faint not, keep watch and pray, Be wise the err - ing soul to win;

It is the way the Mas - ter went; Should not the servant tread it still?
Men heed thee, love thee, praise thee not; The Master prais - es: what are men?
Speed, speed thy work, cast sloth a - way; It is not thus that souls are won.
Go forth in - to the world's highway, Compel the wan - derer to come in. A-MEN.

The Church of Christ

The Rites: Marriage

356

DOROTHY BLOMFIELD GURNEY, 1883   11. 10. 11. 10.   PERFECT LOVE (SANDRINGHAM)
JOSEPH BARNBY, 1889

In moderate time

1. O perfect Love, all hu-man thought tran-scend-ing,
2. O perfect Life, be Thou their full as-sur-ance
3. Grant them the joy which bright-ens earth-ly sor-row,

Low-ly we kneel in prayer be-fore Thy throne,
Of ten-der char-i-ty and stead-fast faith,
Grant them the peace which calms all earth-ly strife;

That theirs may be the love which knows no end-ing
Of pa-tient hope, and qui-et, brave en-dur-ance,
And to life's day the glo-rious un-known mor-row

Whom Thou for-ev-er-more dost join in one.
With child-like trust that fears nor pain nor death.
That dawns up-on e-ter-nal love and life. A-MEN.

Dedications
Church

357

WILLIAM CULLEN BRYANT, 1820

C. M.

NUN DANKET ALL' (GRÄFENBERG)
JOHANN CRÜGER'S
Praxis Pietatis Melica, 1653

May be sung in unison. Majestically

1. Thou, whose un-meas-ured tem-ple stands, Built o-ver earth and sea,
2. Lord, from Thine in-most glo-ry send, With-in these walls to a-bide,
3. May er-ring minds that wor-ship here Be taught the bet-ter way;
4. May faith grow firm, and love grow warm, And pure de-vo-tion rise,

Ac-cept the walls that hu-man hands Have raised, O God, to Thee.
The peace that dwell-eth with-out end Se-rene-ly by Thy side.
And they who mourn, and they who fear Be strength-ened as they pray.
While round these hal-lowed walls the storm Of earth-born pas-sion dies. A-MEN.

Alternative tune, St. Anne.

358

JOHN PIERPONT, 1785–1866

7.7.7.7.

GOTT SEI DANK DURCH ALLE WELT
Freylinghausen's *Gesangbuch*, Halle, 1704

May be sung in unison. With spirit

1. On this stone now laid with prayer Let Thy Church rise strong and fair;
2. May Thy Ho-ly Son who came Man from er-ror to re-claim,
3. May Thy Spir-it here give rest To the hearts by sin op-pressed,
4. By wise mas-ter-build-ers squared, Here be liv-ing stones pre-pared

Ev-er, Lord, Thy name be known, Where we lay this cor-ner-stone.
And for sin-ners to a-tone, Bless, with Thee, this cor-ner-stone.
And the seeds of truth be sown, Where we lay this cor-ner-stone.
For the tem-ple near Thy throne, Je-sus Christ its cor-ner-stone. A-MEN.

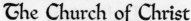

The Church of Christ

359

FREDERICK W. GOADBY, 1879, alt. 7.6.7.6.D. AURELIA
SAMUEL S. WESLEY, 1864

In moderate time, with breadth and dignity

1. O Thou, whose hand hath brought us Un - to this joy - ful day,
2. For this new house we praise Thee, Reared at Thine own com-mand,
3. And oft as here we gath - er, And hearts in wor - ship blend,

Ac - cept our glad thanks-giv - ing, And lis - ten as we pray;
For ev - ery gen - erous spir - it, And ev - ery will - ing hand;
May truth re - veal its pow - er, And fer - vent prayer as - cend;

And may our prep - a - ra - tion For this day's serv - ice be
O Lord with - in this tem - ple, Thy glo - ry may we see,
Here may Thy bur - dened chil - dren Rise to the things a - bove;

With one ac - cord to of - fer Our-selves, O Lord, to Thee.
For all its strength and beau - ty Are noth - ing with - out Thee.
The young, the old, be strength-ened, And all men learn Thy love. A-MEN.

360 Dedications
Organ

Henry Ware, Jr., 1822
Stanza 3, alt.

C. M. D.

BETHLEHEM (SERAPH)
Gottfried W. Fink, 1842

Joyously

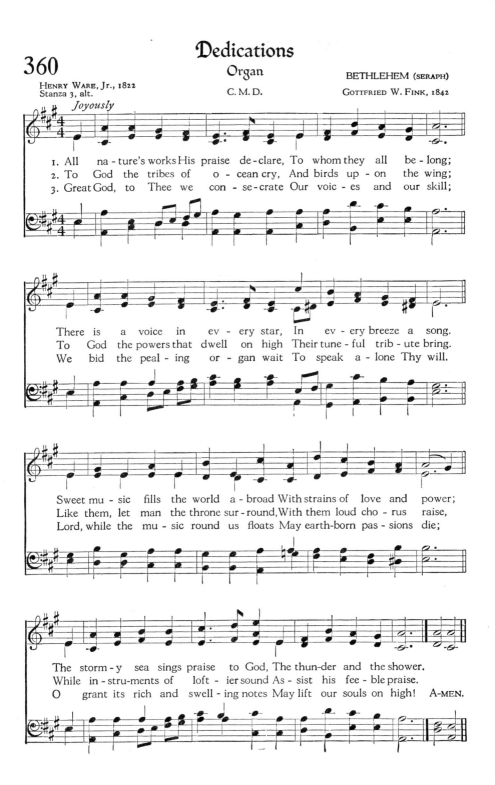

1. All na - ture's works His praise de - clare, To whom they all be - long;
2. To God the tribes of o - cean cry, And birds up - on the wing;
3. Great God, to Thee we con - se - crate Our voic - es and our skill;

There is a voice in ev - ery star, In ev - ery breeze a song.
To God the powers that dwell on high Their tune - ful trib - ute bring.
We bid the peal - ing or - gan wait To speak a - lone Thy will.

Sweet mu - sic fills the world a - broad With strains of love and power;
Like them, let man the throne sur - round, With them loud cho - rus raise,
Lord, while the mu - sic round us floats May earth-born pas - sions die;

The storm - y sea sings praise to God, The thun - der and the shower.
While in - stru - ments of loft - ier sound As - sist his fee - ble praise.
O grant its rich and swell - ing notes May lift our souls on high! A - MEN.

The Church of Christ

361

Thomas H. Gill, 1868   8. 7. 8. 7. 8. 8. 7.

NUN FREUT EUCH
Melody by Martin Luther in
Geistliche Lieder, Wittenberg, 1535

Moderately fast

1. We come un-to our fa-thers' God, Their Rock is our sal-va-tion;
2. Their joy un-to the Lord we bring, Their song to us de-scend-eth;
3. Ye saints to come, take up the strain, The same sweet theme en-deav-or;

Th' e-ter-nal arms, their dear a-bode, We make our hab-i-ta-tion.
The Spir-it who in them did sing To us His mu-sic lend-eth:
Un-bro-ken be the gold-en chain! Keep on the song for-ev-er!

We bring Thee, Lord, the praise they brought, We seek Thee as Thy
His song in them, in us, is one; We raise it high, we
Safe in the same dear dwell-ing place, Rich with the same e-

saints have sought In ev-ery gen-e-ra-tion.
send it on— The song that nev-er end-eth.
ter-nal grace, Bless the same bound-less Giv-er. A-men.

Anniversaries

362

Jay Glover Eldridge, 1937   8.7.8.7.D.   HYMN TO JOY
Ludwig van Beethoven, 1824

1. God of years, Thy love hath led us, Thou hast been our bul-wark strong,
2. On-ward lead, O King e-ter-nal! Lo, we heed Thy high com-mand:
3. Lead us forth, a church u-nit-ed, Strong, cou-ra-geous in Thy might;

Wall of fire a-gainst the wick-ed, Sword of power a-gainst the wrong.
Bear good news to ev-ery peo-ple, Far and near, in ev-ery land.
Lo, the fields are white with har-vest, Sheaves to gar-ner ere the night;

Thou hast blest of old Thy serv-ants, As they bore Thy mes-sage far;
Thine they are, Thy love doth seek them, Thou wouldst bring them to the light;
One our pur-pose, one our Lead-er, Thus Thy church shall nev-er fail;

We who fol-low in their foot-steps Ev-er-more their debt-ors are.
Lead us on till dark-ness bright-ens, On, till faith is lost in sight.
Lead us on, O King e-ter-nal, So shall love, world-wide, pre-vail. A-men.

The Kingdom of God on Earth

363

JOHN HOWARD MASTERMAN   L. M.   T. WILLIAMS' *Psalmodia Evangelica*, 1789

TRURO

In moderate time

1. Al - might - y Fa - ther, who dost give The gift of life to
2. Lift up our hearts, O King of kings, To bright - er hopes and
3. Thy world is wea - ry of its pain, Of self - ish greed and
4. Hear Thou the prayer Thy serv - ants pray, Up - ris - ing from all

all who live, Look down on all earth's sin and strife,
kind - lier things; To vi - sions of a larg - er good,
fruit - less gain, Of tar - nished hon - or, false - ly strong,
lands to - day, And o'er the van - quished powers of sin

And lift us to a ho - lier life.
And ho - lier dreams of broth - er - hood.
And all its an - cient deeds of wrong.
O bring Thy great sal - va - tion in. A-MEN.

Words used by permission of Mrs. John Howard Masterman.

364

THOMAS HUGHES, 1823–1896   C. M.   ST. FULBERT
H. J. GAUNTLETT, 1852

In moderate time

1. O God of truth, whose liv - ing word Up - holds what-e'er hath breath,
2. Set up Thy stand - ard, Lord, that we, Who claim a heaven - ly birth,
3. We fight for truth? We fight for God?—Poor slaves of lies and sin!
4. Then, God of truth, for whom we long, Thou who wilt hear our prayer,
5. Still smite, still burn, till naught is left But God's own truth and love;

The Reign of Righteousness

Look down on Thy cre - a - tion, Lord, En-slaved by sin and death.
May march with Thee to smite the lies That vex Thy groan-ing earth.
He who would fight for Thee on earth Must first be true with - in.
Do Thine own bat - tle in our hearts, And slay the false-hood there.
Then, Lord, as morn-ing dew come down, Rest on us from a - bove! A-MEN.

365

FRANK MASON NORTH, 1917   L. M.   WINCHESTER NEW
Musikalisches Handbuch, Hamburg, 1690

In moderate time

1. Thou Lord of light, a - cross the years Thy shin - ing path of
2. We thank Thee for these years of power, For stal - wart souls, for
3. For men who gird the world with flame, Who count for Thee all
4. High cour - age grant, the out - look broad, The strength of joy, the

love we see; Bright glows a - mid our joys and fears
gen - tle life, For men trans - formed to meet the hour
things but loss, Who chal - lenge na - tions in Thy name
zest for right, The faith that burns, the sense of God,

The ar - dor of our faith in Thee.
Of blast - ing wrong, of surg - ing strife;
To hear the sto - ry of Thy cross.
Thy fel - low - ship, Thou Lord of light. A-MEN.

The Kingdom of God on Earth

366

James Montgomery, 1822   7.6.7.6. D.   ROCKPORT
T. Tertius Noble, 1938

UNISON. *Majestically*

1. Hail to the Lord's a - noint - ed, Great Da - vid's great - er Son!
2. Kings shall fall down be - fore Him, And gold and in - cense bring;
3. He shall come down like show - ers Up - on the fruit - ful earth,
4. O'er ev - ery foe vic - to - rious, He on His throne shall rest,

HARMONY

Hail, in the time ap - point - ed, His reign on earth be - gun!
All na - tions shall a - dore Him, His praise all peo - ple sing;
And love, joy, hope, like flow - ers, Spring in His path to birth;
From age to age more glo - rious, All bless - ing and all - blest;

He comes to break op - pres - sion, To set the cap - tive free,
For He shall have do - min - ion O'er riv - er, sea, and shore,
Be - fore Him on the moun - tains Shall peace, the her - ald, go;
The tide of time shall nev - er His cov - en - ant re - move;

UNISON

To take a - way trans-gres - sion, And rule in e - qui - ty.
Far as the ea - gle's pin - ion Or dove's light wing can soar.
And right-eous-ness in foun-tains From hill to val - ley flow.
His name shall stand for-ev - er; That name to us is love. A - MEN.

Music copyright, 1941, by Eden Publishing House.
Alternative tune, *Webb*.

The Reign of Righteousness

367

Henry Hallam Tweedy

8. 6. 8. 6. D.

SARAH
Rhys Thomas

Not too slow

1. E - ter - nal God, whose power up - holds Both flower and flam - ing star,
2. O God of love, whose Spir - it wakes In ev - ery hu - man breast,
3. O God of truth, whom sci - ence seeks, And rev - erent souls a - dore,
4. O God of beau - ty, oft re - vealed In dreams of hu - man art,
5. O God of right - eous - ness and grace, Seen in the Christ, Thy Son,

To whom there is no here nor there, No time, no near nor far,
Whom love, and love a - lone can know, In whom all hearts find rest,
Who light - est ev - ery ear - nest mind Of ev - ery clime and shore,
In speech that flows to mel - o - dy, In ho - li - ness of heart,
Whose life and death re - veal Thy face, By whom Thy will was done,

No al - ien race, no for - eign shore, No child un - sought, un - known,
Help us to spread Thy gra - cious reign Till greed and hate shall cease,
Dis - pel the gloom of er - ror's night, Of ig - no - rance and fear,
Teach us to ban all ug - li - ness That blinds our eyes to Thee,
In - spire Thy her - alds of good news To live Thy life di - vine,

Oh, send us forth, Thy pro - phets true, To make all lands Thine own!
And kind - ness dwell in hu - man hearts, And all the earth find peace!
Un - til true wis - dom from a - bove Shall make life's path - way clear!
Till all shall know the love - li - ness Of lives made fair and free.
Till Christ is formed in all man - kind And ev - ery land is Thine! A-men.

The Kingdom of God on Earth

368

James Montgomery, 1843
St. 4, line 3 alt.

C.M.D.

ELLACOMBE
*Gesangbuch der Herzogl. Wirtembergischen
Katholischen Hofkapelle,* 1784

DESCANT

2. A ho - ly war those serv - ants wage; Mys - te - rious - ly at strife,
4. O fear not, faint not, halt not now; Quit you like men, be strong!

1. Lift up your heads, ye gates of brass, Ye bars of i - ron, yield,
2. A ho - ly war those serv - ants wage; Mys - te - rious - ly at strife,
3. Though few and small and weak your bands, Strong in your Cap-tain's strength
4. O fear not, faint not, halt not now; Quit you like men, be strong!

The powers of heaven and hell en - gage For more than death or life.
To Christ shall all the na - tions bow, And sing with you this song:

And let the King of glo - ry pass; The cross is in the field:
The powers of heaven and hell en - gage For more than death or life.
Go to the con - quest of all lands; All must be His at length;
To Christ shall all the na - tions bow, And sing with you this song:

Ye arm - ies of the liv - ing God, His sac - ra - men - tal host,
"Up - lift - ed are the gates of brass, The bars of i - ron yield;

That ban - ner, bright-er than the star That leads the train of night,
Ye arm - ies of the liv - ing God, His sac - ra - men - tal host,
Those spoils at His vic - to - rious feet You shall re - joice to lay;
"Up - lift - ed are the gates of brass, The bars of i - ron yield;

The Reign of Righteousness

Where hal - lowed foot-steps nev - er trod Take your ap - point - ed post.
Be - hold the King of glo - ry pass; The cross hath won the field." A-MEN.

Shines on their march, and guides from far His serv-ants to the fight.
Where hal - lowed foot-steps nev - er trod Take your ap - point-ed post.
And lay your-selves, as tro-phies meet, In His great judgment-day.
Be - hold the King of glo - ry pass; The cross hath won the field." A-MEN.

369

FREDERICK L. HOSMER, 1891

C.M.

CHESTERFIELD
THOMAS HAWEIS, 1792

Joyously

1. "Thy King-dom come," on bend - ed knee The pass - ing a - ges pray;
2. But the slow watch - es of the night Not less to God be - long;
3. And lo! al - read - y on the hills The flags of dawn ap-pear;
4. The day in whose clear - shin - ing light All wrong shall stand re-vealed;
5. When knowledge, hand in hand with peace, Shall walk the earth a - broad;

And faith-ful souls have yearned to see On earth that King-dom's day.
And for the ev - er - last - ing right The si - lent stars are strong.
Gird up your loins, ye proph - et souls, Pro-claim the day is near:
When jus - tice shall be clothed with might, And ev - ery hurt be healed;
The day of per - fect right - eous-ness, The prom-ised day of God. A-MEN.

The Kingdom of God on Earth

370

LLANGLOFFAN
Welsh Hymn Melody

GILBERT K. CHESTERTON, 1906   7.6.7.6.D.   D. EVANS' *Hymnau a Thonau*, 1865

With breadth and earnestness

1. O God of earth and al - tar, Bow down and hear our cry,
2. From all that ter - ror teach - es, From lies of tongue and pen,
3. Tie in a liv - ing teth - er The priest and prince and thrall,

Our earth - ly rul - ers fal - ter, Our peo - ple drift and die;
From all the eas - y speech - es That com - fort cru - el men,
Bind all our lives to - geth - er, Smite us and save us all;

The walls of gold en - tomb us, The swords of scorn di - vide,
From sale and prof - a - na - tion Of hon - or and the sword;
In ire and ex - ul - ta - tion A - flame with faith, and free,

Take not Thy thun - der from us, But take a - way our pride.
From sleep and from dam - na - tion, De - liv - er us, good Lord!
Lift up a liv - ing na - tion, A sin - gle sword to Thee. A-MEN.

Missions

371

Psalm lxxii
ISAAC WATTS, 1719

L. M.

DUKE STREET
JOHN HATTON, d. 1793

With exultation

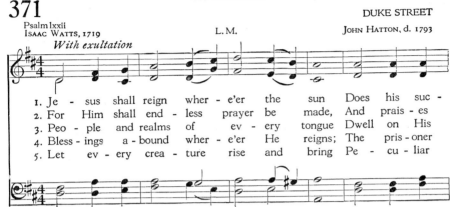

1. Je - sus shall reign wher - e'er the sun Does his suc -
2. For Him shall end - less prayer be made, And prais - es
3. Peo - ple and realms of ev - ery tongue Dwell on His
4. Bless - ings a - bound wher - e'er He reigns; The pris - oner
5. Let ev - ery crea - ture rise and bring Pe - cu - liar

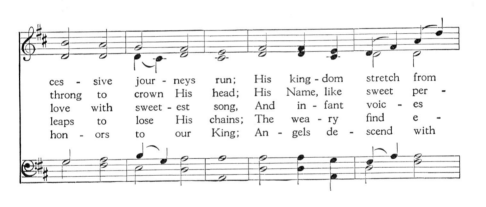

ces - sive jour - neys run; His king - dom stretch from
throng to crown His head; His Name, like sweet per -
love with sweet - est song, And in - fant voic - es
leaps to lose His chains; The wea - ry find e -
hon - ors to our King; An - gels de - scend with

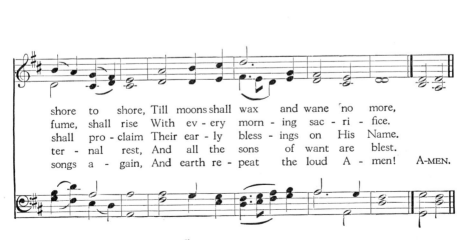

shore to shore, Till moons shall wax and wane 'no more,
fume, shall rise With ev - ery morn - ing sac - ri - fice.
shall pro - claim Their ear - ly bless - ings on His Name.
ter - nal rest, And all the sons of want are blest.
songs a - gain, And earth re - peat the loud A - men! A-MEN.

The Kingdom of God on Earth

372

SAMUEL WOLCOTT, 1869   6. 6. 4. 6. 6. 4.   CUTTING
WILLIAM F. SHERWIN, 1826–1888

First Tune

In moderate time. With spirit.

1. Christ for the world we sing; The world to Christ we bring
2. Christ for the world we sing; The world to Christ we bring
3. Christ for the world we sing; The world to Christ we bring
4. Christ for the world we sing; The world to Christ we bring

With lov - ing zeal; The poor and them that mourn, The faint and
With fer - vent prayer; The way - ward and the lost, By rest - less
With one ac - cord; With us the work to share, With us re -
With joy - ful song; The new - born souls whose days, Re - claimed from

o - ver-borne, Sin - sick and sor - row-worn, Whom Christ doth heal.
pas - sions tossed, Re - deemed at count - less cost From dark de - spair.
proach to dare, With us the cross to bear, For Christ our Lord.
er - ror's ways, In - spired with hope and praise, To Christ be - long. A-MEN.

373

SERUG
Composer unknown
SAMUEL SEBASTIAN WESLEY'S
European Psalmist, 1872

SAMUEL WOLCOTT, 1869   6. 6. 4. 6. 6. 4.   *Second Tune*

In moderate time

1. Christ for the world we sing; The world to Christ we bring
2. Christ for the world we sing; The world to Christ we bring
3. Christ for the world we sing; The world to Christ we bring
4. Christ for the world we sing; The world to Christ we bring

Missions

With lov - ing zeal; The poor and them that mourn, The faint and
With fer - vent prayer; The way - ward and the lost, By rest - less
With one ac - cord; With us the work to share, With us re -
With joy - ful song; The new - born souls whose days, Re - claimed from

o - ver-borne, Sin - sick and sor - row-worn, Whom Christ doth heal.
pas - sions tossed, Redeemed at count-less cost From dark de - spair.
proach to dare, With us the cross to bear, For Christ our Lord.
er - ror's ways, In-spired with hope and praise, To Christ be - long. A - MEN.

374

MARGARET E. SANGSTER, 1838–1912   L. M.   MISSIONARY CHANT
HEINRICH CHRISTOPHER ZEUNER, 1832

Rather slowly

1. O Christ, for - get not them who stand Thy van-guard in the dis - tant land.
2. Thine is the work they strive to do, Their foes so man - y, they so few.

In flood, in flame, in dark, in dread, Sus - tain, we pray, each lift - ed head.
Be with Thine own, Thy loved, who stand, Christ's vanguard, in the storm-swept land. AMEN.

Words used by permission of Miss Margaret E. Sangster.

375 The Kingdom of God on Earth

WILLIAM CULLEN BRYANT, 1859   L. M.   LOUVAN
VIRGIL C. TAYLOR, 1847

In moderate time

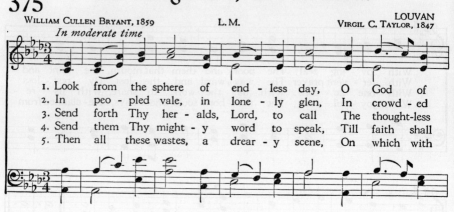

1. Look from the sphere of end - less day, O God of
2. In peo - pled vale, in lone - ly glen, In crowd - ed
3. Send forth Thy her - alds, Lord, to call The thought-less
4. Send them Thy might - y word to speak, Till faith shall
5. Then all these wastes, a drear - y scene, On which with

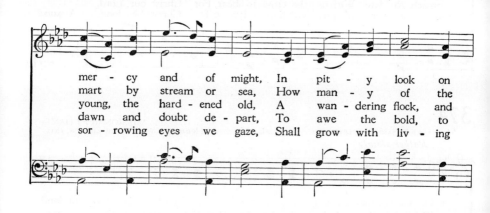

mer - cy and of might, In pit - y look on
mart by stream or sea, How man - y of the
young, the hard - ened old, A wan - dering flock, and
dawn and doubt de - part, To awe the bold, to
sor - rowing eyes we gaze, Shall grow with liv - ing

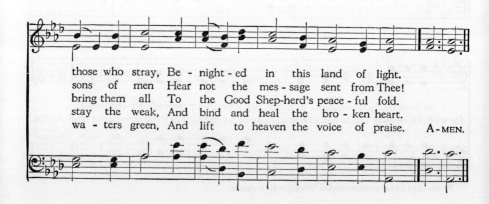

those who stray, Be - night - ed in this land of light.
sons of men Hear not the mes - sage sent from Thee!
bring them all To the Good Shep-herd's peace - ful fold.
stay the weak, And bind and heal the bro - ken heart.
wa - ters green, And lift to heaven the voice of praise. A - MEN.

Missions

376

ROBERT MURRAY, 1880

7. 6. 7. 6. D.

LANCASHIRE
HENRY SMART, 1836

Broadly, with exultation

1. From o-cean un-to o-cean Our land shall own Thee Lord,
2. O Christ, for Thine own glo-ry, And for our coun-try's weal,
3. Our Sav-iour King, de-fend us, And guide where we should go;

And, filled with true de-vo-tion, O-bey Thy sov-ereign word.
We hum-bly plead be-fore Thee, Thy-self in us re-veal;
Forth with Thy mes-sage send us, Thy love and light to show;

Our prai-ries and our moun-tains, For-est and fer-tile field,
And may we know, Lord Je-sus, The touch of Thy dear hand;
Till, fired with true de-vo-tion, En-kin-dled by Thy word,

Our riv-ers, lakes, and foun-tains, To Thee shall trib-ute yield.
And, healed of our dis-eas-es, The Temp-ter's power with-stand.
From o-cean un-to o-cean Our land shall own Thee Lord. A-MEN.

The Kingdom of God on Earth

377

JOHN WRIGHT BUCKHAM, 1916

L. M.

DUKE STREET
JOHN HATTON, -1793

With dignity

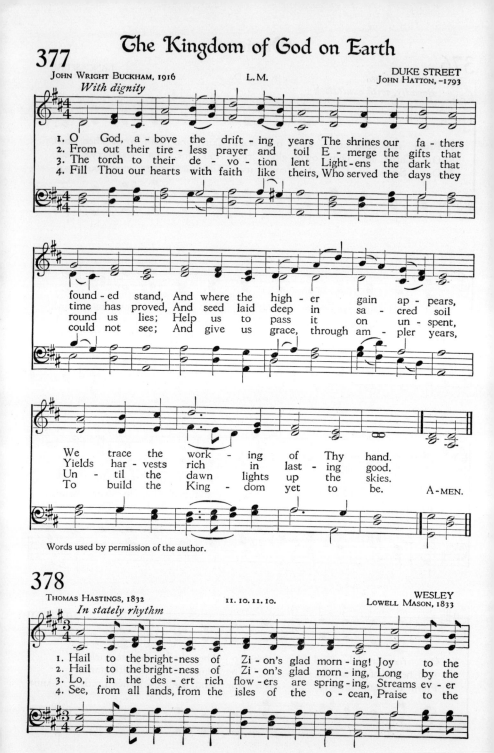

1. O God, a-bove the drift-ing years The shrines our fa-thers
2. From out their tire-less prayer and toil E-merge the gifts that
3. The torch to their de-vo-tion lent Light-ens the dark that
4. Fill Thou our hearts with faith like theirs, Who served the days they

found-ed stand, And where the high-er gain ap-pears,
time has proved, And seed laid deep in sa-cred soil
round us lies; Help us to pass it on un-spent,
could not see; And give us grace, through am-pler years,

We trace the work-ing of Thy hand.
Yields har-vests rich in last-ing good.
Un-til the dawn lights up the skies.
To build the King-dom yet to be. A-MEN.

Words used by permission of the author.

378

THOMAS HASTINGS, 1832

11. 10. 11. 10.

WESLEY
LOWELL MASON, 1833

In stately rhythm

1. Hail to the bright-ness of Zi-on's glad morn-ing! Joy to the
2. Hail to the bright-ness of Zi-on's glad morn-ing, Long by the
3. Lo, in the des-ert rich flow-ers are spring-ing, Streams ev-er
4. See, from all lands, from the isles of the o-cean, Praise to the

Missions

lands that in dark-ness have lain! Hushed be the ac-cents of
proph-ets of Is-rael fore-told! Hail to the mil-lions from
co-pious are glid-ing a-long; Loud from the moun-tain tops
Sav-iour as-cend-ing on high; Fall-en the en-gines of

sor-row and mourning; Zi-on in tri-umph be-gins her mild reign.
bond-age re-turn-ing! Gen-tiles and Jews the blest vi-sion be-hold.
ech-oes are ring-ing, Wastes rise in ver-dure, and min-gle in song.
war and com-mo-tion, Shouts of sal-va-tion are rend-ing the sky. A-MEN.

379

MARY C. GATES, 1890   8. 8. 8. 6.   ELMHURST
EDWIN DREWETT, 1887

In moderate time

1. Send Thou, O Lord, to ev-ery place Swift mes-sen-gers be-fore Thy face,
2. Send men whose eyes have seen the King, Men in whose ears His sweet words ring;
3. To bring good news to souls in sin; The bruised and bro-ken hearts to win;
4. Gird each one with the Spir-it's sword, The sword of Thine own death-less Word;

The her-alds of Thy won-drous grace, Where Thou Thy-self wilt come.
Send such Thy lost ones home to bring; Send them where Thou wilt come:
In ev-ery place to bring them in Where Thou Thy-self wilt come.
And make them conquerors, conquering, Lord, Where Thou Thy-self wilt come. A-MEN.

380 The Kingdom of God on Earth

MARY ANN THOMSON, 1870   11. 10. 11. 10. 9. 11.   TIDINGS (ANGELIC SONGS)
JAMES WALCH, 1875

Brightly, but with dignity

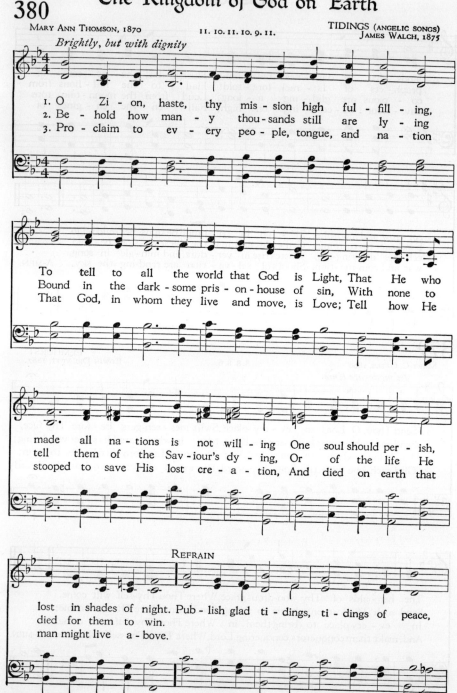

1. O Zi - on, haste, thy mis - sion high ful - fill - ing,
2. Be - hold how man - y thou - sands still are ly - ing
3. Pro - claim to ev - ery peo - ple, tongue, and na - tion

To tell to all the world that God is Light, That He who
Bound in the dark - some pris - on - house of sin, With none to
That God, in whom they live and move, is Love; Tell how He

made all na - tions is not will - ing One soul should per - ish,
tell them of the Sav - iour's dy - ing, Or of the life He
stooped to save His lost cre - a - tion, And died on earth that

REFRAIN

lost in shades of night. Pub - lish glad ti - dings, ti - dings of peace,
died for them to win.
man might live a - bove.

Missions

Ti - dings of Je - sus, re - demp - tion and re - lease. A-MEN.

381

GEORGE W. DOANE, 1848   L. M.   WALTHAM
J. BAPTISTE CALKIN, 1872

Moderately fast, with dignity

1. Fling out the ban - ner! let it float Sky - ward and sea - ward,
2. Fling out the ban - ner! an - gels bend In anx - ious si - lence
3. Fling out the ban - ner! dis - tant lands Shall see from far the
4. Fling out the ban - ner! let it float Sky - ward and sea - ward,
5. Fling out the ban - ner! wide and high, Sea - ward and sky - ward,

high and wide; The sun that lights its shin - ing folds,
o'er the sign, And vain - ly seek to com - pre - hend
glo - rious sight, And na - tions, crowd - ing to be born,
high and wide, Our glo - ry, on - ly in the cross;
let it shine: Nor skill, nor might, nor mer - it ours;

The Cross on which the Sav - iour died.
The won - der which of the Love di - vine.
Bap - tize their spir - its in its light.
Our on - ly hope, the Cru - ci - fied!
We con - quer on - ly in that sign. A-MEN.

The Kingdom of God on Earth

382

FRANK MASON NORTH, 1850–1935   8.8.8.8.8.8.   MELITA
JOHN B. DYKES, 1861

In moderate time

1. O Mas - ter of the wak - ing world, Who hast the na - tions
2. On ev - ery side the walls are down, The gates swing wide to
3. We hear the throb of surg - ing life, The clank of chains, the
4. Thy wit - ness in the souls of men, Thy Spir - it's cease - less,

in Thy heart— The heart that bled and broke to send
ev - ery land, The rest - less tribes and rac - es feel
curse of greed, The moan of pain, the fu - tile cries
brood - ing, power, In lands where shad - ows hide the light,

God's love to earth's re - mot - est part: Show us a - new in
The pres - sure of Thy pierc - ed hand; Thy way is in the
Of su - per - sti - tion's cru - el creed; The peo - ples hun - ger
A - wait a new cre - a - tive hour: O might - y God, set

Cal - va - ry The won - drous power that makes men free.
sea and air, Thy world is o - pen ev - ery - where.
for Thee, Lord, The isles are wait - ing for Thy Word.
us a - flame To show the glo - ry of Thy Name. A-MEN.

Missions

383

Daniel March, 1868 8.7.8.7. D. WHITE FIELDS
David Bruning, 1915

Moderately fast

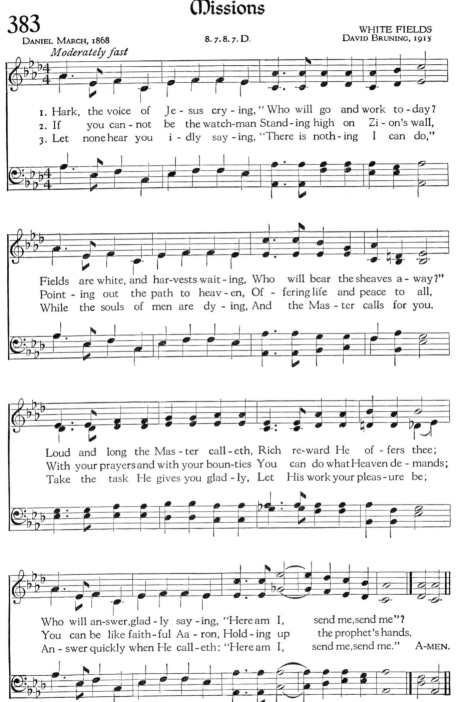

1. Hark, the voice of Je-sus cry-ing, "Who will go and work to-day?
2. If you can-not be the watch-man Stand-ing high on Zi-on's wall,
3. Let none hear you i-dly say-ing, "There is noth-ing I can do,"

Fields are white, and har-vests wait-ing, Who will bear the sheaves a-way?"
Point-ing out the path to heav-en, Of-fering life and peace to all,
While the souls of men are dy-ing, And the Mas-ter calls for you.

Loud and long the Mas-ter call-eth, Rich re-ward He of-fers thee;
With your prayers and with your boun-ties You can do what Heaven de-mands;
Take the task He gives you glad-ly, Let His work your pleas-ure be;

Who will an-swer, glad-ly say-ing, "Here am I, send me, send me"?
You can be like faith-ful Aa-ron, Hold-ing up the prophet's hands.
An-swer quickly when He call-eth: "Here am I, send me, send me." A-men.

384
The Kingdom of God on Earth

SAMUEL FRANCIS SMITH, 1832   7.6.7.6.D.   WEBB
GEORGE J. WEBB, 1837

Jubilantly

1. The morn - ing light is break - ing; The dark - ness dis - ap - pears;
2. See men and na - tions bend - ing Be - fore the God we love,
3. Blest riv - er of sal - va - tion, Pur - sue thine on - ward way;

The sons of earth are wak - ing To pen - i - ten - tial tears;
And thou - sand hearts as - cend - ing In gra - ti - tude a - bove;
Flow thou to ev - ery na - tion, Nor in thy rich - ness stay:

Each breeze that sweeps the o - cean Brings ti - dings from a - far
While sin - ners, now con - fess - ing, The gos - pel call o - bey,
Stay not till all the low - ly Tri - umph - ant reach their home;

Of na - tions in com - mo - tion, Pre - pared for Zi - on's war.
And seek the Sav - iour's bless - ing, A na - tion in a day.
Stay not till all the ho - ly Pro - claim, "The Lord is come." A-MEN.

Missions

385

Laura S. Copenhaver, 1894

10. 10. 10. 10.

NATIONAL HYMN
George William Warren, 1892

In march rhythm

Trumpets, before each stanza

1. Her - alds of Christ, who bear the King's com-mands,
2. Through des - ert ways, dark fen, and deep mo-rass,
3. Where once the crook - ed trail in dark-ness wound
4. Lord, give us faith and strength the road to build,

Im - mor - tal ti - dings in your mor - tal hands,
Through jun - gles, slug - gish seas, and moun - tain pass,
Let march - ing feet and joy - ous song re - sound,
To see the prom - ise of the day ful - filled,

Pass on and car - ry swift the news ye bring:
Build ye the road, and fal - ter not, nor stay;
Where burn the fu - neral pyres, and cen - sers swing,
When war shall be no more and strife shall cease

Make straight, make straight the high - way of the King.
Pre - pare a - cross the earth the King's high - way.
Make straight, make straight the high - way of the King.
Up - on the high - way of the Prince of Peace. A-men.

Words used by permission of Mrs. Horatio W. Parker.

The Kingdom of God on Earth

386

From Psalm cxvii
ISAAC WATTS, 1719

8. 8. 4. 4. 8. 8. with Alleluias

LASST UNS ERFREUEN
Geistliche Kirchengesäng,
COLOGNE, 1623

In unison. Jubilantly

1. From all that dwell be-low the skies Let the Cre - a-tor's praise a - rise:
2. In ev-ery land be-gin the song, To ev-ery land the strains be-long:
3. E - ter-nal are Thy mer-cies,Lord! E - ter-nal truth at-tends Thy word:

HARMONY   UNISON

Al - le - lu - ia! Al - le - lu - ia! Let the Re-deem-er's Name be
Al - le - lu - ia! Al - le - lu - ia! In cheer-ful sound all voic - es
Al - le - lu - ia! Al - le - lu - ia! Thy praise shall sound from shore to

HARMONY

sung Through ev - ery land, in ev-ery tongue. Al - le - lu - ia! Al - le -
raise And fill the world with joy-ful praise. Al - le - lu - ia! Al - le -
shore, Till suns shall rise and set no more. Al - le - lu - ia! Al - le -

UNISON   HARMONY

lu - ia! Al - le - lu - ia! Al - le - lu - ia! Al - le - lu - ia!
lu - ia! Al - le - lu - ia! Al - le - lu - ia! Al - le - lu - ia!
lu - ia! Al - le - lu - ia! Al - le - lu - ia! Al - le - lu - ia! A - MEN.

Descant version, No. 15.

Social Service and Brotherhood

387

John Haynes Holmes, 1913

7. 6. 7. 6. D.

MEIRIONYDD
Welsh Hymn Melody

Not too fast. With dignity

1. The voice of God is call-ing Its sum-mons un-to men;
2. I hear my peo-ple cry-ing In cot and mine and slum;
3. We heed O Lord, Thy sum-mons, And an-swer: Here are we!
4. From ease and plen-ty save us; From pride of place ab-solve;

As once He spake in Zi - on, So now He speaks a-gain:
No field or mart is si - lent, No cit-y street is dumb.
Send us up-on Thine er - rand, Let us Thy serv-ants be.
Purge us of low de-sire; Lift us to high re-solve;

Whom shall I send to suc - cor My peo-ple in their need?
I see my peo-ple fall - ing In dark-ness and de-spair.
Our strength is dust and ash - es, Our years a pass-ing hour;
Take us, and make us ho - ly; Teach us Thy will and way.

Whom shall I send to loos - en The bonds of shame and greed?
Whom shall I send to shat - ter The fet-ters which they bear?
But Thou canst use our weak-ness To mag-ni-fy Thy power.
Speak, and, be-hold! we an - swer; Command, and we o - bey! A-men.

The Kingdom of God on Earth

388

EMILY V. CLARK, 1891   L.M.   QUEBEC (HESPERUS)
HENRY BAKER, 1866

In moderate time

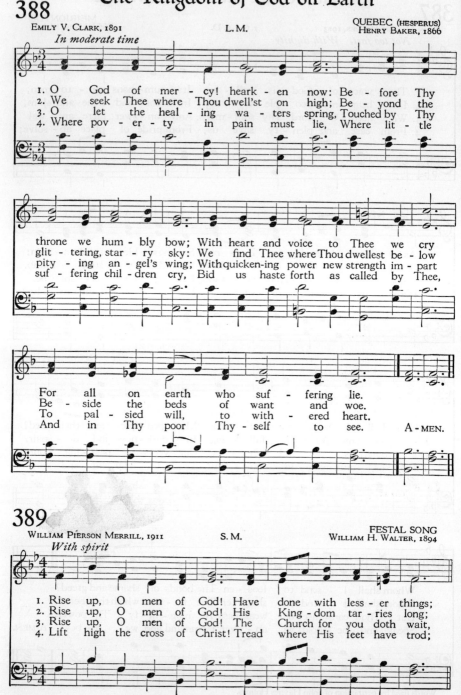

1. O God of mer - cy! heark - en now: Be - fore Thy
2. We seek Thee where Thou dwell'st on high; Be - yond the
3. O let the heal - ing wa - ters spring, Touched by Thy
4. Where pov - er - ty in pain must lie, Where lit - tle

throne we hum - bly bow; With heart and voice to Thee we cry
glit - tering, star - ry sky: We find Thee where Thou dwellest be - low
pity - ing an - gel's wing; With quicken-ing power new strength im - part
suf - fering chil - dren cry, Bid us haste forth as called by Thee,

For all on earth who suf - fering lie.
Be - side the beds of want and woe.
To pal - sied will, to with - ered heart.
And in Thy poor Thy - self to see. A - MEN.

389

WILLIAM PIERSON MERRILL, 1911   S.M.   FESTAL SONG
WILLIAM H. WALTER, 1894

With spirit

1. Rise up, O men of God! Have done with less - er things;
2. Rise up, O men of God! His King - dom tar - ries long;
3. Rise up, O men of God! The Church for you doth wait,
4. Lift high the cross of Christ! Tread where His feet have trod;

Social Service and Brotherhood

Give heart and soul and mind and strength To serve the King of kings.
Bring in the day of broth-er-hood And end the night of wrong.
Her strength un-e-qual to her task; Rise up, and make her great!
As broth-ers of the Son of Man, Rise up, O men of God! A-MEN.

Words used by permission of The Presbyterian Tribune.

390

WILLIAM G. TARRANT, 1892   C. M.   CHRISTMAS
GEORGE FREDERICK HANDEL, 1728

With joyous rhythm

1. Come, let us join with faith-ful souls Our song of faith to
2. Faith-ful are all who love the truth And dare the truth to
3. And faith-ful are the gen-tle hearts To whom the power is
4. O Lord of hosts, our faith re-new, And grant us, in Thy

sing, One broth-er-hood in heart are we,
tell, Who stead-fast stand at God's right hand
given, Of ev-ery hearth to make a home,
love, To sing the songs of vic-to-ry

And one our Lord and King, And one our Lord and King.
And strive to serve Him well, And strive to serve Him well.
Of ev-ery home a heaven, Of ev-ery home a heaven.
With faith-ful souls a-bove, With faith-ful souls a-bove. A-MEN.

Words used by permission of Miss Dorothy Tarrant.

The Kingdom of God on Earth

NYLAND
Finnish Hymn Melody
Har. David Evans

S. Ralph Harlow

7. 6. 7. 6. D.

Not too slowly, with flowing rhythm

1. O young and fear-less Proph-et Of an-cient Gal-i-lee:
2. We mar-vel at the pur-pose That held Thee to Thy course
3. Cre-ate in us the splen-dor That dawns when hearts are kind,
4. O young and fear-less Proph-et, We need Thy pres-ence here,

Thy life is still a sum-mons To serve hu-man-i-ty,
While ev-er on the hill-top Be-fore Thee loomed the cross;
That knows not race nor sta-tion As boun-daries of the mind;
A-mid our pride and glo-ry To see Thy face ap-pear;

To make our thoughts and ac-tions Less prone to please the crowd,
Thy stead-fast face set for-ward Where love and du-ty shone,
That learns to val-ue beau-ty, In heart, or brain, or soul,
Once more to hear Thy chal-lenge A-bove our noi-sy day,

To stand with hum-ble cour-age For truth, with hearts un-cowed.
While we be-tray so quick-ly And leave Thee there a-lone.
And longs to bind God's chil-dren In-to one per-fect whole.
A-gain to lead us for-ward A-long God's ho-ly way. A-MEN.

392

Henry van Dyke, 1909   8.7.8.7. D.   George F. Le Jeune, 1872

LOVE DIVINE

In moderate time

1. Je - sus, Thou di - vine Com-pan - ion, By Thy low - ly hu - man birth
2. They who tread the path of la - bor Fol - low where Thy feet have trod;
3. Ev - ery task, how - ev - er sim - ple, Sets the soul that does it free;

Thou hast come to join all work - ers, Bur - den-bear - ers of the earth.
They who work with-out com-plain-ing Do the ho - ly will of God.
Ev - ery deed of love and kind-ness Done to man is done to Thee.

Thou, the Car - pen - ter of Naz-areth, Toil - ing for Thy dai - ly food,
Thou, the Peace that pass - eth knowl-edge, Dwell-est in the dai - ly strife;
Je - sus, Thou di - vine Com-pan - ion, Help us all to work our best;

By Thy pa-tience and Thy cour -age, Thou hast taught us toil is good.
Thou, the Bread of heaven, art bro-ken In the sac - ra-ment of life.
Bless us in our dai - ly la - bor, Lead us to our Sab-bath rest. A-men.

The Kingdom of God on Earth

JOHN GREENLEAF WHITTIER, 1807–1892   11.10.11.10.   WELWYN
ALFRED SCOTT–GATTY, 1902

May be sung in unison. Not too slowly

1. O broth-er man, fold to thy heart thy broth-er;
2. For he whom Je-sus loved has tru-ly spo-ken:
3. Fol-low with rev-erent steps the great ex-am-ple
4. Then shall all shack-les fall; the storm-y clan-gor

Where pit-y dwells, the peace of God is there; ..
The ho-lier wor-ship which He deigns to bless ..
Of Him whose ho-ly work was do-ing good; ..
Of wild war mu-sic o'er the earth shall cease; ..

To wor-ship right-ly is to love each oth-er,
Re-stores the lost, and binds the spir-it bro-ken,
So shall the wide earth seem our Fa-ther's tem-ple,
Love shall tread out the bale-ful fire of an-ger,

Each smile a hymn, each kind-ly deed a prayer.
And feeds the wid-ow and the fa-ther-less.
Each lov-ing life a psalm of grat-i-tude.
And in its ash-es plant the tree of peace. A-MEN.

Social Service and Brotherhood

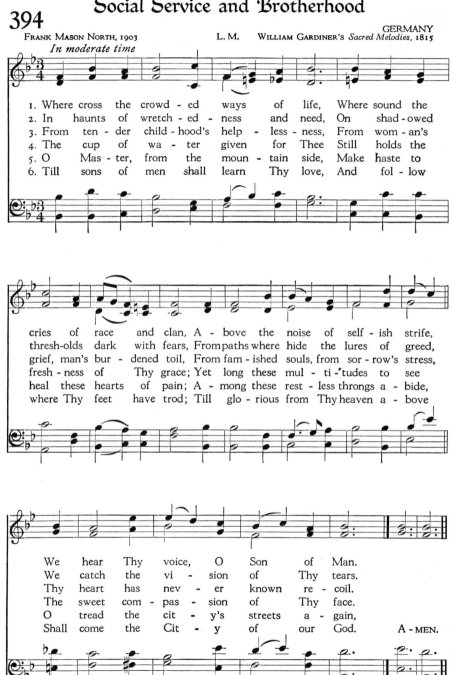

394

FRANK MASON NORTH, 1903   L. M.   GERMANY
WILLIAM GARDINER'S *Sacred Melodies*, 1815

In moderate time

1. Where cross the crowd - ed ways of life, Where sound the
2. In haunts of wretch - ed - ness and need, On shad - owed
3. From ten - der child - hood's help - less - ness, From wom - an's
4. The cup of wa - ter given for Thee Still holds the
5. O Mas - ter, from the moun - tain side, Make haste to
6. Till sons of men shall learn Thy love, And fol - low

cries of race and clan, A - bove the noise of self - ish strife,
thresh-olds dark with fears, From paths where hide the lures of greed,
grief, man's bur - dened toil, From fam - ished souls, from sor - row's stress,
fresh - ness of Thy grace; Yet long these mul - ti - 'tudes to see
heal these hearts of pain; A - mong these rest - less throngs a - bide,
where Thy feet have trod; Till glo - rious from Thy heaven a - bove

We hear Thy voice, O Son of Man.
We catch the vi - sion of Thy tears.
Thy heart has nev - er known re - coil.
The sweet com - pas - sion of Thy face.
O tread the cit - y's streets a - gain,
Shall come the Cit - y of our God.   A - MEN.

Words used by permission of Eric M. North.

The Kingdom of God on Earth

395

Charles Kingsley, 1872   C. M.   BELMONT   William Gardiner, 1812

In flowing rhythm

1. From Thee all skill and sci - ence flow, All pit - y, care and love,
2. And part them, Lord, to each and all, As each and all shall need,
3. And has - ten, Lord, that per - fect day When pain and death shall cease,
4. When ev - er blue the sky shall gleam, And ev - er green the sod,

All calm and cour - age, faith and hope: O pour them from a - bove!
To rise like in - cense, each to Thee, In no - ble thought and deed.
And Thy just rule shall fill the earth With health, and light, and peace;
And man's rude work de - face no more The par - a - dise of God. A-MEN.

396

Edwin P. Parker, 1888   6. 4. 6. 4. 6. 6. 4. 4.   LOVE'S OFFERING   Edwin P. Parker, 1888

In moderate time

1. Mas - ter, no of - fer - ing, Cost - ly and sweet, May we, like
2. Dai - ly our lives would show Weak - ness made strong, Toil - some and
3. Some word of hope for hearts Bur - dened with fears, Some balm of
4. Thus in Thy serv - ice, Lord, Till e - ven - tide Clos - es the

Mag - da - lene, Lay at Thy feet; Yet may love's in - cense rise,
gloom - y ways Bright - ened with song; Some deeds of kind - ness done,
peace for eyes Blind - ed with tears, Some dews of mer - cy shed,
day of life, May we a - bide! And when earth's la - bors cease,

Social Service and Brotherhood

Sweet-er than sac-ri-fice, Dear Lord, to Thee, Dear Lord, to Thee.
Some souls by pa-tience won, Dear Lord, to Thee, Dear Lord, to Thee.
Some way-ward footsteps led, Dear Lord, to Thee, Dear Lord, to Thee.
Bid us de-part in peace, Dear Lord, to Thee, Dear Lord, to Thee. A-MEN.

397

W. RUSSELL BOWIE, 1909   8.6.8.6.8.6.   MORWELLHAM
                           CHARLES STEGGALL, 1826-1905

With exultation

1. O Ho-ly Cit-y seen of John, Where Christ, the Lamb, doth reign,
2. O shame to us who rest con-tent While lust and greed for gain
3. Give us, O God, the strength to build The Cit-y that hath stood
4. Al-read-y in the mind of God That Cit-y ris-eth fair;

With-in whose four-square walls shall come No night, nor need, nor pain,
In street and shop and ten-e-ment Wring gold from hu-man pain,
Too long a dream, whose laws are love, Whose ways are broth-er-hood,
Lo, how its splen-dor chal-len-ges The souls that great-ly dare,

And where the tears are wiped from eyes That shall not weep a-gain!
And bit-ter lips in blind de-spair Cry, "Christ hath died in vain!"
And where the sun that shin-eth is God's grace for hu-man good.
Yea, bids us seize the whole of life And build its glo-ry there. A-MEN.

The Kingdom of God on Earth

398

HENRY SCOTT HOLLAND, 1902   8.7.8.7.8.7.   RHUDDLAN
Welsh Traditional Melody

Majestically but not too slowly
May be sung in unison

1. Judge e-ter-nal, throned in splen-dor, Lord of lords and
King of kings, With Thy liv-ing fire of judg-ment
Purge this realm of bit-ter things: Sol-ace all its
wide do-min-ion With the heal-ing of Thy wings.

2. Still the wea-ry folk are pin-ing For the hour that
brings re-lease; And the cit-y's crowd-ed clan-gor
Cries a-loud for sin to cease; And the home-steads
and the wood-lands Plead in si-lence for their peace.

3. Crown, O God, Thine own en-deav-or; Cleave our dark-ness
with Thy sword; Feed the faint and hun-gry peo-ples
With the rich-ness of Thy Word; Cleanse the bod-y
of this na-tion Through the glo-ry of the Lord. A-MEN.

Alternative tune, *Alleluia Dulce Carmen.*

Social Service and Brotherhood

399

James Russell Lowell, 1845
Stanza 2, line 3, alt.

8. 7. 8. 7. D.

TON-Y-BOTEL

Welsh Hymn Melody

In unison, with great breadth

1. Once to ev-ery man and na-tion Comes the mo-ment to de-cide,
2. By the light of burn-ing mar-tyrs, Je-sus' bleed-ing feet I track,
3. Though the cause of e-vil pros-per, Yet 'tis truth a-lone is strong,

In the strife of truth with false-hood, For the good or e-vil side;
Toil-ing up new Cal-varies ev-er With the cross that turns not back;
Truth for-ev-er on the scaf-fold, Wrong for-ev-er on the throne.

Some great cause, God's new Mes-si-ah, Of-fering each the bloom or blight,
New oc-ca-sions teach new du-ties, Time makes an-cient good un-couth;
Yet that scaf-fold sways the fu-ture, And, be-hind the dim un-known,

And the choice goes by for-ev-er 'Twixt that dark-ness and that light.
They must up-ward still and on-ward, Who would keep a-breast of truth.
Stand-eth God with-in the shad-ow Keep-ing watch a-bove His own. A-men.

Music used by permission of W. Gwenlyn Evans and Sons.

The Kingdom of God on Earth

400

Ozora S. Davis, 1909

C. M. D.

ALL SAINTS NEW
Henry S. Cutler, 1872

With spirit

1. At length there dawns the glo - rious day By proph-ets long fore - told,
2. For what are sun-dering strains of blood, Or an - cient caste and creed?
3. One com - mon faith u - nites us all, We seek one com-mon goal;

At length the cho - rus clear - er grows That shep-herds heard of old.
One claim u - nites all men in God To serve each hu - man need.
One ten - der com - fort broods up - on The strug-gling hu - man soul.

The day of dawn-ing broth - er-hood Breaks on our ea - ger eyes,
Then here to-geth - er, broth - er men, We pledge the Lord a - new
To this clear call of broth - er-hood Our hearts re - spon-sive ring;

And hu - man ha - treds flee be - fore The ra - diant east - ern skies.
Our loy - al love, our stal - wart faith, Our serv - ice strong and true.
We join the glo - rious new cru - sade Of our great Lord and King. A - MEN.

World Friendship and Peace

401
LAURENCE HOUSMAN, 1921 11.10.11.10.10. LANGHAM
GEOFFREY SHAW, 1921

UNISON. *Moderately slow*

1. Fa - ther e - ter - nal, Rul - er of cre - a - tion, Spir - it of
2. Rac - es and peo - ples, lo! we stand di - vi - ded, And shar - ing
3. En - vious of heart, blind - eyed, with tongues con - found - ed, Na - tion by
4. How shall we love Thee, ho - ly, hid - den Be - ing, If we love

life, which moved ere form was made; Through the thick dark - ness,
not our griefs, no joys can share; By wars and tu - mults
na - tion still goes un - for - given; In wrath and fear, by
not the world which Thou hast made? O give us broth - er -

cov - ering ev - ery na - tion, Light to man's blind - ness, O be Thou our
Love is mocked, di - vi - ded, His con - quering cross no king - dom wills to
jeal - ous - ies sur - round - ed, Build - ing proud towers which shall not reach to
love for bet - ter see - ing Thy Word made flesh, and in a man - ger

aid: Thy king - dom come, O Lord, Thy will be done.
bear: Thy king - dom come, O Lord, Thy will be done.
heaven: Thy king - dom come, O Lord, Thy will be done.
laid: Thy king - dom come, O Lord, Thy will be done. A - MEN.

The Kingdom of God on Earth

WILLIAM M. VORIES, 1908   L.M.   PENTECOST
WILLIAM BOYD, 1868

With spirit

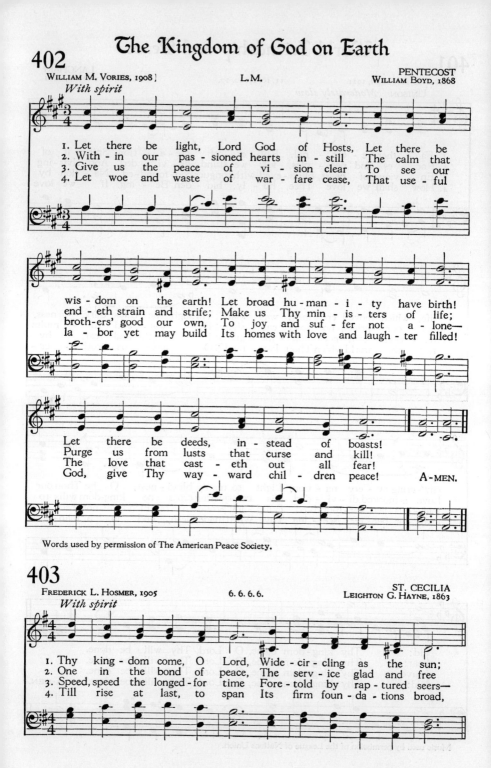

1. Let there be light, Lord God of Hosts, Let there be
2. With - in our pas - sioned hearts in - still The calm that
3. Give us the peace of vi - sion clear To see our
4. Let woe and waste of war - fare cease, That use - ful

wis - dom on the earth! Let broad hu - man - i - ty have birth!
end - eth strain and strife; Make us Thy min - is - ters of life;
broth-ers' good our own, To joy and suf - fer not a - lone—
la - bor yet may build Its homes with love and laugh - ter filled!

Let there be deeds, in - stead of boasts!
Purge us from lusts that curse and kill!
The love that cast - eth out all fear!
God, give Thy way - ward chil - dren peace!   A - MEN.

Words used by permission of The American Peace Society.

FREDERICK L. HOSMER, 1905   6. 6. 6. 6.   ST. CECILIA
LEIGHTON G. HAYNE, 1863

With spirit

1. Thy king - dom come, O Lord, Wide - cir - cling as the sun;
2. One in the bond of peace, The serv - ice glad and free
3. Speed, speed the longed - for time Fore - told by rap - tured seers—
4. Till rise at last, to span Its firm foun - da - tions broad,

World Friendship and Peace

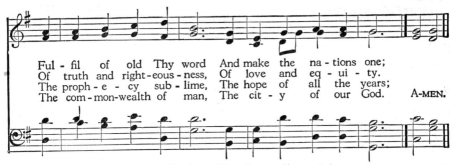

Ful - fil of old Thy word And make the na - tions one;
Of truth and right-eous-ness, Of love and eq - ui - ty.
The proph - e - cy sub - lime, The hope of all the years;
The com-mon-wealth of man, The cit - y of our God. A-MEN.

From *Hymns of the Spirit*, copyright The Beacon Press, Inc., used by permission.

404

HENRY W. BAKER, 1861   L. M.   QUEBEC (HESPERUS)
HENRY BAKER, 1862

In moderate time

1. O God of love, O King of peace, Make wars through-
2. Re - mem - ber, Lord, Thy works of old, The won - ders
3. Whom shall we trust but Thee, O Lord? Where rest but
4. Where saints and an - gels dwell a - bove All hearts are

out the world to cease; The wrath of sin - ful man re-strain;
that our fa - thers told; Re - mem - ber not our sin's dark stain;
on Thy faith-ful word? None ev - er called on Thee in vain;
knit in ho - ly love; O bind us in that heaven - ly chain;

Give peace, O God, give peace a - gain. A - MEN.

The Kingdom of God on Earth

405

HENRY F. CHORLEY, 1842
JOHN ELLERTON, 1870; alt.

RUSSIAN HYMN

ALEXIS LWOFF, 1833

11.10.11.9.

Majestically

1. God the Om-nip - o - tent! King, who or-dain-est Thun-der Thy
2. God the All-mer - ci - ful! earth hath for-sak-en Thy ways all-
3. God the All-right-eous One! man hath de-fied Thee; Yet to e-
4. So shall Thy peo - ple, with thank-ful de - vo - tion, Praise Him who

clar - ion, the light-ning Thy sword; Show forth Thy pit - y on
ho - ly, and slight-ed Thy word; Let not Thy wrath in its
ter - ni - ty stand-eth Thy word; False-hood and wrong shall not
saved them from per - il and sword, Sing - ing in cho - rus from

high where Thou reign-est; Give to us peace in our time, O Lord.
ter - rors a - wak - en; Give to us peace in our time, O Lord.
tar - ry be - side Thee; Give to us peace in our time, O Lord.
o - cean to o - cean Peace to the na-tions, and praise to the Lord. A-MEN.

406

JOHN OXENHAM, 1908

ST. PETER
ALEXANDER R. REINAGLE, 1836

C.M.

In moderate time

1. In Christ there is no East or West, In Him no South or North;
2. In Him shall true hearts ev - ery-where Their high com-mun - ion find;
3. Join hands, then, broth - ers of the faith, What-e'er your race may be.
4. In Christ now meet both East and West, In Him meet South and North;

World Friendship and Peace

But one great fel-low-ship of love Through-out the whole wide earth.
His serv-ice is the gold-en cord Close bind-ing all man-kind.
Who serves my Fa-ther as a son Is sure-ly kin to me.
All Christ-ly souls are one in Him Through-out the whole wide earth. A-MEN.

Words from *Bees in Amber*. Used by permission of the American Tract Society.

407

DE PAUW

JOHN ADDINGTON SYMONDS, 1880   L. M.   ROBERT G. McCUTCHAN, 1930

With well-defined rhythm

1. These things shall be: a loft - ier race Than e'er the
2. They shall be gen - tle, brave, and strong, To spill no
3. Na - tion with na - tion, land with land, In - armed shall
4. New arts shall bloom of loft - ier mold, And might - ier

world hath known shall rise With flame of free - dom
drop of blood, but dare All that may plant man's
live as com - rades dare free; In ev - ery heart and
mu - sic thrill the skies, And ev - ery life shall

in their souls And light of know - ledge in their eyes.
lord - ship firm On earth, and fire, and sea, and air.
brain shall throb The pulse of one fra - ter - ni - ty.
be a song, When all the earth is par - a - dise. A-MEN.

Music copyright, 1930, by Robert G. McCutchan. Used by permission.

The Kingdom of God on Earth

408

JOHN GREENLEAF WHITTIER, 1807–1892　　II. II. II. II.

ST. DENIO
Welsh Hymn Melody

With spirit

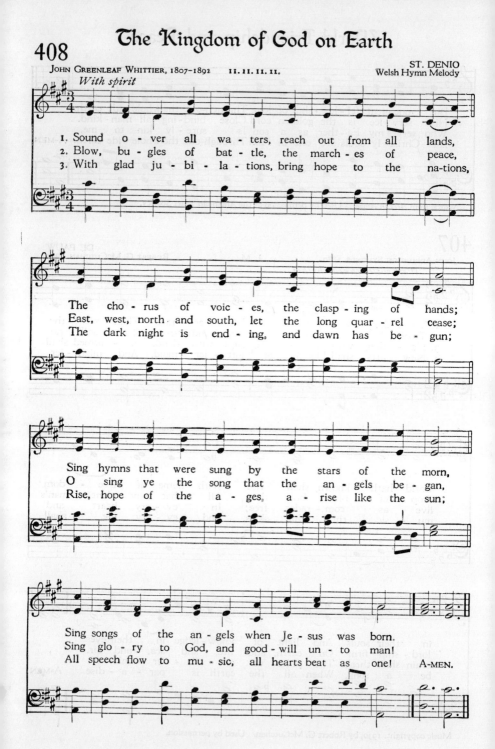

1. Sound o-ver all wa-ters, reach out from all lands,
   The cho-rus of voic-es, the clasp-ing of hands;
   Sing hymns that were sung by the stars of the morn,
   Sing songs of the an-gels when Je-sus was born.

2. Blow, bu-gles of bat-tle, the march-es of peace,
   East, west, north and south, let the long quar-rel cease;
   O sing ye the song that the an-gels be-gan,
   Sing glo-ry to God, and good-will un-to man!

3. With glad ju-bi-la-tions, bring hope to the na-tions,
   The dark night is end-ing, and dawn has be-gun;
   Rise, hope of the a-ges, a-rise like the sun;
   All speech flow to mu-sic, all hearts beat as one! A-MEN.

World Friendship and Peace

409

HARRY EMERSON FOSDICK, 1930   C. M. D.   PETERSHAM
CLEMENT WILLIAM POOLE, 1875

In moderate time

1. The Prince of Peace His ban-ner spreads, His way-ward folk to lead
   From war's em-bat-tled hates and dreads, Its bul-warked ire and greed.
   O mar-shal us, the sons of sires Who braved the can-non's roar,
   To ven-ture all that peace re-quires As they dared death for war.

2. Lead on, O Christ! That haunt-ing song No cen-tu-ries can dim,
   Which long a-go the heaven-ly throng Sang o-ver Beth-le-hem;
   Cast down our ran-cor, fear, and pride, Ex-alt good-will a-gain!
   Our wor-ship doth Thy name de-ride, Bring we not peace to men.

3. Thy par-don, Lord, for war's dark shame, Its death-strewn, blood-y fields!
   Yet thanks to Thee for souls a-flame Who dared with swords and shields!
   O Christ, who died to give men life, Bring that vic-to-rious hour,
   When man shall use for peace, not strife, His val-or, skill, and power. A-MEN.

Words used by permission of the author.
Music by permission of the Misses Horder.

410 The Kingdom of God on Earth

CLIFFORD BAX, 1919   10. 10. 10. 10. 10.   Melody in *Genevan Psalter*, 1552

OLD 124TH

May be sung in unison. With spirit, but broadly

1. Turn back, O man, for-swear thy fool-ish ways. Old now is earth, and none may count her days, Yet thou, her child, whose head is crowned with flame, Still wilt not hear thine in-ner God pro-claim—"Turn back, O man, for-swear thy fool-ish ways."

2. Earth might be fair and all men glad and wise. Age aft-er age their trag-ic em-pires rise, Built while they dream, and in that dream-ing weep: Would man but wake from out his haunt-ed sleep, Earth might be fair and all men glad and wise.

3. Earth shall be fair, and all her peo-ple one: Nor till that hour shall God's whole will be done. Now, ev-en now, once more from earth to sky, Peals forth in joy man's old, un-daunt-ed cry— "Earth shall be fair, and all her folk be one!" A-MEN.

Words used by permission of A. D. Peters.

Christian Unity

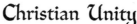

411

JOHN W. CHADWICK, 1864   10. 10. 10. 10. 10. 10.   YORKSHIRE
JOHN WAINWRIGHT, 1723–1768

Majestically

1. E - ter -nal Rul - er of the cease-less round Of cir'- cling plan-ets sing-ing
2. We are of Thee, the chil-dren of Thy love, The broth-ers of Thy well - be -
3. We would be one in ha-tred of all wrong, One in our love of all things

on their way, Guide of the na - tions from the night pro - found
lov - ed Son; De - scend, O Ho - ly Spir - it, like a dove,
sweet and fair, One with the joy that break-eth in - to song,

In - to the glo - ry of the per - fect day, Rule in our hearts that
In - to our hearts that we may be as one— As one with Thee, to
One with the grief that trem-bles in - to prayer, One in the power that

we may ev - er be Thus guid - ed, strength-ened, and up-held by Thee.
whom we ev - er tend, As one with Him, our Broth-er and our Friend.
makes Thy chil-dren free To fol - low truth, and thus to fol - low Thee. A-MEN.

The Kingdom of God on Earth

412

CHRISTOPHER WORDSWORTH, 1871   8.8.8.4.   ALMSGIVING   JOHN B. DYKES, 1865

In moderate time

1. Fa - ther of all, from land and sea The na - tions sing, "Thine,
2. O Son of God, whose love so free For men did make Thee
3. Join high with low, join young with old, In love that nev - er
4. O Spir - it blest, who from a - bove Camest gen - tly glid - ing

Lord, are we; Countless in num - ber, but in Thee May we be one."
man to be, U - nit - ed to our God in Thee May we be one.
wax - es cold; Un - der one Shep-herd, in one fold, Make us all one.
like a dove, Calm all our strife, give faith and love; O make us one! A-MEN.

413

Composite based on   ST. LO   JOHN GREENLEAF WHITTIER, 1807–1892, alt.   8.8.8.   Old Breton Melody as in *School Worship*, 1926

Rather slowly. Not too fast

1. O Lord our God, in time to be May one great tem - ple
2. White flowers of love its walls shall climb, Soft bells of peace shall
3. A sweet - er song shall then be heard, Con - fess - ing, in a
4. That song shall swell from shore to shore, One hope, one faith, one

rise to Thee—One Church for all hu - man - i - ty.
ring its chime, Its days shall all be ho - ly time.
world's ac - cord, The in - ward Christ, the liv - ing Word.
love re - store The seam - less robe that Je - sus wore. A-MEN.

Christian Unity

414

HENRY VAN DYKE, 1852-1933
7. 6. 8. 6. D.
ALFORD
JOHN B. DYKES, 1875

In moderate time

1. Wher - ev - er men a - dore Thee, Our souls with them would kneel;
2. The mind that is in Je - sus Will guide us in - to truth,
3. No form of hu - man fram - ing, No bond of out - ward might
4. For - give us, Lord, the fol - ly That quar - rels with Thy friends,

Wher - ev - er men im - plore Thy help, Their trou - ble we would feel;
The hum - ble, o - pen, joy - ful mind Of ev - er - learn - ing youth;
Can bind Thy Church to - geth - er, Lord, And all her flocks u - nite;
And draw us near - er to Thy heart, Where ev - ery dis - cord ends;

And where men do Thy serv - ice, Though know-ing not Thy sign,
The heart that is in Je - sus Will lead us out of strife,
But, Je - sus, Thou hast told us How u - ni - ty must be:
Thou art the crown of man-hood, And Thou of God the Son:

Our hand is with them in good work, For they are al - so Thine.
The giv - ing and for - giv - ing heart That fol - lows love in life.
Thou art with God the Fa - ther one, And we are one in Thee.
O Mas - ter of our man - y lives, In Thee our life is one. A-MEN.

The Kingdom of God on Earth

415

BERNHARDT S. INGEMANN, 1825
Tr. SABINE BARING-GOULD, 1867, 1875   8.7.8.7.D.

ST. ASAPH
WILLIAM S. BAMBRIDGE, 1872

With exultation

1. Through the night of doubt and sor - row On - ward goes the pil - grim band,
2. One the light of God's own pres-ence O'er His ran-somed peo - ple shed,
3. One the strain that lips of thou-sands Lift as from the heart of one,
4. On - ward, there-fore, pil - grim broth-ers, On - ward, with the cross our aid;

Sing - ing songs of ex - pec - ta - tion, March-ing to the prom-ised land:
Chas - ing far the gloom and ter - ror, Bright-ening all the path we tread;
One the con - flict, one the per - il, One the march in God be - gun;
Bear its shame, and fight its bat - tle, Till we rest be - neath its shade;

Clear be - fore us through the dark-ness Gleams and burns the guid-ing light;
One the ob - ject of our jour-ney, One the faith which nev - er tires,
One the glad - ness of re - joic - ing On the far e - ter - nal shore,
Soon shall come the great a - wak - ing, Soon the rend-ing of the tomb,

Broth - er clasps the hand of broth-er, Step-ping fear-less through the night.
One the ear - nest look-ing for-ward, One the hope our God in - spires;
Where the One Al-might-y Fa - ther Reigns in love for - ev - er - more.
Then the scat-tering of all shad-ows, And the end of toil and gloom. A-MEN.

Eternal Life

416

HENRY ALFORD, 1867

7.6.8.6.D.

ALFORD
JOHN B. DYKES, 1875

In moderate time; with exultation

1. Ten thou - sand times ten thou - sand In spark - ling rai - ment bright,
2. What rush of al - le - lu - ias Fills all the earth and sky!
3. O then what rap - tured greet - ings On Ca - naan's hap - py shore;
4. Bring near Thy great sal - va - tion, Thou Lamb for sin - ners slain;

The ar - mies of the ran - somed saints Throng up the steeps of light;
What ring - ing of a thou - sand harps Be - speaks the tri - umph nigh!
What knit - ting sev - ered friend - ships up Where part - ings are no more!
Fill up the roll of Thine e - lect, Then take Thy power and reign;

'Tis fin - ished, all is fin - ished, Their fight with death and sin:
O day, for which cre - a - tion And all its tribes were made;
Then eyes with joy shall spar - kle, That brimmed with tears of late;
Ap - pear, De - sire of na - tions, Thine ex - iles long for home;

Fling o - pen wide the gold - en gates, And let the vic - tors in.
O joy, for all its for - mer woes A thou - sand - fold re - paid!
Or - phans no long - er fa - ther - less, Nor wid - ows des - o - late.
Show in the heaven Thy prom - ised sign; Thou Prince and Sav - iour, come. A-MEN.

Eternal Life

417

WILLIAM WALSHAM HOW, 1864

10. 10. 10. 4.
First Tune

SARUM
JOSEPH BARNBY, 1869

In moderate time; with exultation

1. For all the saints who from their la - bors rest, Who Thee by
2. Thou wast their Rock, their For - tress, and their Might; Thou, Lord, their
3. O may Thy sol - diers, faith - ful, true, and bold, Fight as the
4. O blest com - mun - ion, fel - low-ship di - vine! We fee - bly
5. From earth's wide bounds, from o - cean's far - thest coast, Through gates of

faith be - fore the world con - fessed, Thy Name, O Je - sus,
Cap - tain in the well - fought fight; Thou, in the dark - ness
saints who no - bly fought of old, And win with them the
strug - gle, they in glo - ry shine; Yet all are one in
pearl streams in the count - less host, Sing - ing to Fa - ther,

be for - ev - er blest. Al - le - lu - ia! Al - le - lu - ia!
drear, their one true Light. Al - le - lu - ia! Al - le - lu - ia!
vic - tor's crown of gold. Al - le - lu - ia! Al - le - lu - ia!
Thee, for all are Thine. Al - le - lu - ia! Al - le - lu - ia!
Son, and Ho - ly Ghost, Al - le - lu - ia! Al - le - lu - ia! A-MEN.

Eternal Life

418

WILLIAM WALSHAM HOW, 1864

10. 10. 10. 4.
Second Tune

SINE NOMINE
R. VAUGHAN WILLIAMS, 1906

Voices in unison. In moderate time

1. For all the saints who from their la - bors rest, Who Thee by faith be -
2. Thou wast their Rock, their For-tress, and their Might; Thou, Lord, their Cap-tain
3. O may Thy sol - diers, faith-ful, true, and bold, Fight as the saints who
4. O blest com-mun - ion, fel-low-ship di - vine! We fee-bly strug-gle,
5. From earth's wide bounds, from o-cean's far-thest coast, Through gates of pearl streams

fore the world con - fessed, Thy Name, O Je - sus, be for-ev - er blest.
in the well-fought fight; Thou, in the dark - ness drear, their one true Light.
no - bly fought of old, And win with them the vic-tor's crown of gold.
in the count-less host, Sing-ing to Fa - ther, Son, and Ho - ly Ghost,

Harmony

Al - le - lu - ia! Al - le - lu - ia! A-MEN.

Harmony

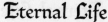

Eternal Life

419

JOHN GREENLEAF WHITTIER, 1882

11.10.11.6.

JOURNEY'S END
WILLIAM K. ANDERSON

With quiet confidence

1. When on my day of life the night is fall - ing,
2. Thou, who hast made my home of life so pleas - ant,
3. I have but Thee, my Fa - ther! let Thy Spir - it
4. Suf - fice it if— my good and ill un - reck - oned,
5. There, from the mu - sic round a - bout me steal - ing,

And, in the wind from un-sunned spac - es blown, I hear far
Leave not its ten - ant when its walls de - cay; O Love Di -
Be with me then to com - fort and up - hold; No gate of
And both for - given through Thine a - bound-ing grace— I find my -
I fain would learn the new and ho - ly song, And find at

voic - es out of dark-ness call - ing My feet to paths un-known;
vine, O Help - er ev - er pres - ent, Be Thou my strength and stay.
pearl, no branch of palm I mer - it, Nor street of shin - ing gold.
self by hands fa - mil - iar beck-oned Un - to my fit - ting place;
last, be-neath Thy trees of heal - ing, The life for which I long. A-MEN.

Eternal Life

420

FREDERICK W. FABER, 1854

11. 10. 11. 10. 9. 11.

PILGRIMS (SMART)
HENRY SMART, 1868

In moderate time

1. Hark, hark, my soul, an - gel - ic songs are swell-ing O'er earth's green fields and o - cean's wave-beat shore: How sweet the truth those bless-ed strains are tell - ing Of that new life when sin shall be no more.

2. On - ward we go, for still we hear them sing-ing, "Come, wea-ry souls, for Je - sus bids you come"; And through the dark, its ech-oes sweet-ly ring-ing, The mu - sic of the gos - pel leads us home.

3. Far, far a - way, like bells at eve - ning peal-ing, The voice of Je - sus sounds o'er land and sea; And lad - en souls, by thou-sands meek-ly steal-ing, Kind Shep-herd, turn their wea - ry steps to Thee.

4. An - gels, sing on, your faith-ful watch - es keep-ing; Sing us sweet frag-ments of the songs a - bove, Till morn-ing's joy shall end the night of weep-ing, And life's long shad-ows break in cloud-less love.

REFRAIN

An - gels of Je - sus, An - gels of light, Sing - ing to wel-come the pil-grims of the night! A - MEN.

Eternal Life

Benjamin Schmolck, 1731
Tr. Frances E. Cox, 1841

7. 8. 7. 8. 7. 7.

JESUS MEINE ZUVERSICHT (RATISBON)
Johann Crüger's
Praxis Pietatis Melica, c. 1653

Not too slowly; with steady movement

1. Heaven-ward still our path-way tends; Here on earth we
2. Heaven-ward still! God calls to me, In His word so
3. Heaven-ward still, when life shall close, Death to my true

are but stran-gers, Till our road in Ca-naan ends,
clear-ly speak-ing; Glimps-es in that word I see
home shall guide me: Then, tri-um-phant o'er my woes,

Safe-ly past this wild of dan-gers: Here we but as
Of the home I'm ev-er seek-ing; While my heart that
Last-ing bliss shall God pro-vide me. Christ Him-self the

pil-grims rove, For our home is there a-bove.
call at-tends, Still to heaven my path as-cends.
way has led; Joy-ful in His steps I tread. A-men.

Eternal Life

422

BERNARD OF CLUNY, 12th century
Tr. JOHN MASON NEALE, 1851

7. 6. 7. 6. D.

EWING

ALEXANDER EWING, 1853

Jubilantly

1. Je - ru - sa - lem the gold - en, With milk and hon - ey blest!
2. They stand, those halls of Zi - on, All ju - bi - lant with song,
3. There is the throne of Da - vid; And there, from care re - leased,
4. O sweet and bless - ed coun - try, The home of God's e - lect!

Be - neath thy con - tem - pla - tion Sink heart and voice op - pressed.
And bright with many an an - gel And all the mar - tyr throng.
The song of them that tri - umph, The shout of them that feast;
O sweet and bless - ed coun - try That ea - ger hearts ex - pect!

I know not, O I know not, What joys a - wait us there;
The Prince is ev - er in them, The day - light is se - rene;
And they who with their Lead - er Have con - quered in the fight,
Je - sus, in mer - cy bring us To that dear land of rest;

What ra - dian - cy of glo - ry, What bliss be - yond com - pare.
The pas - tures of the bless - ed Are decked in glo - rious sheen.
For - ev - er and for - ev - er Are clad in robes of white.
Who art, with God the Fa - ther, And Spir - it, ev - er blest. A - MEN.

423

JAMES D. BURNS, 1861, alt.   8. 7. 8. 7. D.   HYFRYDOL
ROWLAND HUGH PRICHARD, 1811–1887

In moderate time; joyfully

1. At Thy feet, our God and Fa-ther, Who hast blessed us all our days,
2. Je-sus, for Thy love most ten-der, On the cross for sin-ners shown,
3. Ev-ery day will be the bright-er When Thy gra-cious face we see;

We with grate-ful hearts would gath-er, To be-gin the year with praise:
We would praise Thee, and sur-ren-der All our hearts to be Thine own:
Ev-ery bur-den will be light-er When we find our strength in Thee.

Praise for light so bright-ly shin-ing On our steps from heaven a-bove;
With so blest a Friend pro-vid-ed, We up-on our way would go,
Spread Thy love's broad ban-ner o'er us, Give us strength to serve and wait,

Praise for mer-cies dai-ly twin-ing Round us gold-en cords of love.
Sure of be-ing safe-ly guid-ed, Guard-ed well from ev-ery foe.
Till the glo-ry breaks be-fore us Through the Cit-y's o-pen gate. A-MEN.

The Changing Year

424

Frances R. Havergal, 1874   7.6.7.6.D.   TOURS   Berthold Tours, 1872

Not too slowly

1. An-oth-er year is dawn-ing! Dear Fa-ther, let it be
2. An-oth-er year of mer-cies, Of faith-ful-ness and grace;
3. An-oth-er year of serv-ice, Of wit-ness for Thy love;

In work-ing or in wait-ing An-oth-er year with Thee!
An-oth-er year of glad-ness In the shin-ing of Thy face.
An-oth-er year of train-ing For holi-er work a-bove.

An-oth-er year of lean-ing Up-on Thy lov-ing breast,
An-oth-er year of pro-gress, An-oth-er year of praise,
An-oth-er year is dawn-ing! Dear Fa-ther, let it be

An-oth-er year of trust-ing, Of qui-et, hap-py rest.
An-oth-er year of prov-ing Thy pres-ence 'all the days.'
On earth, or else in heav-en, An-oth-er year for Thee. A-men.

425

PHILIP DODDRIDGE, 1702–1751

L.M.

WAREHAM
WILLIAM KNAPP, 1738

With dignity

1. Great God, we sing that might-y hand By which sup-port-ed still we stand;
2. By day, by night, at home, a-broad, Still are we guard-ed by our God;
3. With grate-ful hearts the past we own; The fu-ture, all ' to us un-known,
4. In scenes ex-alt-ed or de-pressed, Thou art our Joy, and Thou our Rest;

The ope-ning year Thy mer-cy shows; That mer-cy crowns it till it close.
By His in-ces-sant boun-ty fed, By His un-err-ing coun-sel led.
We to Thy guard-ian care com-mit, And peace-ful leave be-fore Thy feet.
Thy good-ness all our hopes shall raise, A-dored through all our chang-ing days. A-MEN.

Alternative tune, *Truro.*

426

HENRY DOWNTON, 1843

7.7.7.7.

SEYMOUR
CARL M. VON WEBER, 1826

Not too fast

1. For Thy mer-cy and Thy grace, Faith-ful through an-oth-er year,
2. Lo, our sins on Thee we cast, Thee, our per-fect Sac-ri-fice;
3. Dark the fu-ture; let Thy light Guide us, bright and morn-ing Star;
4. In our weak-ness and dis-tress, Rock of strength, be Thou our Stay;
5. Keep us faith-ful, keep us pure, Keep us ev-er-more Thine own;

Hear our song of thank-ful-ness, Fa-ther and Re-deem-er, hear!
And, for-get-ting all the past, Press to-wards our glo-rious prize.
Fierce our foes, and hard the fight; Arm us, Sav-iour, for the war.
In the path-less wil-der-ness Be our true and liv-ing Way.
Help, O help us to en-dure, Fit us for the prom-ised crown. A-MEN.

The Changing Year

427

FRANCES RIDLEY HAVERGAL, 1873 6.5.6.5. with Refrain

THE NEW YEAR
ARTHUR H. MANN, 1885

In march rhythm

1. Stand-ing at the por-tal Of the open-ing year, . . Words of com-fort
2. For the year be-fore us, O what rich sup-plies! . . For the poor and
3. He will nev-er fail us, He will not for-sake; . . His e-ter-nal

meet us, Hush-ing ev-ery fear; Spo-ken through the si-lence
need-y Liv-ing streams shall rise; For the sad and sin-ful
cove-nant He will nev-er break; Rest-ing on His prom-ise,

By our Fa-ther's voice, . . Ten-der, strong, and faith-ful,
Shall His grace a-bound; . . For the faint and fee-ble
What have we to fear? . . God is all-suf-fi-cient

REFRAIN

Mak-ing us re-joice. On-ward, then, and fear not, Chil-dren of the
Per-fect strength be found.
For the com-ing year.

day; For His word shall nev-er, Nev-er pass a-way. A-MEN.

428

ALFRED TENNYSON, 1849

L. M. D.

CANTATE DOMINO (JORDAN)
JOSEPH BARNBY, 1872

With well-defined rhythm

1. Ring out, wild bells, to the wild sky, The fly-ing cloud, the frost-y light;
2. Ring out the grief that saps the mind, For those that here we see no more;
3. Ring out old shapes of foul dis-ease, Ring out the narrow-ing lust of gold;

The year is dy-ing in the night: Ring out, wild bells, and let him die.
Ring out the feud of rich and poor, Ring in re-dress to all man-kind.
Ring out the thou-sand wars of old, Ring in the thou-sand years of peace.

Ring out the old, ring in the new, Ring, hap-py bells, a-cross the snow:
Ring out false pride in place and blood, The civ-ic slan-der and the spite;
Ring in the val-iant man and free, The larg-er heart, the kind-lier hand;

The year is go-ing, let him go; Ring out the false, ring in the true.
Ring in the love of truth and right, Ring in the com-mon love of good.
Ring out the dark-ness of the land, Ring in the Christ that is to be. A-MEN.

The Seasons

Winter

429

FRANCES WHITMARSH WILE, 1912

C. M. D.

FOREST GREEN
English Traditional Melody

In moderate time; brightly

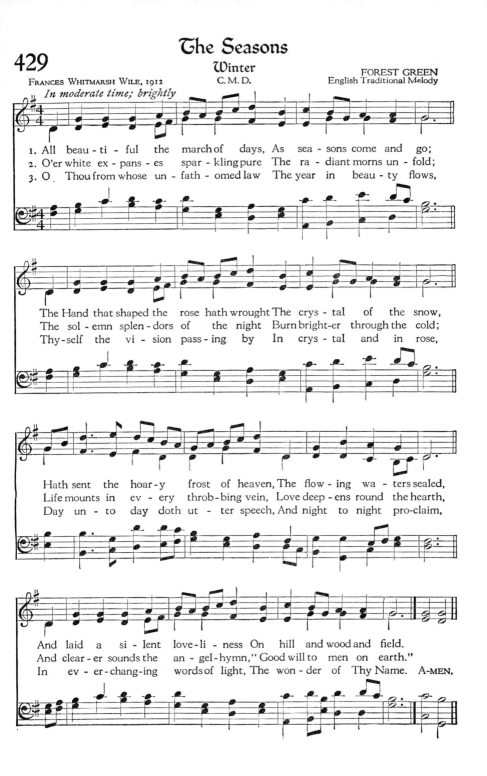

1. All beau - ti - ful the march of days, As sea - sons come and go;
2. O'er white ex - pans - es spar - kling pure The ra - diant morns un - fold;
3. O. Thou from whose un - fath - omed law The year in beau - ty flows,

The Hand that shaped the rose hath wrought The crys - tal of the snow,
The sol - emn splen - dors of the night Burn bright-er through the cold;
Thy-self the vi - sion pass - ing by In crys - tal and in rose,

Hath sent the hoar-y frost of heaven, The flow - ing wa - ters sealed,
Life mounts in ev - ery throb-bing vein, Love deep - ens round the hearth,
Day un - to day doth ut - ter speech, And night to night pro-claim,

And laid a si - lent love-li - ness On hill and wood and field.
And clear - er sounds the an - gel-hymn, "Good will to men on earth."
In ev - er-chang-ing words of light, The won - der of Thy Name. A-MEN.

430
Spring
C. M. D.

THOMAS H. GILL, 1867

BETHLEHEM (SERAPH)
GOTTFRIED W. FINK, 1842

Joyously

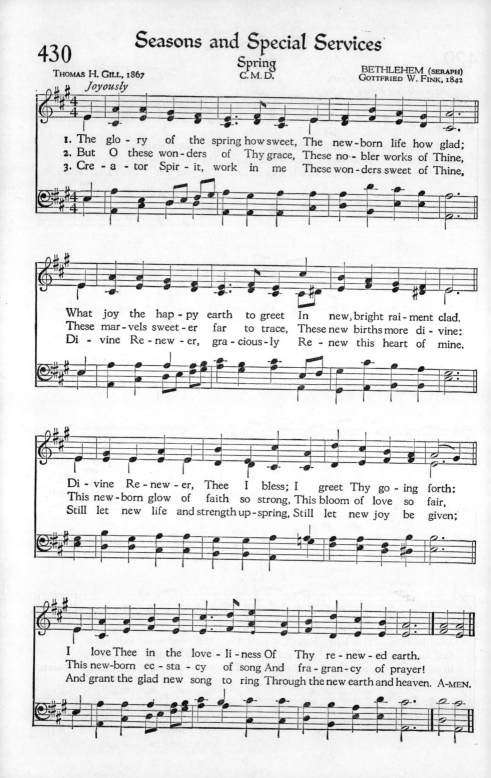

1. The glo-ry of the spring how sweet, The new-born life how glad;
2. But O these won-ders of Thy grace, These no--bler works of Thine,
3. Cre-a-tor Spir-it, work in me These won-ders sweet of Thine,

What joy the hap-py earth to greet In new, bright rai-ment clad.
These mar-vels sweet-er far to trace, These new births more di-vine:
Di-vine Re-new-er, gra-cious-ly Re-new this heart of mine.

Di-vine Re-new-er, Thee I bless; I greet Thy go-ing forth:
This new-born glow of faith so strong, This bloom of love so fair,
Still let new life and strength up-spring, Still let new joy be given;

I love Thee in the love-li-ness Of Thy re-new-ed earth.
This new-born ec-sta-cy of song And fra-gran-cy of prayer!
And grant the glad new song to ring Through the new earth and heaven. A-MEN.

The Seasons

431

Summer

FOREST GREEN
English Traditional Melody

SAMUEL LONGFELLOW, 1819-1892

C. M. D.

In moderate time; brightly

1. The sum-mer days are come a-gain; Once more the glad earth yields
2. The sum-mer days are come a-gain; The birds are on the wing;

Her gold-en wealth of ripen-ing grain, And breath of clo-ver fields,
God's prais-es, in their lov-ing strain, Un-con-scious-ly they sing.

And deepen-ing shade of sum-mer woods, And glow of sum-mer air,
We know who giv-eth all the good That doth our cup o'er-brim;

And wing-ing thoughts, and hap-py moods Of love and joy and prayer.
For sum-mer joy in field and wood, We lift our song to Him. A-MEN.

Matthias Claudius, 1782
Tr. Jane M. Campbell, 1861

WIR PFLÜGEN (DRESDEN)

7.6.7.6. with Refrain

Johann A. P. Schulz, 1800

Brightly

1. We plow the fields, and scat - ter The good seed on the land,
2. He on - ly is the Mak - er Of all things near and far;
3. We thank Thee, then, O Fa - ther, For all things bright and good,

But it is fed and wa - tered By God's al - might - y hand;
He paints the way - side flow - er, He lights the eve - ning star;
The seed - time and the har - vest, Our life, our health, our food;

He sends the snow in win - ter, The warmth to swell the grain,
The winds and waves o - bey Him, By Him the birds are fed;
Ac - cept the gifts we of - fer For all Thy love im - parts,

The breez - es and the sun - shine, And soft re - fresh - ing rain.
Much more to us, His chil - dren, He gives our dai - ly bread.
And that which Thou de - sir - est, Our hum - ble, thank - ful hearts.

REFRAIN

All good gifts a - round us Are sent from heaven a - bove;

Harvest and Thanksgiving

Then thank the Lord, O thank the Lord For all His love. A-MEN.

433

WILLIAM CHATTERTON DIX, 1864   8. 7. 8. 7. D.   BISHOPGARTH
ARTHUR S. SULLIVAN, 1897

Joyfully

1. To Thee, O Lord, our hearts we raise In hymns of ad - o - ra - tion,
2. And now, on this our fes - tal day, Thy boun-teous hand con - fess - ing,

To Thee bring sac - ri - fice of praise With shouts of ex - ul - ta - tion;
Up - on Thine al - tar, Lord, we lay The first-fruits of Thy bless - ing;

Bright robes of gold the fields a - dorn, The hills with joy are ring - ing,
By Thee the souls of men are fed With gifts of grace su - per - nal:

The val - leys stand so thick with corn That ev - en they are sing - ing.
Thou, Who dost give us dai - ly bread, Give us the Bread E - ter - nal. A-MEN.

434

Henry Alford, 1844
Alt. Hugh Hartshorne, 1915

7.7.7.7. D.

ST. GEORGE'S WINDSOR
George J. Elvey, 1858
Descant by H. A. Chambers, 1931

DESCANT

3. These to Thee, our God, we owe, Source whence all our bless-ings flow;

1. Come, ye thank-ful peo-ple, come, Raise the song of har-vest home:
2. All the bless-ings of the field, All the stores the gar-dens yield;
3. These to Thee, our God, we owe, Source whence all our bless-ings flow;

And for these our souls shall raise Grate-ful vows and sol-emn praise.

All is safe-ly gath-ered in Ere the win-ter storms be-gin;
All the fruits in full sup-ply, Rip-ened 'neath the sum-mer sky;
And for these our souls shall raise Grate-ful vows and sol-emn praise.

Come, then, thank-ful peo-ple, come, Raise the song of har-vest home;

God, our Mak-er, doth pro-vide For our wants to be sup-plied;
All that Spring with boun-teous hand Scat-ters o'er the smil-ing land;
Come, then, thank-ful peo-ple, come, Raise the song of har-vest home;

Harvest and Thanksgiving

Come to God's own tem - ple, come, Raise the song of har - vest home. A-MEN.

Come to God's own tem - ple, come, Raise the song of har - vest home.
All that lib - eral au - tumn pours From her rich o'er - flow-ing stores,
Come to God's own tem - ple, come, Raise the song of har - vest home. A-MEN.

435

ANNA L. BARBAULD, 1773   7.7.7.7.7.7.   DIX
Arr. from CONRAD KOCHER, 1838

Joyously

1. Praise to God, im - mor - tal praise, For the love that crowns our days;
2. All the plen - ty sum - mer pours; Au-tumn's rich o'er - flow - ing stores;
3. As Thy pros-pering hand hath blest, May we give Thee of our best;

Boun - teous source of ev - ery joy, Let Thy praise our tongues em - ploy;
Flocks that whit - en all the plain; Yel - low sheaves of ri - pened grain;
And by deeds of kind - ly love, For Thy mer - cies grate-ful prove;

All to Thee, our God, we owe, Source whence all our bless-ings flow.
Lord, for these our souls shall raise Grate - ful vows and sol - emn praise.
Sing - ing thus through all our days, Praise to God, im - mor - tal praise. A-MEN.

436

LEONARD BACON, 1833   L. M.   DUKE STREET
JOHN HATTON, d. 1793

With dignity

1. O God, be-neath Thy guid-ing hand Our ex-iled fa-thers
2. Thou heardest, well-pleased, the song, the prayer; Thy bless-ing came; and
3. Laws, free-dom, truth, and faith in God Camewith those ex-iles
4. And here Thy Name, O God of love, Their chil-dren's chil-dren

crossed the sea; And, when they trod the win-try strand,
still its power Shall on-ward through all a-ges bear
o'er the waves, And where their pil-grim feet have trod,
shall a-dore, Till these e-ter-nal hills re-move,

With prayer and psalm they wor-shiped Thee.
The mem-ory of that ho-ly hour.
The God they trust-ed guards their graves.
And spring a-dorns the earth no more. A-MEN.

437

ALFRED A. WOODHULL, 1810–1836   L. M.   MENDON
German Traditional Melody
Arr. SAMUEL DYER, 1828

Joyously

1. Great God of na-tions, now to Thee Our hymn of grat-i-tude we raise;
2. Thy Name we bless, Al-might-y God, For all the kind-ness Thou hast shown
3. Here free-dom spreads her ban-ner wide, And casts her soft and hal-lowed ray;
4. Great God, pre-serve us in Thy fear; In dan-ger still our guard-ian be:

The Nation

With hum-ble heart and bend-ing knee We of-fer Thee our song of praise.
To this fair land the Pil-grims trod, This land we fond-ly call our own.
Here Thou our fa-thers' steps didst guide In safe-ty through their dangerous way.
O spread Thy truth's bright pre-cepts here; Let all the peo - ple wor - ship Thee. A-MEN.

438

AMOS R. WELLS, 1862–1933
Stanza 1, alt.

L. M.

DEUS TUORUM MILITUM

Grenoble Church Melody

UNISON. *With dignity*

1. God help our coun - try to be strong 'Gainst all the bat - tle -
2. God hold our na - tion's aim sin - cere, God save her heart from
3. From foe with - out and foe with - in, From o - pen shame and

hosts of wrong; In all we pledge or think or do
cow - ard fear, God pros - per her with true suc - cess,
hid - den sin, From boast - ful pride and greed - y store,

God help our coun - try to be true.
And crown her head with worth - i - ness.
God keep our na - tion ev - er - more! A - MEN.

Stanzas 1 and 2, SIEGFRIED A. MAHLMANN, 1815
Stanza 3, WILLIAM E. HICKSON, 1836   6. 6. 4. 6. 6. 6. 4.

AMERICA

Thesaurus Musicus, 1740

1. God bless our na - tive land; Firm may she
2. For her our prayers shall rise To God a -
3. Not for this land a - lone, But be God's

ev - er stand Through storm and night: When the wild
bove the skies; On Him we wait; Thou who art
mer - cies shown From shore to shore; And may the

tem - pests rave, Rul - er of wind and wave,
ev - er nigh, Guard - ing with watch - ful eye,
na - tions see That men should broth - ers be,

Do Thou our coun - try save By Thy great might.
To Thee a - loud we cry, God save the State!
And form one fam - i - ly The wide world o'er.   A - MEN.

The Nation

440

Daniel C. Roberts, 1876

10. 10. 10. 10.

NATIONAL HYMN
George William Warren, 1892

In march rhythm

Trumpets, before
each stanza

1. God of our fa-thers, whose al-might-y hand
2. Thy love di-vine hath led us in the past;
3. From war's a-larms, from dead-ly pes-ti-lence,
4. Re-fresh Thy peo-ple on their toil-some way,

Leads forth in beau-ty all the star-ry band
In this free land by Thee our lot is cast;
Be Thy strong arm our ev-er sure de-fense;
Lead us from night to nev-er-end-ing day;

Of shin-ing worlds in splen-dor through the skies,
Be Thou our Rul-er, Guard-ian, Guide, and Stay;
Thy true re-li-gion in our hearts in-crease,
Fill all our lives with love and grace di-vine,

Our grate-ful songs be-fore Thy throne a-rise.
Thy word our law, Thy paths our cho-sen way.
Thy boun-teous good-ness nour-ish us in peace.
And glo-ry, laud, and praise be ev-er Thine. A-men.

441

SAMUEL F. SMITH, 1832   6. 6. 4. 6. 6. 6. 4.   AMERICA
                                                      Thesaurus Musicus, 1740

1. My coun - try, 'tis of thee, Sweet land of
2. My na - tive coun - try, thee, Land of the
3. Let mu - sic swell the breeze, And ring from
4. Our fa - thers' God, to Thee, Au - thor of

lib - er - ty, Of thee I sing; Land where my
no - ble free, Thy name I love; I love thy
all the trees Sweet free - dom's song: Let mor - tal
lib - er - ty, To Thee we sing: Long may our

fa - thers died, Land of the pil - grims' pride,
rocks and rills, Thy woods and tem - pled hills;
tongues a - wake; Let all that breathe par - take;
land be bright With free - dom's ho - ly light;

From ev - ery moun - tain side Let free - dom ring.
My heart with rap - ture thrills Like that a - bove.
Let rocks their si - lence break, The sound pro - long.
Pro - tect us by Thy might, Great God, our King.   A - MEN.

The Nation

442

WILLIAM PIERSON MERRILL, 1911   8. 7. 8. 7. D.   HYFRYDOL
ROWLAND HUGH PRICHARD, 1811–1887

With dignity

1. Not a - lone for might-y em - pire, Stretching far o'er land and sea;
2. Not for bat - tle-ship and for - tress, Not for con-quests of the sword;
3. For the ar - mies of the faith-ful, Souls that passed and left no name;
4. God of jus - tice, save the peo - ple From the clash of race and creed,

Not a - lone for boun-teous har-vests, Lift we up our hearts to Thee.
But for con-quests of the spir - it Give we thanks to Thee, O Lord;
For the glo - ry that il - lu - mines Pa - triot lives of death-less fame;
From the strife of class and fac - tion: Make our na - tion free in-deed.

Stand-ing in the liv - ing pres-ent, Mem - o - ry and hope be - tween,
For the price-less gift of free-dom, For the home, the church, the school;
For our proph-ets and a - pos - tles, Loy - al to the liv - ing Word;
Keep her faith in sim - ple man-hood Strong as when her life be - gan,

Lord, we would with deep thanks-giv - ing Praise Thee most for things unseen.
For the o - pen door to man-hood In a land the peo - ple rule.
For all he - roes of the Spir - it, Give we thanks to Thee, O Lord.
Till it find its full fru - i - tion In the broth-er-hood of man. A - MEN.

443

KATHARINE LEE BATES, 1895   C. M. D.   MATERNA
S. A. WARD, 1882

Joyously, with dignity

1. O beau-ti-ful for spa-cious skies, For am-ber waves of grain,
2. O beau-ti-ful for pil-grim feet, Whose stern, im-pas-sioned stress
3. O beau-ti-ful for he-roes, proved In lib-er-at-ing strife,
4. O beau-ti-ful for pa-triot dream That sees be-yond the years

For pur-ple moun-tain maj-es-ties A-bove the fruit-ed plain!
A thor-ough-fare for free-dom beat A-cross the wil-der-ness!
Who more than self their coun-try loved, And mer-cy more than life!
Thine al-a-bas-ter cit-ies gleam Un-dimmed by hu-man tears!

A-mer-i-ca! A-mer-i-ca! God shed His grace on thee,
A-mer-i-ca! A-mer-i-ca! God mend thine ev-ery flaw,
A-mer-i-ca! A-mer-i-ca! May God thy gold re-fine,
A-mer-i-ca! A-mer-i-ca! God shed His grace on thee,

And crown thy good with broth-er-hood From sea to shin-ing sea!
Con-firm thy soul in self-con-trol, Thy lib-er-ty in law!
Till all suc-cess be no-ble-ness, And ev-ery gain di-vine!
And crown thy good with broth-er-hood From sea to shin-ing sea! A-MEN.

The Home and Family

Dedication of a Home

444

Louis F. Benson, 1925

8.6.8.8.6.

REST (ELTON)
Frederick C. Maker, 1887

In moderate time

1. O Thou whose gra - cious pres - ence blest The home at Beth - a - ny, This shel - ter from the world's un - rest, This home made read - y for its Guest, We ded - i - cate to Thee.

2. When Thou didst pass the tem - ple gate, To pray be - neath its dome, It was Thy Fa - ther's house, more great Be - cause by love made con - se - crate; It was Thine on - ly home.

3. We build an al - tar here, and pray That Thou wilt show Thy face. Dear Lord, if Thou wilt come to stay, This home we con - se - crate to - day Will be a ho - ly place. A-MEN.

Words used by permission of Mrs. Robert F. Jeffreys.

445

The Home and Family

Carl J. P. Spitta, 1833
Tr. Sarah L. Findlater, 1858

HENLEY

11. 10. 11. 10.

Lowell Mason, 1854

In moderate time; joyfully

1. O hap-py home, where Thou art loved the dear-est,
2. O hap-py home, where each one serves Thee, low-ly,
3. O hap-py home, where Thou art not for-got-ten
4. Un-til at last, when earth's day's work is end-ed,

Thou lov-ing Friend and Sav-iour of our race,
What-ev-er his ap-point-ed work may be,
When joy is o-ver-flow-ing, full, and free;
All meet Thee in the bless-ed home a-bove,

And where a-mong the guests there nev-er com-eth
Till ev-ery com-mon task seems great and ho-ly,
O hap-py home, where ev-ery wound-ed spir-it
From whence Thou cam-est, where Thou hast as-cend-ed,

One who can hold such high and hon-ored place.
When it is done, O Lord, as un-to Thee.
Is brought, Phys-i-cian, Com-fort-er, to Thee,
Thy ev-er-last-ing home of peace and love! A-MEN.

Youth and Schools

Walter J. Mathams, 1913

S. M. D.

DIADEMATA
George J. Elvey, 1868

446

With spirit

1. Now in the days of youth, When life flows fresh and free, Thou Lord of all our hearts and lives We give our-selves to Thee; Our fer-vent gift re-ceive, And fit us to ful-fill, Through all our days, in all our ways, Our Heaven-ly Fa-ther's will.

2. Teach us wher-e'er we live, To act as in Thy sight, And do what Thou wouldst have us do With ra-di-ant de-light; Not choos-ing what is great, Nor spurn-ing what is small, But take as from Thy hands our tasks, And glo-ri-fy them all.

3. Teach us to love the true, The beau-ti-ful and pure, And let us not for one short hour An e-vil thought en-dure. But give us grace to stand De-cid-ed, brave and strong, The lov-ers of all ho-ly things, The foes of all things wrong.

4. Spir-it of Christ, do Thou Our first bright days in-spire, That we may live the life of love And loft-i-est de-sire; And be by Thee pre-pared For larg-er years to come, And for the life in-ef-fa-ble With-in the Fa-ther's home. A-men.

Youth and Schools

447

Johann Wolfgang von Goethe, 1858
Tr. anon.

6. 5. 6. 5. D.

LYNDHURST

Anon.

Not too fast

1. Pu - rer yet and pu - rer I would be in mind,
2. Calm - er yet and calm - er In the hour of pain,
3. High - er yet and high - er Out of clouds and sight,
4. Swift - er yet and swift - er Ev - er on - ward run,

Dear - er yet and dear - er Ev - ery du - ty find;
Sur - er yet and sur - er Peace at last to gain;
Near - er yet and near - er Ris - ing to the light:
Firm - er yet and firm - er Step as I go on:

Hop - ing still, and trust - ing God with - out a fear,
Suf - fering still and do - ing, To His will re - signed,
Light se - rene and ho - ly, Where my soul may rest,
Oft these ear - nest long - ings Swell with - in my breast,

Pa - tient - ly be - liev - ing He will make all clear.
And to joy sub - du - ing Heart and will and mind.
Pu - ri - fied and ho - ly, Sanc - ti - fied and blest.
Yet their in - ner mean - ing Ne'er can be ex - pressed. A-MEN.

Youth and Schools

448

HOWARD ARNOLD WALTER, 1917

11. 10. 11. 10.

PEEK

JOSEPH YATES PEEK, 1911

In moderate time

1. I would be true, for there are those who trust me;
2. I would be friend of all, the foe, the friend-less;

I would be pure, for there are those who care;
I would be [giv - ing, and for - get the gift;

I would be strong, for there is much to suf - fer;
I would be hum - ble, for I know my weak - ness;

I would be brave, for there is much to dare,
I would look up, and laugh, and love, and lift,

I would be brave, for there is much to dare. A - MEN.
I would look up, and laugh, and love, and lift.

Youth and Schools

449

Harry Thomas Stock, alt.

LOBT GOTT IHR CHRISTEN ALLZUGLEICH
8.6.8.8.6.

Nicolaus Hermann, 1554

Joyfully

1. O gra - cious God, whose con - stant care Sup - plies our gold - en days,
2. We thank Thee, Fa - ther, for each word, Each thought-re - veal - ing truth,
3. Com-pan - ion of this sa - cred hour, Re - new in us each day

Whose joy - ous fel - low - ship we share At work, at rest, in
For proph - et voic - es glad - ly heard, For dar - ing dreams, for
Our loft - y pur - pose; grant us power That worth - y thoughts in

play and prayer— Ac - cept our heart - felt praise.
friends who stirred The frag - ile wills of youth.
deeds may flower, In Christ - like lives, we pray. A-men.

450

M. Woolsey Stryker, 1851–1929

C.M.

PATTEN
Peter C. Lutkin, 1858–1931

With spirit

1. Al - might - y Lord, with one ac - cord
2. Thy cause doth claim our souls by name,
3. Let fall on ev - ery col - lege hall
4. Our hearts be ruled, our spir - its schooled

Youth and Schools

We of-fer Thee our youth, And pray that Thou wouldst
Be-cause that we are strong; In all the land, one
The lus-ter of Thy cross, That love may dare Thy
A-lone Thy will to seek; And when we find Thy

give us now The war-fare of the truth.
stead-fast band, May we to Christ be-long.
work to share, And count all else as lost.
bless-ed mind, In-struct our lips to speak. A-MEN.

Music used by permission of Mrs. Peter C. Lutkin.

451

Louis F. Benson, 1894   C. M.   ST. MAGNUS
                                          Jeremiah Clark, 1670-1707

In moderate time

1. O Thou whose feet have climbed life's hill, And trod the path of youth,
2. The call is Thine: be Thou the Way, And give us men, to guide;
3. Who learn of Thee the truth shall find, Who fol-low, gain the goal;
4. A-wake the pur-pose high which strives, And, fall-ing, stands a-gain;
5. Thy life the bond of fel-low-ship, Thy love the law that rules,

Our Sav-iour and our Broth-er still, Now lead us in-to truth.
Let wis-dom broad-en with the day, Let hu-man faith a-bide.
With rev-erence crown the ear-nest mind, And speak with-in the soul.
Con-firm the will of ea-ger lives To quit themselves like men:
Thy Name, pro-claimed by ev-ery lip, The Mas-ter of our schools. A-MEN.

Words used by permission of Mrs. Robert E. Jeffreys.

452

PURD E. DEITZ

FINLANDIA
JEAN SIBELIUS
Arranged for *The Hymnal, 1933*

May be sung in unison   10. 10. 10. 10. 10. 10.
In moderate time, with flowing rhythm

1. We would be build - ing; tem - ples still un - done   O'er crum-bling
2. Teach us to build; up - on the sol - id rock   We set the
3. O keep us build - ing, Mas - ter; may our hands   Ne'er fal - ter

walls their cross - es scarce - ly lift,   Wait - ing till love can
dream that hard - ens in - to deed,   Ribbed with the steel that
when the dream is in our hearts,   When to our ears there

raise the bro - ken stone,   And hearts cre - a - tive bridge the hu - man rift;
time and change doth mock,   Th'un-fail-ing pur - pose of our no - blest creed;
come di - vine com - mands   And all the pride of sin - ful will de - parts;

We would be build - ing; Mas - ter, let Thy plan
Teach us to build; O Mas - ter, lend us sight
We build with Thee; O grant en - dur - ing worth

Youth and Schools

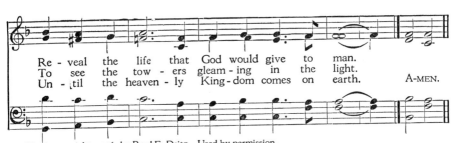

Re - veal the life that God would give to man.
To see the tow - ers gleam - ing in the light.
Un - til the heaven - ly King - dom comes on earth. A-MEN.

453

SERUG

Derived from CLEMENT OF ALEXANDRIA, Second century A. D.   From SAMUEL SEBASTIAN WESLEY'S
Tr. HENRY M. DEXTER, 1846   6. 6. 4. 6. 6. 6. 4.   *European Psalmist, 1872*

With flowing rhythm

1. Shep - herd of ea - ger youth, Guid - ing in love and truth
2. Thou art our ho - ly Lord, The all - sub - du - ing Word,
3. Ev - er be Thou our Guide, Our Shep - herd and our Pride,
4. So now, and till we die, Sound we Thy prais - es high,

Through de - vious ways; Christ our tri - um - phant King, We come Thy
Heal - er of strife; Thou didst Thy - self a - base, That from sin's
Our Staff and Song; Je - sus, Thou Christ of God, By Thine en -
And joy - ful sing; Let all the ho - ly throng, Who to Thy

name to sing, Hith - er our chil - dren bring To shout Thy praise.
deep dis - grace Thou might - est save our race, And give us life.
dur - ing word, Lead us where Thou hast trod, Make our faith strong.
Church be - long, U - nite to swell the song To Christ our King! A-MEN.

The earliest known Christian hymn.

Youth and Schools

454

JAMES GORDON GILKEY, 1912   7.6.8.6. D.   GRESHAM
GEOFFREY TURTON SHAW

UNISON. *With spirit*

1. O God, in whose great pur - pose An age is but a day, Who
2. A - gain, with vi - sion kin - dled, We sons of la - ter days Lift

watch - est sun give place to sun And plan - ets burn a - way; In
ea - ger hands as here we wait Be - side the part - ing ways. A -

Thee our fa - thers trust - ed, For Thee they dared the sea, And
cross Thine earth we scat - ter To meet the tasks of men: O

Thou didst teach their fee - ble hands To shape a world for Thee.
God of strength, be Thou to us Our fa - thers' God a - gain! A - MEN.

Words used by permission of the author.
Music, used by permission, from Curwen Edition No. 6300, published by J. Curwen and Sons, Ltd.

Children

455

WILLIAM GEORGE TARRANT, 1888   7. 6. 7. 6. D.   TOURS

BERTHOLD TOURS, 1872

Joyfully

1. With hap-py voic-es ring-ing, Thy chil-dren, Lord, ap-pear;
2. For though no eye be-holds Thee, No hand Thy touch may feel,

Their joy-ous prais-es bring-ing In an-thems sweet and clear.
Thy u-ni-verse un-folds Thee, Thy star-ry heavens re-veal;

For skies of gold-en splen-dor, For az-ure roll-ing sea,
The earth in all its glo-ry, Our homes and all we love,

For blos-soms sweet and ten-der, O Lord, we wor-ship Thee.
Tell forth the won-drous sto-ry Of One who reigns a-bove. A-MEN.

Words used by permission of Miss Dorothy Tarrant.

Children

456

J. EDGAR PARK, 1913

11. 10. 11. 10.

CUSHMAN
HERBERT B. TURNER, 1905

In moderate time

1. We would see Je - sus; lo! His star is shin - ing
2. We would see Je - sus, Ma - ry's Son most ho - ly,
3. We would see Je - sus on the moun - tain teach - ing,
4. We would see Je - sus in His work of heal - ing,
5. We would see Je - sus; in the ear - ly morn - ing

A - bove the sta - ble while the an - gels sing;
Light of the vil - lage life from day to day,
With all the lis - tening peo - ple gath - ered round,
At ev - en - tide be - fore the sun was set;
Still as of old He call - eth, "Fol - low Me";

There in a man - ger on the hay re - clin - ing,
Shin - ing re - vealed through ev - ery task most low - ly,
While birds and flowers and sky a - bove are preach - ing
Di - vine and hu - man, in His deep re - veal - ing
Let us a - rise, all mean - er serv - ice scorn - ing;

Haste, let us lay our gifts be - fore the King.
The Christ of God, the Life, the Truth, the Way.
The bless - ed - ness which sim - ple trust has found.
Of God and man in lov - ing serv - ice met.
Lord, we are Thine, we give our - selves to Thee! A - MEN.

Children

457

ANGEL VOICES

Francis Pott, 1861   8. 5. 8. 5. 8. 4. 3.   Arthur S. Sullivan, 1872

Joyfully

1. An - gel voic - es, ev - er sing - ing
2. Lord, we know Thy love re - joic - es
3. Here, great God, to - day we of - fer
4. Hon - or, glo - ry, might, and mer - it,

Round Thy throne of light, An - gel harps, for - ev - er ring - ing,
O'er each work of Thine; Thou didst ears and hands and voic - es,
Of Thine own to Thee; And for Thine ac - cept - ance prof - fer,
Thine shall ev - er be, Fa - ther, Son, and Ho - ly Spir - it,

Rest not day nor night; Thou - sands on - ly live to bless Thee,
For Thy praise com - bine; Crafts - man's art and mu - sic's meas - ure
All un - wor - thi - ly, Hearts and minds, and hands, and voic - es,
Bless - ed Trin - i - ty: Of the best that Thou hast giv - en,

And con - fess Thee Lord of might.
For Thy pleas - ure Didst de - sign.
In our choic - est Mel - o - dy.
Earth and heav - en Ren - der Thee. A - MEN.

Children

458

JOHN PAGE HOPPS, 1877   7.7.7.7.   *Magdaïen Chapel Hymns, c. 1760*

LYNE

In moderate time

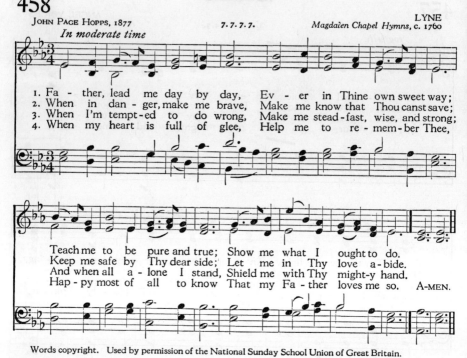

1. Fa - ther, lead me day by day, Ev - er in Thine own sweet way;
2. When in dan - ger, make me brave, Make me know that Thou canst save;
3. When I'm tempt-ed to do wrong, Make me stead - fast, wise, and strong;
4. When my heart is full of glee, Help me to re - mem - ber Thee,

Teach me to be pure and true; Show me what I ought to do.
Keep me safe by Thy dear side; Let me in Thy love a - bide.
And when all a - lone I stand, Shield me with Thy might-y hand.
Hap - py most of all to know That my Fa - ther loves me so. A-MEN.

Words copyright. Used by permission of the National Sunday School Union of Great Britain.

459

MARY LUNDIE DUNCAN, 1839   8.7.8.7.   *Liederbuch für Kleinkinderschulen, 1842*

DIJON

With quiet confidence

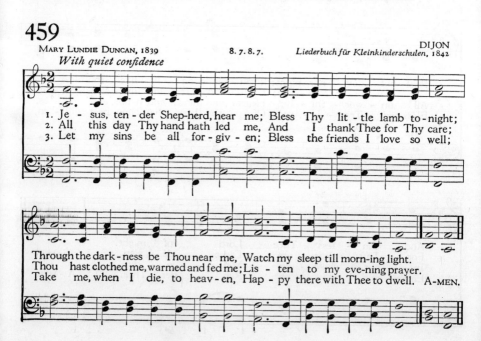

1. Je - sus, ten - der Shep-herd, hear me; Bless Thy lit - tle lamb to-night;
2. All this day Thy hand hath led me, And I thank Thee for Thy care;
3. Let my sins be all for - giv - en; Bless the friends I love so well;

Through the dark - ness be Thou near me, Watch my sleep till morn-ing light.
Thou hast clothed me, warmed and fed me; Lis - ten to my eve-ning prayer.
Take me, when I die, to heav - en, Hap - py there with Thee to dwell. A-MEN.

Children

460

SWEET STORY
A Greek Folk Song
Arr. WILLIAM B. BRADBURY, 1859

JEMIMA LUKE, 1841   Irregular

In the style of a carol

1. I think when I read that sweet story of old,
2. I wish that His hands had been placed on my head,
3. Yet still to His foot-stool in prayer I may go,
4. I long for the joy of that glo-ri-ous time,

When Je-sus was here a-mong men,
That His arm had been thrown a-round me,
And ask for a share in His love;
The sweet-est and bright-est and best,

How He called lit-tle chil-dren as lambs to His fold,
And that I might have seen His kind look when He said,
And if I now ear-nest-ly seek Him be-low,
When the dear lit-tle chil-dren of ev - - ery clime

I should like to have been with them then.
"Let the lit-tle ones come un-to Me."
I shall see Him and hear Him a-bove.
All shall crowd to His arms and be blest.   A-MEN.

Children

461

From *Hymns for the Young,* 1836
Ascribed to DOROTHY A. THRUPP

8. 7. 8. 7. D.

BRADBURY
WILLIAM B. BRADBURY, 1859
Reharmonized

In moderate time; with simplicity

1. Sav - iour, like a shep-herd lead us, Much we need Thy ten-der care;
2. We are Thine; do Thou be - friend us, Be the Guard-ian of our way;
3. Ear - ly let us seek Thy fa - vor; Ear - ly let us do Thy will;

In Thy pleas-ant pas-tures feed us, For our use Thy folds pre-pare.
Keep Thy flock, from sin de - fend us, Seek us when we go a - stray.
Bless - ed Lord and on - ly Sav - iour, With Thy love our bos - oms fill.

Bless - ed Je - sus, Bless - ed Je - sus, Thou hast bought us, Thine we are;
Bless - ed Je - sus, Bless - ed Je - sus, Hear Thy chil - dren when they pray;
Bless - ed Je - sus, Bless - ed Je - sus, Thou hast loved us, love us still;

Bless - ed Je - sus, Bless - ed Je - sus, Thou hast bought us, Thine we are.
Bless - ed Je - sus, Bless - ed Je - sus, Hear Thy chil - dren when they pray.
Bless - ed Je - sus, Bless - ed Je - sus, Thou hast loved us, love us still. A-MEN.

Miscellaneous Hymns

462

FANNY J. CROSBY, 1820–1915   7. 6. 7. 6. with Refrain   NEAR THE CROSS
WILLIAM H. DOANE, 1832–1915

1. Je - sus, keep me near the cross; There a pre - cious foun - tain,
2. Near the cross, a trem - bling soul, Love and mer - cy found me;
3. Near the cross! O Lamb of God, Bring its scenes be - fore me;
4. Near the cross I'll watch and wait, Hop - ing, trust - ing ev - er,

Free to all— a heal - ing stream—Flows from Cal - vary's moun - tain.
There the bright and morn - ing Star Shed its beams a - round me.
Help me walk from day to day With its shad - ow o'er me.
Till I reach the heaven - ly land, Just be - yond the riv - er.

REFRAIN

In the cross, in the cross, be my glo - ry ev - er,

Till my 'rap - tured soul shall find Rest be - yond the riv - er.

463

John M. Wigner, 1872

6. 6. 6. 6. D.

COME TO THE SAVIOUR
Frederick C. Maker, 1881

1. Come to the Sav - iour now, He gen - tly call - eth thee;
2. Come to the Sav - iour now, Ye who have wan - dered far;
3. Come to the Sav - iour, all, What - e'er your bur - dens be;

In true re - pent - ance bow, Be - fore Him bend the knee;
Re - new your sol - emn vow, For His by right you are;
Hear now His lov - ing call, "Cast all your care on Me."

He wait - eth to be - stow Sal - va - tion, peace and love,
Come, like poor wan - dering sheep Re - turn - ing to His fold;
Come, and for ev - ery grief, In Je - sus you will find

True joy on earth be - low, A home in heaven a - bove.
His arm will safe - ly keep, His love will ne'er grow cold.
A sure and safe re - lief, A lov - ing Friend and kind.

Miscellaneous Hymns

464

MARTHA J. LANKTON

8. 7. 8. 7. with Refrain

DWELL IN ME
GEORGIA GUINEY BERKEY

1. Dwell in me, O bless-ed Spir - it, How I need Thy help di - vine!
2. Let me feel Thy sa - cred pres - ence; Then my faith will ne'er de - cline;
3. Round the cross where Thou hast led me, Let my pur - est feel - ings twine;
4. Dwell in me, O bless-ed Spir - it, Gra - cious Teach - er, Friend di - vine,

In the way of life e - ter - nal, Keep, oh, keep this heart of mine.
Com - fort Thou and help me on - ward, Fill with love this heart of mine.
With the blood from sin that cleansed me, Seal a - new this heart of mine.
For the home of bliss that waits me O pre - pare this heart of mine.

REFRAIN

Dwell in me, oh, dwell in me; Hear and grant my prayer to Thee;

Spir - it, now from heaven de - scend-ing, Come, oh, come and dwell in me.

465

FRANCIS H. ROWLEY

HYFRYDOL
ROWLAND HUGH PRICHARD, 1811–1887

8. 7. 8. 7. with Refrain

1. I will sing the won-drous sto - ry Of the Christ who died for me,
2. I was lost, but Je - sus found me, Found the sheep that went a - stray;
3. I was bruised, but Je - sus healed me; Faint was I from many a fall;
4. Days of dark - ness still come o'er me, Sor-row's paths I of - ten tread,

How He left His home in glo - ry For the cross on Cal - va - ry.
Threw His lov - ing arms a - round me, Drew me back in - to His way.
Sight was gone, and fears pos - sessed me, But He freed me from them all.
But the Sav - iour still is with me, By His hand I'm safe - ly led.

REFRAIN

Yes, I'll sing the won-drous sto - ry Of the Christ who died for me,

Sing it with the saints in glo - ry, Gath-ered by the crys - tal sea.

466

JOSEPH H. GILMORE, 1861   L. M. D.   HE LEADETH ME
WILLIAM B. BRADBURY, 1864

1. He lead - eth me: O bless - ed thought, O words with heaven-ly com-fort fraught!
2. Lord, I would clasp Thy hand in mine, Nor ev - er mur - mur nor re - pine;
3. And when my task on earth is done, When by Thy grace the vic-tory's won,

What - e'er I do, wher-e'er I be, Still 'tis God's hand that lead-eth me.
Con - tent, what-ev - er lot I see, Since 'tis my God that lead-eth me.
E'en death's cold wave I will not flee Since God through Jor - dan lead-eth me.

REFRAIN

He lead-eth me, He lead - eth me; By His own hand He lead-eth me:

His faith-ful fol-lower I would be, For by His hand He lead - eth me.

467

KATHERINE HANKEY, 1866; refrain added
7. 6. 7. 6. D. with Refrain

I LOVE TO TELL THE STORY
WILLIAM G. FISHER, 1869

1. I love to tell the sto-ry Of un-seen things a-bove,
2. I love to tell the sto-ry, 'Tis pleas-ant to re-peat
3. I love to tell the sto-ry, For those who know it best

Of Je-sus and His glo-ry, Of Je-sus and His love.
What seems, each time I tell it, More won-der-ful-ly sweet.
Seem hun-ger-ing and thirst-ing To hear it, like the rest.

I love to tell the sto-ry, Be-cause I know 'tis true;
I love to tell the sto-ry, For some have nev-er heard
And when, in scenes of glo-ry, I sing the new, new song,

It sat-is-fies my long-ings As noth-ing else would do.
The mes-sage of sal-va-tion From God's own Ho-ly Word.
'Twill be the old, old sto-ry That I have loved so long.

REFRAIN

I love to tell the sto-ry, 'Twill be my theme in glo-ry

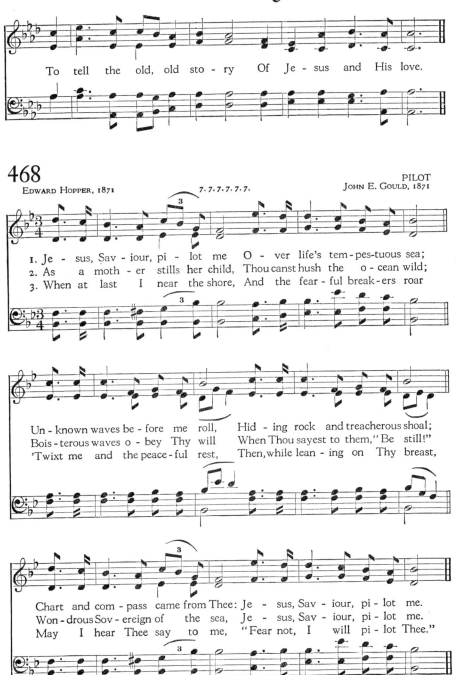

To tell the old, old story Of Jesus and His love.

468

EDWARD HOPPER, 1871
7.7.7.7.7.7.
PILOT
JOHN E. GOULD, 1871

1. Jesus, Saviour, pilot me O - ver life's tem - pes-tuous sea;
2. As a moth - er stills her child, Thou canst hush the o - cean wild;
3. When at last I near the shore, And the fear - ful break-ers roar

Un - known waves be - fore me roll, Hid - ing rock and treacherous shoal;
Bois - terous waves o - bey Thy will When Thou sayest to them, "Be still!"
'Twixt me and the peace - ful rest,

Chart and com - pass came from Thee: Je - sus, Sav - iour, pi - lot me.
Won - drous Sov - ereign of the sea, Je - sus, Sav - iour, pi - lot me.
May I hear Thee say to me, "Fear not, I will pi - lot Thee."

469

ANNIE S. HAWKS, 1872
Refrain added by ROBERT LOWRY   6. 4. 6. 4. with Refrain

NEED

ROBERT LOWRY, 1872

1. I need Thee ev - ery hour, Most gra - cious Lord;
2. I need Thee ev - ery hour, Stay Thou near by;
3. I need Thee ev - ery hour, In joy or pain;
4. I need Thee ev - ery hour, Teach me Thy will;
5. I need Thee ev - ery hour, Most Ho - ly One;

No ten - der voice like Thine Can peace af - ford.
Temp - ta - tions lose their power When Thou art nigh.
Come quick - ly and a - bide, Or life is vain.
And Thy rich prom - is - es In me ful - fil.
O, make me Thine in - deed, Thou bless - èd Son.

REFRAIN

I need Thee, O I need Thee; Ev - ery hour I need Thee;

O bless me now, my Sav - iour! I come to Thee.

Miscellaneous Hymns

470

SYLVANUS D. PHELPS, 1862   6. 4. 6. 4. 6. 6. 6. 4

SOMETHING FOR JESUS
ROBERT LOWRY, 1872

1. Sav - iour, Thy dy - ing love Thou gav - est me,
2. At the blest mer - cy - seat, Plead - ing for me,
3. Give me a faith - ful heart, Like - ness to Thee,
4. All that I am and have, Thy gifts so free,

Nor should I aught with - hold, Dear Lord, from Thee;
My fee - ble faith looks up, Je - sus, to Thee.
That each de - part - ing day Hence - forth may see
In joy, in grief, through life, Dear Lord, for Thee!

In love my soul would bow, My heart ful - fil its vow,
Help me the cross to bear, Thy won - drous love de - clare,
Some work of love be - gun, Some deed of kind - ness done,
And when Thy face I see, My ran - somed soul shall be,

Some of - fering bring Thee now, Some - thing for Thee.
Some song to raise, or prayer, Some - thing for Thee.
Some wan - derer sought and won, Some - thing for Thee.
Through all e - ter - ni - ty, Some - thing for Thee.

471

ELIZABETH P. PRENTISS, 1869   6.4.6.4.6.6.6.4.

MORE LOVE TO THEE
W. H. DOANE, 1868

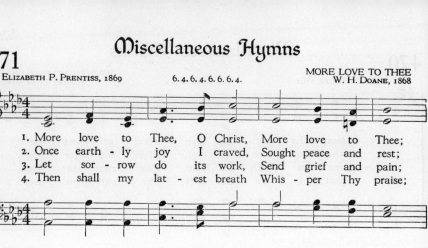

1. More love to Thee, O Christ, More love to Thee;
2. Once earth - ly joy I craved, Sought peace and rest;
3. Let sor - row do its work, Send grief and pain;
4. Then shall my lat - est breath Whis - per Thy praise;

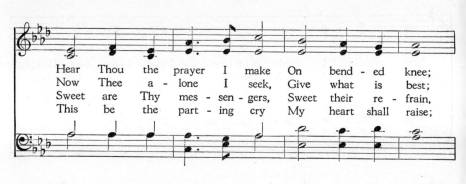

Hear Thou the prayer I make On bend - ed knee;
Now Thee a - lone I seek, Give what is best;
Sweet are Thy mes - sen - gers, Sweet their re - frain,
This be the part - ing cry My heart shall raise;

This is my ear - nest plea, More love, O Christ, to Thee,
This all my prayer shall be, More love, O Christ, to Thee,
When they can sing with me, More love, O Christ, to Thee,
This still its prayer shall be, More love, O Christ, to Thee,

More love to Thee, More love to Thee!

Miscellaneous Hymns

472

JOSEPH SCRIVEN, 1855

8. 7. 8. 7. D.

WHAT A FRIEND (ERIE)
C. C. CONVERSE, 1868

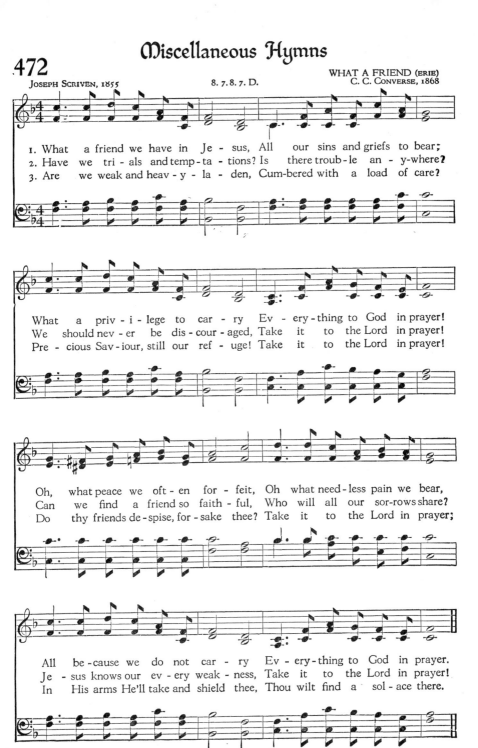

1. What a friend we have in Je - sus, All our sins and griefs to bear;
2. Have we tri - als and temp - ta - tions? Is there troub - le an - y-where?
3. Are we weak and heav - y - la - den, Cum-bered with a load of care?

What a priv - i - lege to car - ry Ev - ery-thing to God in prayer!
We should nev - er be dis - cour - aged, Take it to the Lord in prayer!
Pre - cious Sav - iour, still our ref - uge! Take it to the Lord in prayer!

Oh, what peace we oft - en for - feit, Oh what need - less pain we bear,
Can we find a friend so faith - ful, Who will all our sor-rows share?
Do thy friends de - spise, for - sake thee? Take it to the Lord in prayer;

All be - cause we do not car - ry Ev - ery-thing to God in prayer.
Je - sus knows our ev - ery weak - ness, Take it to the Lord in prayer!
In His arms He'll take and shield thee, Thou wilt find a sol - ace there.

473

GERHARD TERSTEEGEN, 1697–1769
TR. SARAH B. FINDLATER, 1855

4.4.8.8.8.

CLOLATA

ST. CLAIR PALMER

1. God call - ing yet! Shall I not hear? Earth's pleas - ures
2. God call - ing yet! Shall I not rise? Can I His
3. God call - ing yet! And shall He knock, And I my
4. God call - ing yet! And shall I give No heed, but
5. God call - ing yet! I can - not stay; My heart I

shall I still hold dear? Shall life's swift pass - ing
lov - ing voice de - spise, And base - ly His kind
heart the clos - er lock? He still is wait - ing
still in bond - age live? I wait, but He does
yield with - out de - lay: Vain world, fare - well, from

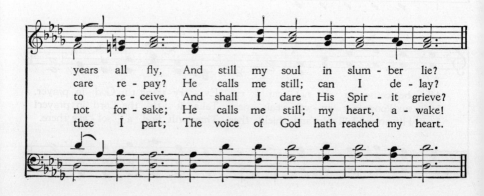

years all fly, And still my soul in slum - ber lie?
care re - pay? He calls me still; can I de - lay?
to re - ceive, And shall I dare His Spir - it grieve?
not for - sake; He calls me still; my heart, a - wake!
thee I part; The voice of God hath reached my heart.

474

JAMES G. SMALL, 1866   8.7.8.7.D.   CONSTANCE
ARTHUR S. SULLIVAN, 1875

1. I've found a Friend, O such a Friend! He loved me ere I knew Him;
2. I've found a Friend, O such a Friend! He bled, He died to save me;
3. I've found a Friend, O such a Friend! So kind and true and ten-der,

He drew me with the cords of love, And thus He bound me to Him;
And not a-lone the gift of life, But His own self He gave me!
So wise a Coun-sel-lor and Guide, So might-y a De-fend-er!

And round my heart still close-ly twine Those ties which naught can sev-er,
Naught that I have mine own I call, I'll hold it for the Giv-er,
From Him who loves me now so well What power my soul can sev-er?

For I am His, and He is mine For-ev-er and for-ev-er.
My heart, my strength, my life, my all Are His, and His for-ev-er.
Shall life or death, shall earth or hell? No! I am His for-ev-er.

475

W. W. Walford   L. M. D.   SWEET HOUR
Wm. B. Bradbury, 1859

1. Sweet hour of prayer, sweet hour of prayer, That calls me from a world of care,
2. Sweet hour of prayer, sweet hour of prayer, Thy wings shall my pe - ti - tion bear
3. Sweet hour of prayer, sweet hour of prayer, May I thy con - so - la - tion share

And bids me at my Fa-ther's throne Make all my wants and wish - es known;
To Him whose truth and faith-ful-ness En - gage the wait - ing soul to bless.
Till from Mount Pis-gah's loft - y height I view my home and take my flight.

In sea-sons of dis-tress and grief My soul has oft - en found re - lief,
And since He bids me seek His face, Be - lieve His word and trust His grace,
This robe of flesh I'll drop, and rise To seize the ev - er - last - ing prize,

And oft es-caped the tempt-er's snare By thy re - turn, sweet hour of prayer.
I'll cast on Him my ev - ery care, And wait for thee, sweet hour of prayer.
And, dwell-ing in the man-sions fair, Still think of thee, sweet hour of prayer!

476

ROBERT ROBINSON, 1758

8.7.8.7.D.

NETTLETON
JOHN WYETH, 1812

1. Come, thou Fount of ev-ery bless-ing, Tune my heart to sing Thy grace;
2. Here I raise my Eb-en-e-zer; Hith-er by Thy help I'm come;
3. O to grace how great a debt-or Dai-ly I'm con-strained to be!

Streams of mer-cy nev-er ceas-ing Call for songs of loud-est praise:
And I hope, by Thy good pleas-ure, Safe-ly to ar-rive at home.
Let that grace now, like a fet-ter, Bind my wan-dering heart to Thee.

Teach me some me-lo-dious son-net, Sung by flam-ing tongues a-bove.
Je-sus sought me when a stran-ger, Wan-dering from the fold of God;
Prone to wan-der, Lord, I feel it; Prone to leave the God I love;

Praise the mount; I'm fixed up-on it, Mount of God's un-chang-ing love.
He, to res-cue me from dan-ger, In-ter-posed with pre-cious blood.
Here's my heart; O take and seal it, Seal it from Thy courts a-bove.

Miscellaneous Hymns

ANNA L. COGHILL, 1860   7. 6. 7. 5. D.   WORK SONG
LOWELL MASON, 1864

1. Work, for the night is com - ing, Work through the morn - ing hours;
2. Work, for the night is com - ing, Work through the sun - ny noon;
3. Work, for the night is com - ing, Un - der the sun - set skies;

Work while the dew is spark - ling, Work 'mid spring - ing flowers;
Fill bright - est hours with la - bor, Rest comes sure and soon.
While their bright tints are glow - ing, Work, for day - light flies.

Work when the day grows bright - er, Work in the glow - ing sun;
Give ev - ery fly - ing min - ute, Some - thing to keep in store;
Work till the last beam fad - eth, Fad - eth to shine no more;

Work, for the night is com - ing, When man's work is done.
Work, for the night is com - ing, When man works no more.
Work while the night is dark - ening, When man's work is o'er.

Miscellaneous Hymns

478

HARRE MEINE SEELE (WAIT ON GOD)

Stanzas 1, 2 FRIEDRICH RÄDER, 1845
Tr. J. H. HORSTMANN, 1908
Stanzas 3 and 4, J. C. HANSEN, 1916
10. 11. 9. 11. 9. 10.
CÉSAR MALAN, 1827

1. Wait on God, and trust Him through all thy days; Cast thy cares up - on Him
2. Wait on God, and trust Him through all thy days; Cast thy cares up - on Him
3. Wait on God, and trust Him through all thy days; Cast thy cares up - on Him
4. Wait on God, and trust Him through all thy days; Cast thy cares up - on Him

who guides all thy ways. Do not de - spair; as the morn - ing fair
who guides all thy ways. Per - ish what will, God is ref - uge still;
who guides all thy ways. Take up Thy cross; count it not a loss,
who guides all thy ways. On bend - ed knee, Lord, I cry to Thee;

Scat - ters fog and dark - ness, God re - moves thy care. 'Midst all thy tri - als,
Great - er than the Help - er is not an - y ill. Faith - ful, e - ter - nal
For the heat of sor - row melts a - way the dross. Je - sus, dear Sav - iour,
Shield my soul from e - vil; to Thy cross I flee. Gra - cious Re - deem - er,

in all thy care God re - mains thy faith - ful Friend ev - ery - where.
Sav - iour and Friend, Save my soul from e - vil un - to the end.
pa - tient and mild, Let me be o - be - dient, a trust - ing child.
might - y and strong, Let me sing re - joic - ing the vic - tor's song.

479

CECIL FRANCES ALEXANDER, 1848   C. M. with Refrain   GREEN HILL
                                                             GEORGE C. STEBBINS, 1878

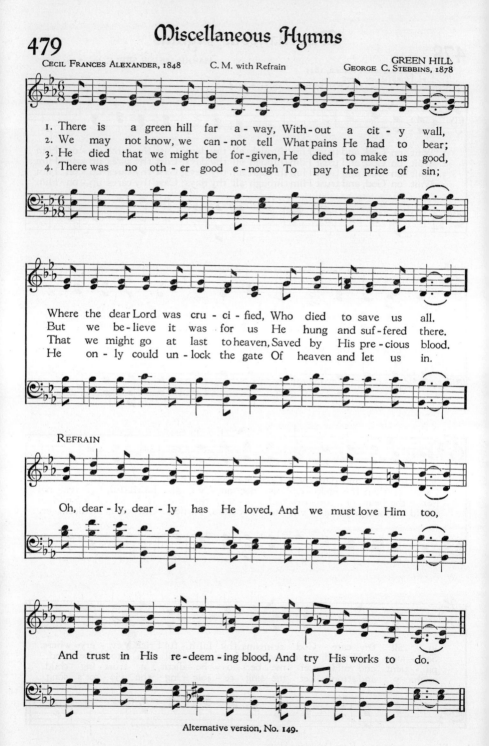

1. There is a green hill far a - way, With - out a cit - y wall,
2. We may not know, we can - not tell What pains He had to bear;
3. He died that we might be for - given, He died to make us good,
4. There was no oth - er good e - nough To pay the price of sin;

Where the dear Lord was cru - ci - fied, Who died to save us all.
But we be - lieve it was for us He hung and suf - fered there.
That we might go at last to heaven, Saved by His pre - cious blood.
He on - ly could un - lock the gate Of heaven and let us in.

REFRAIN

Oh, dear - ly, dear - ly has He loved, And we must love Him too,

And trust in His re - deem - ing blood, And try His works to do.

Alternative version, No. 149.

480

HORATIUS BONAR, 1846   C. M. D.   INVITATION
LOUIS SPOHR, 1835

1. I heard the voice of Je - sus say, "Come un - to Me and rest;
2. I heard the voice of Je - sus say, "Be - hold, I free - ly give
3. I heard the voice of Je - sus say, "I am this dark world's Light;

Lay down, thou wea - ry one, lay down Thy head up - on My breast."
The liv - ing wa - ter; thirst - y one, Stoop down, and drink, and live.'
Look un - to me, thy morn shall rise, And all thy day be bright."

I came to Je - sus as I was, Wea - ry, and worn, and sad;
I came to Je - sus, and I drank Of that life - giv - ing stream;
I looked to Je - sus, and I found In Him my Star, my Sun;

I found in Him a rest - ing place, And He has made me glad.
My thirst was quenched, my soul re - vived, And now I live in Him.
And in that light of life I'll walk, Till trav - el - ing days are done.

Alternative version No. 236

Miscellaneous Hymns

481

MARY A. LATHBURY, 1877

7.7.7.7.4. with Refrain

EVENING PRAISE (CHAUTAUQUA)
WILLIAM F. SHERWIN, 1877

Quietly and reverently

1. Day is dy-ing in the west; Heaven is touch-ing earth with rest: Wait and wor-ship while the night Sets her eve-ning lamps a-light Through all the sky.

2. Lord of life, be-neath the dome Of the u-ni-verse, Thy home, Gath-er us who seek Thy face To the fold of Thy em-brace, For Thou art nigh.

3. While the deep-ening shad-ows fall, Heart of Love, en-fold-ing all, Through the glo-ry and the grace Of the stars that veil Thy face, Our hearts as-cend.

4. When for-ev-er from our sight Pass the stars, the day, the night, Lord of an-gels, on our eyes Let e-ter-nal morn-ing rise, And shad-ows end.

REFRAIN

Ho-ly, ho-ly, ho-ly Lord God of Hosts! Heaven and earth are full of Thee!

Heaven and earth are prais-ing Thee, O Lord Most High!

Used by permission of the Chautauqua Institution.

Responses
and
Canticles

Chanting

Chanting is the recitation of the words of a psalm or canticle to a series of tones; it is indeed nothing more or less than rhythmical reading. The words are, therefore, of supreme importance. They should be sung at a uniform rate of speed throughout, with every syllable clearly enunciated. This should not be done prosaically, however; the rhythm should be unfailingly maintained and the sense clear, so that the whole is vibrant, full of life and significance.

A comma should be observed only as a means of phrasing; the pause should be so slight that the effect is rather that of an almost imperceptible lengthening of the previous syllable. Breath should be taken only at the end of a line.

The presence of a hyphen in a place where it does not simply mark the division of syllables of a word indicates that the syllable before the hyphen should be extended over the following note or notes of the music to which no syllables are allotted. When both the division of syllables of a word and the prolongation of a syllable over more than one note must be indicated two hyphens are used, a short and a long.

Opening Responses

482

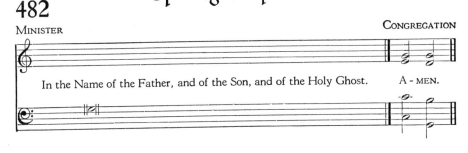

MINISTER — CONGREGATION

In the Name of the Father, and of the Son, and of the Holy Ghost. A - MEN.

483*

MINISTER: Behold the tabernacle of God is with men, and He shall dwell with them, and they shall be His people, and God Himself shall be with them and be their God.

IPPOLITOFF–IVANOFF

CHOIR: *p Very slowly*

Bless the Lord, O . . . my soul, Bless-ed art Thou, O . . Lord.

MINISTER: The Lord is nigh unto all that call upon Him, to all that call upon Him in truth. He will hear their cry and will save them.

CHOIR: *mf*

Bless the Lord, [O . . . . my soul and all that

pp rit.

is with-in me bless His ho - ly Name Bless the Lord, O my soul.

* These Responses may be used separately or together.

Opening Responses

484

SAMUEL P. WARREN, 1909

Slowly

Seek ye the Lord while He may be found, call ye upon Him while He is near. A-MEN.

485

WILLIAM PENNEFATHER, 1816–1873   6. 5. 6. 5.   BEMERTON (CASWALL)
FRIEDRICH FILITZ, 1804–1876

With reverence

Je-sus, stand a-mong us In Thy ris-en power;

Let this time of wor-ship Be a hal-lowed hour. A-MEN.

486

CALVIN W. LAUFER, 1926

mf Slowly

The Lord is in His ho-ly tem-ple, Let all the

pp

earth keep si-lence be-fore Him; Keep si-lence be-fore Him.

487

With reverence

The Lord is in His ho-ly tem-ple, Let all the earth keep si-lence be-fore Him.

En-ter in-to His gates with thanks-giv-ing And in-to His courts with praise.

488

"Liturgy of St. James"
Trans. Gerard Moultrie, 1829-1885

PICARDY
French Traditional Carol

8.7.8.7.8.7.

Unison. *In rather slow time*

Let all mor-tal flesh keep si-lence, And with fear and trem-bling stand;

Pon-der noth-ing earth-ly mind-ed, For with bless-ing in His hand,

God with-in His tem-ple dwell — eth, Our full hom-age doth de — mand.

489

Old Scottish Chant

1. Glory be to . . . God on high, and on earth peace, good will towards men.
2. { We praise Thee, we } { we glorify Thee, }
   { bless Thee, we } wor-ship Thee, { we give thanks to } Thy great glo - ry.
   { Thee for }

3. O Lord God, heaven-ly King, God the Father Al - might - y:

4. { O Lord, the only-be- } Je - sus Christ: { O Lord God, } Fa - ther:
   { gotten Son, } { Lamb of God, }
   { Son of the }
5. That takest away the sins of the world, have mercy up- on — us;
6. Thou that takest away the sins of the world, re - ceive our prayer;
7. { Thou that sittest at the } Fa - ther, have mercy up- on — us;
   { right hand of God the }

8. For Thou only art ho - ly; Thou on - ly art the Lord.
9. { Thou only, O Christ, } Ho - ly Ghost, { art most high } God the Fa - ther.
   { with the } { in the glory of }

A - MEN.

Alternative Metrical Version, No. 2

490

GLORIA PATRI

Old Scottish Chant

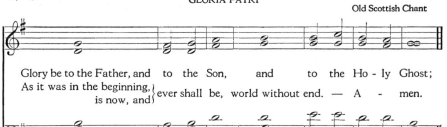

Glory be to the Father, and to the Son, and to the Ho-ly Ghost;
As it was in the beginning, } ever shall be, world without end. — A - men.
is now, and

491

GLORIA PATRI

Anon.

In moderate time

Glo - ry be to the Fa - ther, and to the Son, and to the

Ho - ly Ghost; as it was in the be - gin - ning, is

now, and ev - er shall be, world with - out end. A - men.

492

GLORIA PATRI

CHARLES MEINEKE, 1782–1850

In moderate time

Glo - ry be to the Fa - ther, and to the Son, and to the Ho - ly Ghost; as it

was in the be-gin-ning, is now and ev-er shall be, world with-out end. A-men, A-men.

493

GLORIA PATRI

H. W. GREATOREX, 1851

With spirit

Glo - ry be to the Fa - ther, and to the Son, and to the

Ho - ly Ghost; as it was in the be - gin - ning, is

now, and ev - er shall be, world with-out end. A - men, A - men.

Praise Responses

JEHOVAH

494

G. K. Pfeffel, 1776
Tr. C. G. Haas, 1897

Irregular

Joh. Carl Gerold, 1800

With dignity

Je - ho - vah, Je - ho - vah, Je - ho - vah, Thou art wor - thy
Of hon - or and glo - ry and praise! A - men, A - men! Un -
til the tem - ple of this world By Thy power to dust is hurled,
Help us when these halls we throng, The Ho - ly, Ho - ly, Ho - ly
to pro - long, Hal - le - lu - jah! Hal - le - lu - jah!

Responses to Scripture

495 HALLELUJAH

W. H. MONK

Hal - le - lu - jah, Hal - le - lu - jah, Hal - le - lu - jah!

496 HALLELUJAH

Hal - le - lu - jah, Hal - le - lu - jah, Hal - le - lu - jah!

497 GLORIA TIBI
Before the Gospel

Glo - ry be to Thee, O Lord.

LAUS TIBI
After the Gospel

Praise be to Thee, O Christ.

498 GLORIA TIBI
Before the Gospel

Glo - ry be to Thee, O Lord.

LAUS TIBI
After the Gospel

J. PLAYFORD, 1674-1730

Praise be to Thee, O Christ.

499 DEUS MISEREATUR

God be merciful unto us and } bless us; { and cause His face to } shine up - on us

That Thy way may be known up- } on earth, { Thy saving health a- } mong all na - tions. A-MEN.

Responses to Scripture

From *Call to Worship*
D. TAIT PATTERSON

GEORGE DYSON

Let Thy word a - bide in us, O Lord.

NOTE. The morning and evening canticles No. 528 to No. 538 may also be used after the Scripture Lesson.

501 Prayer Responses

5. 5. 5. 5.

GEORGE WHELPTON, 1847-1930

Hear our prayer, O Lord; Hear our prayer, O Lord;

Hear our prayer, O Lord, And grant us Thy peace. A-MEN.

502

JOSEPH BARNBY, 1838-1896

{Let the words of my}
{mouth and the med-} of my heart {Thy sight, O Lord,} my Re-deem - er. A-MEN.
{ itation} {my strength and}
{be acceptable in}

Prayer Responses

503

Rather slowly

10. 10. 10. 10.

MORECAMBE
Frederick C. Atkinson, 1880

O Thou who hear - est ev - ery heart-felt prayer, With Thy rich grace, Lord,
all our hearts pre - pare; Thou art our Life, Thou art our Love and Light,
O let this Sab - bath hour with Thee be bright. A - MEN.

504

With quiet reverence

10. 9.

Hear, O Lord, our hum - ble sup - pli - ca - tion; Ac -
cept us, O Lord, for Je - sus' sake. A - MEN.

Offertory Responses

505

Ludwig van Beethoven, 1770–1827

All things come of Thee, O Lord: and of Thine own have we giv-en Thee. A-men.

506

William Walsham How, 1864 S. M. ST. ANDREW
Joseph Barnby, 1866

We give Thee but Thine own, What-e'er the gift may be;

All that we have is Thine a-lone, A trust, O Lord, from Thee. A-men.

507

Samuel Longfellow, 1886 L. M. DEUS TUORUM MILITUM
Grenoble Church Melody

With dignity

Bless Thou the gifts our hands have brought; Bless Thou the work our hearts have planned;

Ours is the faith, the will, the thought, The rest, O God, is in Thy hand. A - men.

Offertory Responses

508

JOHN GREENLEAF WHITTIER, 1807–1892   L. M.   HERR JESU CHRIST (CANTIONALE)   Pensum Sacrum, GÖRLITZ, 1648

May be sung in unison

All things are Thine: no gift have we, Lord of all gifts, to of-fer Thee;

And hence with grate-ful hearts to-day, Thine own be-fore Thy feet we lay.

509

Closing Responses

SAMUEL LONGFELLOW, 1864   From *Laudi Spirituali*

p With deep devotion

Fa-ther, give Thy be-ne-dic-tion, Give Thy peace be-fore we part. A-MEN.

510

Z. B. EDWORTHY   7.7.7.7.   ST. BEES   JOHN B. DYKES, 1862

In moderate time

Fa-ther, bless us as we part, Grant us peace that makes us free,

Strength-en ev-ery trust-ing heart With the love that comes from Thee. A-MEN.

Closing Responses

PEACE I LEAVE WITH YOU

511

JOHN xiv : 27
For Women's Voices

Vassar College Tradition
Arr. GEORGE C. GOW

Peace I leave with you, my peace I give un - to you:

not as the world giv - eth, give I un - to you.

Let not your heart be trou - bled, nei - ther let it be a - fraid.

Slower

Peace I leave with you, my peace I give un - to you.

NOTE : For additional closing responses see hymn 32, stanza 1, and hymn 36.

Response to the Commandments

KYRIE

After each commandment, except the last

George J. Elvey, 1816–1893

Lord, have mercy, have mer-cy up - on us, and in - cline our hearts to keep this law.

After the last

Lord, have mer - cy, have mer - cy up - on us, and write all these Thy

laws in our hearts, Thy laws in our hearts, we be - seech Thee.

512

513

Responses for the Communion Service and for General Use

Versicles and Responses I.

MORNING, EVENING, AND COMMUNION SERVICES

MINISTER:

CONGREGATION:

Praise ye the Lord:
O Lord, open Thou our lips:
The Lord be with you:

The Lord's Name be praised.
And our mouth shall show forth Thy praise.
And with thy spirit.

Let us pray:

Create in us a clean heart, O God:
Cast us not away from Thy presence:

And renew a right spirit with - in us.
And take not Thy Holy Spirit from us.

514

FOR THE COMMUNION SERVICE

H. S.

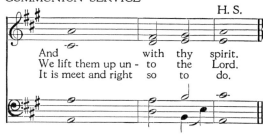

The Lord be with you:
Lift up your hearts:
Let us give thanks unto the Lord:

And with thy spirit.
We lift them up un - to the Lord.
It is meet and right so to do.

515

FOR THE LITANY

H. S.

LITANY PETITIONS
AND
INTERCESSIONS

Have mercy up - on — us.
Good Lord, de - liv - er us.
Spare us, good Lord.
Son of God, we beseech Thee to hear — us.
We beseech Thee to hear us, O Lord.
Grant us Thy peace.

NOTE: The above chants may be interchanged if it is desired.

516

Responses for the Communion Service and for General Use

Versicles and Responses II.

SALUTATION AND CALL TO PRAYER

MINISTER: CONGREGATION: Har. THOMAS TALLIS, c. 1505-1585

The Lord be with you:

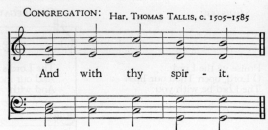

And with thy spir - it.

Let us pray:

Create in us a clean heart, O God:

And re-new a right spir-it with-in us.

Cast us not away from Thy presence:

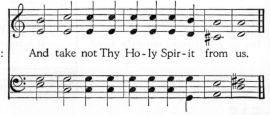

And take not Thy Ho-ly Spir-it from us.

517

CALL TO PRAISE

O Lord, open Thou our lips:

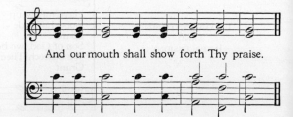

And our mouth shall show forth Thy praise.

Responses for the Communion Service and for General Use

MINISTER:

Praise ye the Lord:

CONGREGATION:

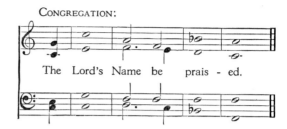

The Lord's Name be prais - ed.

518

KYRIE

From the *American Lutheran Hymnal*

MINISTER:

Lord, have mercy upon us.

CHOIR OR CONGREGATION:

Lord, have mer - cy up - on us.

Christ, have mercy upon us

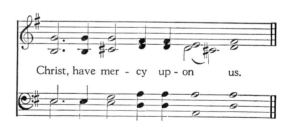

Christ, have mer - cy up - on us.

Lord, have mercy upon us

Lord, have mer - cy up - on us.

Responses for the Communion Service and for General Use

519

KYRIE

O God, the Father in Heaven, have mer-cy up-on us;

O God, the Son, Redeemer of the world, have mer-cy up-on us;

O God, the Holy Ghost, have mer-cy up-on us, And grant us Thy peace. A-men.

520

KYRIE

T. TERTIUS NOBLE, 1915

Lord, have mer-cy up-on us, Christ, have mer-cy up-

on . us, . Lord, have mer-cy up-on . . us.

Responses for the Communion Service
and for General Use
521

SANCTUS

R. TAYLOR

Ho - ly, Ho - ly, Ho - ly, Lord God of hosts,

Heaven and earth are full of Thy glo - ry:

Glo - ry be to Thee, O Lord Most High. A - men, A - men.

522

SERAPHIC HYMN

ALONZO P. HOWARD, 1838-1902

Ho - ly, Ho - ly, Ho - ly, Lord God of Sa - ba-oth; Heav-en and earth are

full, are full of the ma-jes-ty of Thy Glo - ry, Ho -san - na, ho -

Responses for the Communion Service and for General Use

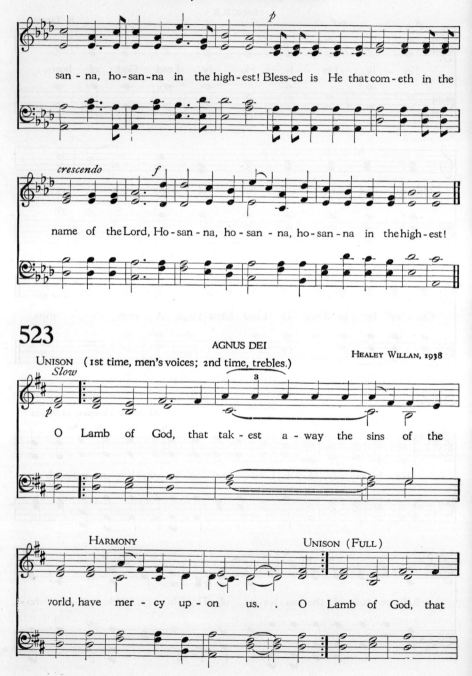

san - na, ho-san-na in the high-est! Bless-ed is He that com-eth in the

name of the Lord, Ho-san - na, ho - san - na, ho-san-na in the high-est!

523

AGNUS DEI

HEALEY WILLAN, 1938

UNISON (1st time, men's voices; 2nd time, trebles.)

Slow

O Lamb of God, that tak - est a - way the sins of the

HARMONY   UNISON (FULL)

world, have mer - cy up - on us. O Lamb of God, that

Responses for the Communion Service and for General Use

Harmony

tak - est a - way the sins of the world, grant us Thy peace.

524

AGNUS DEI

Iohn Merbecke, 1523–c. 1585

p Unison. *In free rhythm*

O Lamb of God, that tak-est a-way the sins of the world, have mer - cy up-on us;

O Lamb of God, that tak-est a - way the sins of the world, have mer-cy up-on us;

rit.

O Lamb of God, that tak - est a - way the sins of the world, grant us Thy peace.

Responses for the Communion Service and for General Use

AGNUS DEI

From a Lutheran Service of 1528

O Christ, Thou Lamb of God, that tak - est a - way the

sin of the world, have mer - cy up - on us;

O Christ, Thou Lamb of God, that tak - est a - way the

sin of the world, have mer - cy up - on us;

O Christ, Thou Lamb of God, that tak - est a - way the

Responses for the Communion Service and for General Use

sin of the world, grant us Thy peace. A - - - - - men.

526

AGNUS DEI

Nicolaus Decius, 1531

Nicolaus Decius, 1531

O Lamb of God who, bleed-ing, Up-on the cross didst lan-guish, Nor scorn nor mal-ice heed-ing, So pa-tient in Thine an-guish, On Thee our guilt was ly-ing; Thou sav-edst us by dy-ing: Have mer-cy on us, Lord Je-sus.

Responses for the Communion Service and for General Use

TE DEUM LAUDAMUS*

E. G. Monk

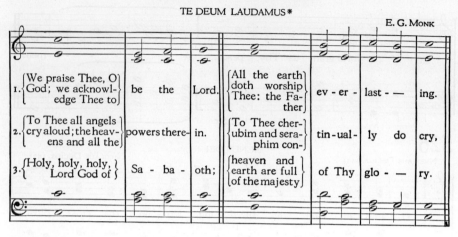

1. {We praise Thee, O God; we acknowledge Thee to} be the Lord. {All the earth doth worship Thee: the Father} ev-er-last-— ing.

2. {To Thee all angels cry aloud; the heavens and all the} powers there-in. {To Thee cherubim and seraphim con-} tin-ual-ly do cry,

3. {Holy, holy, holy, Lord God of} Sa-ba-oth; {heaven and earth are full of the majesty} of Thy glo-— ry.

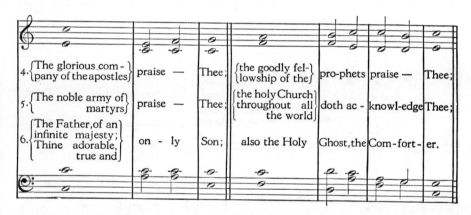

4. {The glorious company of the apostles} praise — Thee; {the goodly fellowship of the} pro-phets praise — Thee;

5. {The noble army of martyrs} praise — Thee; {the holy Church throughout all the world} doth ac-knowl-edge Thee;

6. {The Father, of an infinite majesty; Thine adorable, true and} on-ly Son; also the Holy Ghost, the Com-fort-er.

W. Croft

7. {Thou art the King of Glory,} O — Christ, {Thou art the everlasting} Son of the Fa-— ther.

8. {When Thou tookest upon Thee to de-} liv-er man, {Thou didst humble Thyself to be} born of a Vir-— gin.

9. {When Thou hadst overcome the} sharpness of death, {Thou didst open the kingdom of heaven to} all be-liev-— ers.

Responses for the Communion Service and for General Use

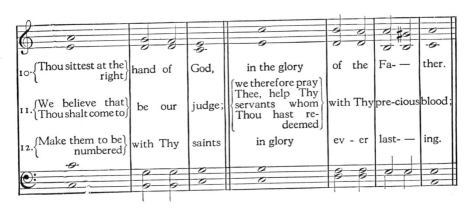

E. G. Monk

10. {Thou sittest at the right} hand of God, in the glory of the Fa- — ther.

11. {We believe that Thou shalt come to} be our judge; {we therefore pray Thee, help Thy servants whom Thou hast re-deemed} with Thy pre-cious blood;

12. {Make them to be numbered} with Thy saints in glory ev - er last- — ing.

13. {O Lord, save Thy peo-ple and bless Thine} her - i - tage; {govern them and lift them} up for - ev- — er.

14. Day by day we magni-fy Thee, {and we worship Thy Name ever} world with-out — end.

15. {Vouchsafe, O Lord, to keep us this day with-} out — sin. {O Lord, have mer-cy upon us, have} mercy up - on — us.

16. {O Lord, let Thy mercy be upon us, as our trust} is in Thee; {O Lord, in Thee have I trusted, let me never} be con - found- — ed.

Note: The Canticle may end with the twelfth verse. Verses 13–16 may be sung either by themselves, or with the other verses.

* For metrical version of this Canticle see Hymn 20.

Morning Canticles

*VENITE EXULTEMUS DOMINO

Double chant to be sung across both pages.

1. O come, let us sing | unto the | Lord; | {let us heartily rejoice in the strength of} | our sal- | va- | tion.

3. For the Lord is a | great — | God; | and a great | King a- | bove all | gods.

5. {The sea is His and He} | made — | it; | and His hands pre- | pared the | dry — | land.

7. For He is the | Lord our | God; | {and we are the people of His pasture, and the} | sheep of | His — | hand.

{Glory be to the Father, and} | to the | Son, | and | to the | Ho-ly | Ghost;

*Metrical Version, Hymn No. 22.

529

VENITE EXULTEMUS DOMINO

Alternative setting, to be sung across both pages.

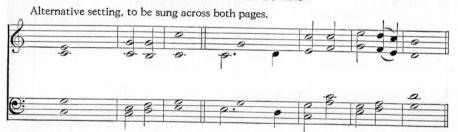

530

VENITE EXULTEMUS DOMINO

Single chant, to be sung across both pages.

Morning Canticles

VENITE EXULTEMUS DOMINO

WILLIAM BOYCE, 1710–1779

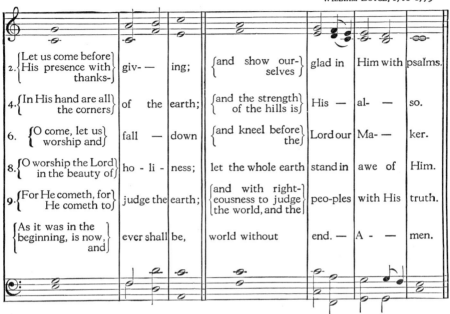

VENITE EXULTEMUS DOMINO

J. TURLE

VENITE EXULTEMUS DOMINO

JOHN GOSS

Morning Canticles

531

BENEDICTUS

LUKE 1: 68–79

Double Chant, to be sung across both pages.

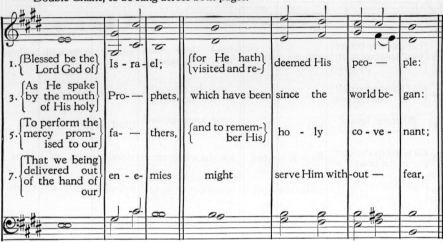

1. {Blessed be the / Lord God of}	Is-ra-el;	{for He hath / visited and re-} deemed His peo-— ple:
3. {As He spake / by the mouth / of His holy}	Pro-—phets,	which have been since the world be-gan:
5. {To perform the / mercy prom-/ised to our}	fa-—thers,	{and to remem-/ber His} ho-ly co-ve-nant;
7. {That we being / delivered out / of the hand of / our}	en-e-—mies	might serve Him with-out—fear,

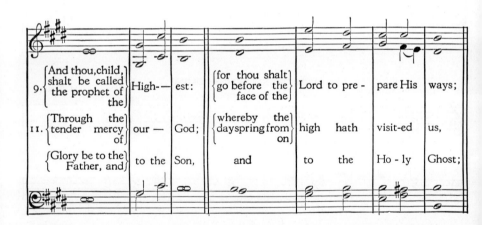

9. {And thou, child, / shalt be called / the prophet of / the}	High-—est:	{for thou shalt / go before the / face of the} Lord to pre-pare His ways;
11. {Through the / tender mercy / of}	our—God;	{whereby the / dayspring from / on} high hath visit-ed us,
{Glory be to the / Father, and}	to the Son,	and to the Ho-ly Ghost;

532

BENEDICTUS

Single Chant, to be sung across both pages.

Verses 1–4 appropriate for Lent.

Morning Canticles

BENEDICTUS

Joseph Barnby, 1838–1896

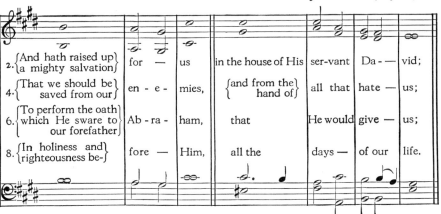

2. {And hath raised up / a mighty salvation} for — us | in the house of His | ser-vant | Da- — vid;

4. {That we should be / saved from our} en - e - mies, {and from the / hand of} all that | hate — us;

6. {To perform the oath / which He sware to / our forefather} Ab - ra - ham, | that | He would | give — us;

8. {In holiness and / righteousness be-} fore — Him, | all the | days — | of our | life.

10. {To give knowledge / of salvation unto / His} peo- — ple | by the re - | mis-sion | of their | sins,

12. {To give light to them / that sit in darkness / and in the} shadow of death, {and to guide / our feet} into the | way of | peace.

{As it was in the be- / ginning, is now, and} ever shall | be, | world without | end. — | A- — | men.

BENEDICTUS

Henry Schwing

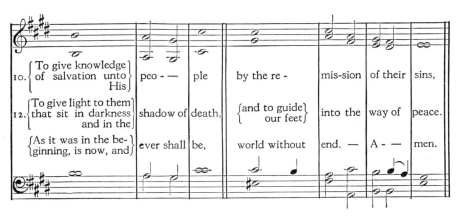

533

JUBILATE DEO

PSALM 100

WILLIAM BYRD, 1538–1623

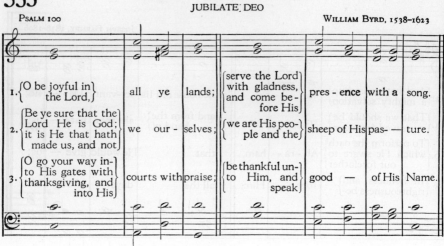

1. O be joyful in the Lord, all ye lands; serve the Lord with gladness, and come before His pres-ence with a song.

2. Be ye sure that the Lord He is God; it is He that hath made us, and not we our-selves; we are His peo-ple and the sheep of His pas-ture.

3. O go your way into His gates with thanksgiving, and into His courts with praise; be thankful unto Him, and speak good — of His Name.

4. For the Lord is gracious, His mer-cy is ever-last-ing; and His truth en-dureth from generation to gen-er-a-tion.

Glory be to the Father, and to the Son, and to the Ho-ly Ghost;

As it was in the be-ginning, is now, and ever shall be, world without end. — A — men.

534

JUBILATE DEO

Alternative setting

GEORGE J. ELVEY, 1816–1893

Evening Canticles

535

PSALM 92

BONUM EST CONFITERI

Anon.

1. { It is a good thing to give thanks } unto the Lord, { and to sing praises unto } name, O Most — High; Thy

2. { To show forth Thy loving kindness in the } morn — ing, and Thy { faithful- ness } ev - ery night,

3. { Upon an instrument of ten strings, and upon the } psal - te - ry, upon the harp with a sol - emn sound.

4. { For Thou, Lord, hast made me glad } through Thy works; I will triumph in the works of Thy hands.

{ Glory be to the Fa- ther, and } to the Son, and to the Ho - ly Ghost;

{ As it was in the be- ginning, is now, and } ever shall be, world without end. — A - — men.

536

LUKE 2: 29–32

NUNC DIMITTIS

Anon.

1. { Lord, now lettest Thou Thy servant de- } part in peace, ac - cord-ing to Thy word:

2. For mine eyes have seen — Thy sal- va — tion,

3. { Which Thou hast pre- } par — ed { before the face of } all — peo — ple;

4. { To be a light to lighten the } Gen — tiles, { and to be the glory of Thy } peo-ple Is - ra - el.

{ Glory be to the Fa- ther, and } to the Son, and to the Ho-ly Ghost;

{ As it was in the be- ginning, is now, and } ever shall be, world without end. — A — men.

Evening Canticles

MAGNIFICAT

Double chant, to be sung across both pages.

LUKE 1; 46–55

1. My soul doth magni- | fy | the | Lord, | {and my spirit hath / rejoiced in} | God my | Sa- — | viour.

3. For behold, from | hence- — | forth | all generations shall | call me | bless- — | ed.

5. {And His mercy is on / them that} | fear — | Him | from generation to | gen-e - | ra - — | tion.

7. {He hath put down / the mighty} | from their | seat; | and hath exalted | them of | low de- | gree.

9. {He hath holpen / His servant} | Is - ra- | el, | in remembrance | of His | mer- — | cy;

{Glory be to the Fa- / ther, and} | to | the | Son, | and | to the | Ho - ly | Ghost;

538

MAGNIFICAT

Alternative setting, to be sung across both pages.

539

MAGNIFICAT

Single chant, to be sung across both pages.

S. WEBBE

Evening Canticles

MAGNIFICAT

JOHN ROBINSON

2. For He hath re - gard - — ed the lowliness of His hand maid- — en.

4. {For He that is mighty hath done to me} great — things, and ho - ly is His Name.

6. {He hath showed strength} with His arm; {He hath scattered the proud in the imagi-} na - tion of their hearts.

8. {He hath filled the hungry with} good — things; and the rich He hath sent — empty a- way.

10. As He spake to our fa - thers, {to Abraham and His} seed for- ev - — er.

{As it was in the be- ginning, is now, and} ever shall be, world without end. — A - — men.

MAGNIFICAT

J. RANDALL

MAGNIFICAT

S. WEBBE

540

MISERERE MEI DEUS

PSALM 51

Double chant, to be sung across both pages

1. Have mercy upon | me, O God, | according to Thy | lov - ing - | kind- — | ness:

3. {Wash me thor-oughly from mine in-} | i - qui-ty, | and | cleanse me | from my | sin.

5. {Against Thee only have I sinned and done this evil} | in Thy sight, | {that Thou might-est be justified when Thou speak-est and} | {clear when Thou} | judg- — | est.

7. {Behold, Thou de-sirest truth in the} | in-ward parts; | {and in the hidden part Thou shalt make me to} | know — | wis - — | dom.

9. {Make me to hear joy and} | glad- —ness; | {that the bones which Thou hast} | bro - ken | may re- | joice.

11. {Create in me a clean} | heart, O God, | and renew a right | spirit with- | in — | me.

13. {Restore unto me the joy of Thy sal-} | va- — tion, | and uphold me with | Thy free | spi - — | rit.

15. {Deliver me from blood - guiltiness, O God, thou God of my sal-} | va- — tion; | {and my tongue shall sing a-} | loud of Thy | right-eous- | ness.

17. {For Thou desirest not sacrifice, else would I} | give — it; | Thou delightest not | in burnt- | of - fer- | ings.

19. {Do good in Thy good pleasure unto} | Zi - — on; | build Thou the | walls of Je- | ru - sa- | lem.

{Glory be to the Fa-ther, and} | to the Son, | and | to the | Ho - ly | Ghost;

541

MISERERE MEI DEUS

Alternative setting, to be sung across both pages.

Penitential Psalms and Hymns

MISERERE MEI DEUS

RICHARD LANGDON

2. {According to the multitude of Thy tender} mer- — cies, | blot out | my trans- | gres- — | sions.

4. {For I acknowl- edge my trans-} gres- — sions, | and my sin is | ever be- | fore — | me.

6. {Behold, I was shapen in in-} i - qui- ty, | {and in sin did my} | mother con- ceive — | me.

8. {Purge me with hyssop and I} shall be clean; | wash me and I | shall be | whiter than | snow.

10. Hide Thy face | from my sin; | {and blot out all} | mine in - | i - qui- | ty.

12. {Cast me not a- way from Thy} pre- — sence, | {and take not Thy} | Ho - ly | Spirit from | me.

14. {Then will I teach trans-} gressors Thy ways, | {And sinners shall be con-} | vert-ed | un - to | Thee.

16. O Lord, open | Thou my lips, | and my mouth | shall show | forth Thy | praise.

18. {The sacrifices of God are a broken} spir- — it; | {a broken and a contrite heart, O God,} | Thou wilt | not des- | pise.

20. {Then shalt Thou be pleased with the sacrifice of righteousness, with burnt-offer- ing and whole burnt-} of - fer- ing; | {then shall they offer bullocks up-} | on Thine | al- — | tar.

{As it was in the beginning, is now and} ever shall be, | world without | end. — | A- — | men.

Alternative, Agnus Dei (O Lamb of God) No. 523

MISERERE MEI DEUS

WILLIAM CROTCH, 1775-1847

Penitential Psalms and Hymns
The Words on the Cross for Good Friday

PART I

Father, forgive them; for they know not what they do.—Luke 23: 34

THOMAS BENSON POLLOCK, 1870   7.7.7.6.   LITANY
St. Alban's Tune Book, 1866

1. Je - sus, in Thy dy - ing woes, Ev - en while Thy life - blood flows,
2. Sav - iour, for our par - don sue, When our sins Thy pangs re - new,
3. O may we, who mer - cy need, Be like Thee in heart and deed,

Crav - ing par - don for Thy foes: Hear us, Ho - ly Je - sus.
For we know not what we do; Hear us, Ho - ly Je - sus.
When with wrong our spir - its bleed; Hear us, Ho - ly Je - sus. A-MEN.

PART II

To-day shalt thou be with Me in Paradise.
—Luke 23: 43

1 JESUS, pitying the sighs
Of the thief who near Thee dies,
Promising him Paradise:
Hear us, Holy Jesus.

2 May we in our guilt and shame,
Still Thy love and mercy claim,
Calling humbly on Thy Name:
Hear us, Holy Jesus.

3 May our hearts to Thee incline,
Looking from our cross to Thine;
Cheer our souls with hope divine:
Hear us, Holy Jesus.

PART III

Woman, behold thy son! Behold thy mother!
—John 19: 26, 27

1 JESUS, loving to the end
Her whose heart Thy sorrows rend,
And Thy dearest human friend:
Hear us, Holy Jesus.

2 May we in Thy sorrows share,
For Thy sake all peril dare,
And enjoy Thy tender care:
Hear us, Holy Jesus.

3 May we all Thy loved ones be,
All one holy family,
Loving for the love of Thee:
Hear us, Holy Jesus.

PART IV

My God, My God, why hast Thou forsaken Me?
—Matt. 27: 46

1 JESUS, whelmed in fears unknown,
With our evil left alone,
While no light from heaven is shown:
Hear us, Holy Jesus.

2 When we seem in vain to pray,
And our hope seems far away,
In the darkness be our stay:
Hear us, Holy Jesus.

3 Though no Father seem to hear,
Though no light our spirits cheer,
May we know that God is near:
Hear us, Holy Jesus.

Penitential Psalms and Hymns

The Words on the Cross for Good Friday

PART V

I thirst. John 19: 28

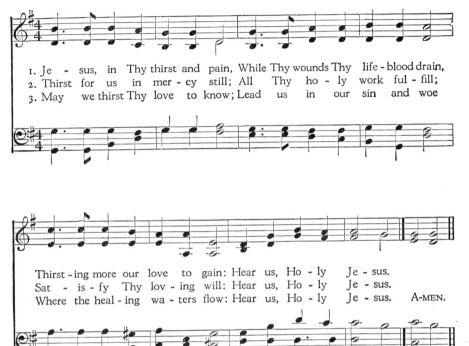

1. Je - sus, in Thy thirst and pain, While Thy wounds Thy life - blood drain,
2. Thirst for us in mer - cy still; All Thy ho - ly work ful - fill;
3. May we thirst Thy love to know; Lead us in our sin and woe

Thirst - ing more our love to gain: Hear us, Ho - ly Je - sus.
Sat - is - fy Thy lov - ing will: Hear us, Ho - ly Je - sus.
Where the heal - ing wa - ters flow: Hear us, Ho - ly Je - sus. A-MEN.

PART VI

It is finished.— John 19: 30

1 JESUS, all our ransom paid,
All Thy Father's will obeyed;
By Thy sufferings perfect made:
    Hear us, Holy Jesus.

2 Save us in our soul's distress:
Be our help to cheer and bless.
While we grow in holiness:
    Hear us, Holy Jesus.

3 Brighten all our heavenward way
With an ever holier ray
Till we pass to perfect day:
    Hear us, Holy Jesus.

PART VII

*Father, into Thy hands I commend My
spirit.*—Luke 23: 46

1 JESUS, all Thy labor vast,
All Thy woe and conflict past;
Yielding up Thy soul at last:
    Hear us, Holy Jesus.

2 When the death-shades round us lower,
Guard us from the tempter's power,
Keep us in that trial hour:
    Hear us, Holy Jesus.

3 May Thy life and death supply
Grace to live and grace to die,
Grace to reach the home on high:
    Hear us, Holy Jesus.

543

Penitential Psalms and Hymns

PSALM 130

DE PROFUNDIS*

J. F. PETRI

1. {Out of the depths / have I cried unto} Thee, O Lord. Lord, hear — my — voice:

2. {Let Thine ears be at-} tent- — ive {to the voice of / my} sup - pli - ca- — tions.

3. {If Thou, Lord, / shouldest mark in-} i - qui- ties, O Lord, — who shall stand?

4. But there is for- {give-ness / with} Thee, that Thou mayest be fear- — ed.

5. {I wait for the / Lord, my} soul doth wait, and in His word — do I hope.

6. {My soul waiteth / for the Lord more / than they that / watch for the} morn- — ing: {I say, more / than they that} watch for the morn- — ing.

7. {Let Israel hope in / the Lord; for with / the Lord there is} mer- — cy, and with Him is plenteous re- demp- tion.

8. {And He shall re- / deem} Is - ra- el from all his in - i - qui- ties.

{Glory be to the / Father, and} to the Son, and to the Ho - ly Ghost;

{As it was in the / beginning, is now / and} ever shall be, world without end. — A- — men.

*For metrical version, see Hymn 210.

Occasional Chants

544
ANNUNCIATIO ANGELI

LUKE 2: 10-12

From Harbaugh's Christmas Service

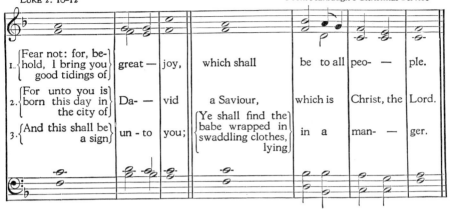

1. {Fear not: for, be-hold, I bring you good tidings of} great — joy, which shall be to all peo- — ple.
2. {For unto you is born this day in the city of} Da- — vid a Saviour, which is Christ, the Lord.
3. {And this shall be a sign} un-to you; {Ye shall find the babe wrapped in swaddling clothes, lying} in a man- — ger.

545
GLORIA IN EXCELSIS DEO

From Harbaugh's Christmas Service

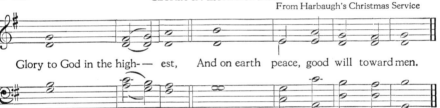

Glory to God in the high- — est, And on earth peace, good will toward men.

546
THE LORD'S PRAYER

Gregorian Chant
Arr. LOWELL MASON

{Our Father who art in heaven,} hallow-ed be Thy Name; {Thy kingdom come; Thy will be done in} {earth, as it} is in heaven;

Give us this day our dai-ly bread. {And forgive us our debts, as} we for-give our debtors.

{And lead us not into temptation, but de-} liv-er us from evil: {For Thine is the kingdom, and the power, and the glory, for} ev-er. A- — men.

Occasional Chants

THE LORD'S PRAYER

THOMAS TALLIS, 1520

{Our Father who art / in heaven, hallowed} be Thy Name; {Thy kingdom come;) / Thy will be done in} {earth, / as it} is in heaven;

Give us this day our dai-ly bread. {And forgive us our / debts, as} we for- give our debtors;

{And lead us not into / temptation, but de- / liver} us from evil: {For Thine is the / kingdom, and the / power, and the glo- / ry, for} ev-er. A—— men.

548

PSALM 23

DOMINUS REGIT ME

LOWELL MASON

1. The Lord is my Shep—herd; I shall—not—want.

2. {He maketh me to / lie down in green} pas-—tures: He leadeth me be-{side the / still} wa-—ters.

3. He re - storeth my soul: {He leadeth me in / the paths of / righteousness} for His Name's— sake.

4. {Yea, though I walk / through the valley / of the shadow of / death, I will fear no} e-—vil: {for Thou art with / me; Thy rod and / Thy} staff they com-fort me.

5. {Thou preparest a / table before me in / the presence of / mine} e - ne-mies: {Thou anointest / my head with / oil; my cup} run-neth o-—ver.

6. {Surely goodness / and mercy shall / follow me all the / days} of my life: {and I will dwell / in the house of / the} Lord for ev-—er.

{Glory be to the Fa- / ther, and} to the Son, and to the Ho - ly Ghost;

{As it was in the / beginning, is now, / and} ever shall be, world without end.—— A—— men.

Occasional Chants

THE GREGORIAN TONES

Arranged for use as Anglican chants
by Richard Appel, 1939

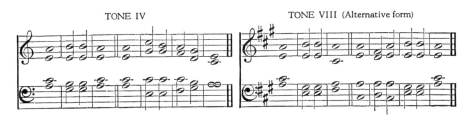

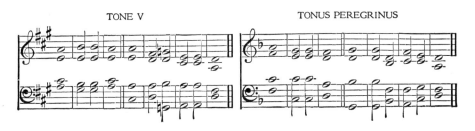

Doxologies and Amens

Long Meter Doxology

OLD HUNDREDTH (Original Rhythm)

550

THOMAS KEN, 1692   L.M.   *Genevan Psalter* Arr. LOUIS BOURGEOIS, 1551

Praise God from whom all bless-ings flow; Praise Him, all crea-tures here be-low;

Praise Him a-bove, ye heaven-ly host: Praise Fa-ther, Son, and Ho-ly Ghost. A-MEN.

551

OLD HUNDREDTH (Altered Rhythm)

THOMAS KEN, 1692   L.M.   *Genevan Psalter* Arr. LOUIS BOURGEOIS, 1551

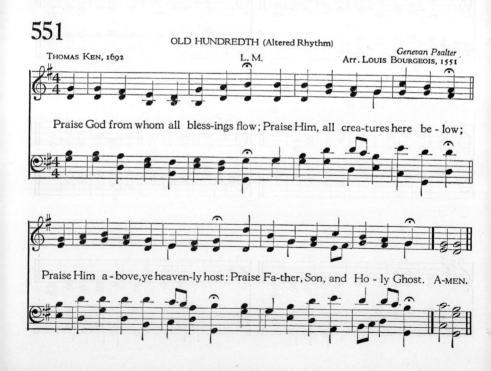

Praise God from whom all bless-ings flow; Praise Him, all crea-tures here be-low;

Praise Him a-bove, ye heaven-ly host: Praise Fa-ther, Son, and Ho-ly Ghost. A-MEN.

Doxologies and Amens

SINGLE AMENS

552 553 554 555 556 DRESDEN AMEN

A-men. A-men. A - men. A - men. A-men, A - men.

557 THREEFOLD AMEN 558 THREEFOLD AMEN

A-men, A-men, A - men. A-men, A-men, A - men.

559 FOURFOLD AMEN JOHN STAINER

A - men, A - men, A - men, A - men.

A - men,

560 SEVENFOLD AMEN JOHN STAINER

A - men, A - men.

A - men, A - men, A - men,

A - men, ..

A - men, A - men, A - men.

... A - men, A - men, A - men.

A Christmas Service

I. Organ Prelude
II. Adeste Fideles
III. Invocation
IV. Gloria, *Mozart* (or appropriate anthem)
V. Hymn
VI. Scripture St. Luke 1: 5-45
VII. Magnificat (St. Luke 1: 46-55), Nos. 537-539
VIII. Scripture St. Luke 1: 56-67
IX. Benedictus (St. Luke 1: 68-79), Nos. 531, 532
X. Scripture St. Luke 1: 80; 2: 1-9
XI. Annunciatio Angeli (St. Luke 2: 10-12), No. 544
XII. Scripture St. Luke 2: 13
XIII. Gloria (St. Luke 2: 14), No. 545
XIV. Scripture St. Luke 2: 15-28
XV. Nunc Dimittis (St. Luke 2: 29-32), No. 536
XVI. Scripture St. Luke 2: 33-40
XVII. Gloria Patri, Nos. 490-493
XVIII. Apostles' Creed
XIX. Collect and Festival Prayer
XX. Hymn
XXI. Epistle Phil. 2: 5-11
XXII. Offertory
XXIII. Lord's Prayer
XXIV. Te Deum Laudamus, No. 527 (Instead of which a hymn or an anthem may be used)
XXV. Benediction
XXVI. Postlude

Arranged by Henry Harbaugh, c. 1834

The Church Year

Introits, Epistles, Gospels, and Secondary Lectionaries

The Church Year with its Introit, Epistle and Gospel *for each given day sets forth the ministry and mission of our Lord and of his Church.*

The word Introit *signifies beginning or entrance. It consists of a Psalm-verse preceded by its* Antiphon *and followed by the* Gloria Patri. *The* Antiphon *announces, in a brief passage of Scripture, the chief thought of the day. The* Introit *should be sung by the choir, or one of its members, or it may be sung or said in a responsive manner. The congregation may join in the singing of the* Gloria Patri.

The Secondary Lectionary *provides readings from the Scriptures for those who may not use the* Epistle *or* Gospel *for any given day.*

THE FIRST SUNDAY IN ADVENT

INTROIT

UNTO thee, O Lord, do I lift up my soul; O my God, I trust in thee. Let me not be ashamed; let not mine enemies triumph over me; yea, let none that wait on thee be ashamed.

Psalm. Show me thy ways, O Lord; teach me thy paths.

Gloria Patri

EPISTLE: Romans 13: 8-14   GOSPEL: Matthew 21: 1-9

SECONDARY LECTIONARY

Hebrews 10: 19-25   Luke 1: 68-79

Jeremiah 31: 31-34

THE SECOND SUNDAY IN ADVENT

INTROIT

DAUGHTER of Zion, behold thy salvation cometh. The Lord shall cause his glorious voice to be heard, and ye shall have gladness of heart.

Psalm. Give ear, O Shepherd of Israel, thou that leadest Joseph like a flock.

Gloria Patri

EPISTLE: Romans 15: 4-13   GOSPEL: Luke 21: 25-36

II Peter 1: 3-11   Luke 17: 20-30

Malachi 4: 1-6

THE THIRD SUNDAY IN ADVENT

INTROIT

REJOICE in the Lord alway; and again I say, Rejoice. Let your moderation be known unto all men. The Lord is at hand. Be careful for nothing, but in everything by prayer and supplication with thanksgiving let your requests be made known unto God.

Psalm. Lord, thou hast been favorable unto thy land; thou hast brought back the captivity of Jacob.

Gloria Patri

EPISTLE: I Corinthians 4: 1-5   GOSPEL: Matthew 11: 2-10

SECONDARY LECTIONARY
II Timothy 4: 5-8   Matthew 3: 1-11

Isaiah 40: 1-8

THE FOURTH SUNDAY IN ADVENT

INTROIT

DROP down, ye heavens, from above, and let the skies pour down righteousness. Let the earth open, and bring forth salvation.

Psalm. The heavens declare the glory of God, and the firmament showeth his handiwork.

Gloria Patri

EPISTLE: Philippians 4: 4-7   GOSPEL: John 1: 19-28

SECONDARY LECTIONARY
I John 1: 1-4   John 1: 15-18

Deuteronomy 18: 15-19

CHRISTMAS DAY. THE NATIVITY OF OUR LORD

I

For the Early Service

INTROIT

THE Lord hath said unto me, Thou art my Son; this day have I begotten thee.

Psalm. The Lord reigneth, he is clothed with majesty. The Lord is clothed with strength, wherewith he hath girded himself.

Gloria Patri

EPISTLE: Titus 2: 11-14   GOSPEL: Luke 2: 1-14

I John 3: 1-5   Matthew 1: 18-23
Isaiah 9: 6-7

II

For the Later Service

INTROIT

UNTO us a Child is born, unto us a Son is given; and the govern-ment shall be upon his shoulder. And his Name shall be called Wonderful, Counsellor, Mighty God, Everlasting Father, Prince of Peace.

Psalm. O sing unto the Lord a new song; for he hath done mar-vellous things.

Gloria Patri

EPISTLE: Hebrews 1: 1-12   GOSPEL: John 1: 1-14

SECONDARY LECTIONARY
Hebrews 1: 1-6   John 1: 1-14
Micah 5: 1-3

THE FIRST SUNDAY AFTER CHRISTMAS

INTROIT

THY testimonies are very sure; holiness becometh thine house, O Lord, forever. Thy throne is established of old; thou art from everlasting.

Psalm. The Lord reigneth, he is clothed with majesty; the Lord is clothed with strength, wherewith he hath girded himself.

Gloria Patri

EPISTLE: Galatians 4: 1-7   GOSPEL: Luke 2: 33-40

SECONDARY LECTIONARY
II Corinthians 5: 1-9; Luke 2: 25-32; or John 12: 35-41;
Isaiah 63: 7-16

THE SECOND SUNDAY AFTER CHRISTMAS

INTROIT *the same as for* THE FIRST SUNDAY AFTER CHRISTMAS.

EPISTLE: I Peter 4:12-19   GOSPEL: Matthew 2:13-23

SECONDARY LECTIONARY
James 4: 13-17   Matthew 16: 1-4
Psalm 73: 23-28

THE EPIPHANY OF OUR LORD

INTROIT

BEHOLD the Lord, the Ruler, hath come; and the kingdom, and the power, and the glory are in his hand.

Psalm. Give the King thy judgments, O God, and thy righteousness unto the King's Son.

Gloria Patri

EPISTLE: Isaiah 60: 1-6   GOSPEL: Matthew 2: 1-12

SECONDARY LECTIONARY

II Corinthians 4: 3-6   Matthew 3: 13-17
Isaiah 2: 2-5

THE FIRST SUNDAY AFTER THE EPIPHANY

INTROIT

I SAW also the Lord, sitting upon a throne, high and lifted up. And I heard the voice of a great multitude, saying, Hallelujah; for the Lord God Omnipotent reigneth.

Psalm. Make a joyful noise unto the Lord, all ye lands; serve the Lord with gladness.

Gloria Patri

EPISTLE: Romans 12: 1-5   GOSPEL: Luke 2: 41-52

SECONDARY LECTIONARY

II Corinthians 6: 14—7: 1   John 1: 35-42
Psalm 122

THE SECOND SUNDAY AFTER THE EPIPHANY

INTROIT

ALL the earth shall worship thee, and shall sing unto thee, O God. They shall sing to thy Name, O thou Most High.

Psalm. Make a joyful noise unto God, all ye lands; sing forth the honor of his Name, make his praise glorious.

Gloria Patri

EPISTLE: Romans 12: 6-16   GOSPEL: John 2: 1-11

SECONDARY LECTIONARY

I Corinthians 2: 6-16   John 1: 43-51
Isaiah 61: 1-6

504

THE THIRD SUNDAY AFTER THE EPIPHANY

INTROIT

WORSHIP him, all ye his angels. Zion heard and was glad. The daughters of Judah rejoiced because of thy judgments, O Lord. *Psalm.* The Lord reigneth, let the earth rejoice; let the multitude of isles be glad thereof.

Gloria Patri

EPISTLE: Romans 12: 16-21   GOSPEL: Matthew 8: 1-13

SECONDARY LECTIONARY

Romans 1: 13-20   John 4: 5-14
II Kings 5: 1-19

THE FOURTH SUNDAY AFTER THE EPIPHANY

INTROIT *the same as for* THE THIRD SUNDAY AFTER THE EPIPHANY.

EPISTLE: Romans 13: 8-10   GOSPEL: Matthew 8: 23-27

SECONDARY LECTIONARY

Romans 7: 7-16   John 4: 31-42
Psalm 93

THE FIFTH SUNDAY AFTER THE EPIPHANY

INTROIT *the same as for* THE THIRD SUNDAY AFTER THE EPIPHANY.

EPISTLE: Colossians 3: 12-17   GOSPEL: Matthew 13: 24-30

SECONDARY LECTIONARY

Romans 8: 1-9   Matthew 7: 24-29
Ezekiel 33: 10-16

THE TRANSFIGURATION OF OUR LORD

The INTROIT, COLLECT, EPISTLE *and* GOSPEL FOR THE TRANSFIGURATION OF OUR LORD *shall be used* THE LAST SUNDAY AFTER THE EPIPHANY *in each year, except when there is only one Sunday after the Epiphany.*

INTROIT

THE lightnings lightened the world, the earth trembled and shook. *Psalm.* How amiable are thy tabernacles, O Lord of hosts. My soul longeth, yea, even fainteth for the courts of the Lord.

Gloria Patri

EPISTLE: II Peter 1: 16-21   GOSPEL: Matthew 17: 1-9

505

II Corinthians 3: 12-18   John 5: 39-47
Exodus 3: 1-6

SEPTUAGESIMA SUNDAY

INTROIT

THE sorrows of death compassed me, the sorrows of hell compassed me about. In my distress I called upon the Lord, and he heard my voice out of his temple.

Psalm. I will love thee, O Lord, my Strength. The Lord is my Rock and my Fortress.

Gloria Patri

EPISTLE: I Corinthians 9: 24—10: 5   GOSPEL: Matthew 20: 1-16

SECONDARY LECTIONARY
Philippians 1: 27—2: 4   Luke 10: 38-42
Jeremiah 9: 23, 24

SEXAGESIMA SUNDAY

INTROIT

AWAKE, why sleepest thou, O Lord? Arise, cast us not off for ever. Wherefore hidest thou thy face and forgettest our affliction? Our soul is bowed down to the dust. Arise for our help and redeem us.

Psalm. We have heard with our ears, O God; our fathers have told us what work thou didst in their days.

Gloria Patri

EPISTLE: II Corinthians 11: 19—12: 9   GOSPEL: Luke 8: 4-15

SECONDARY LECTIONARY
Philippians 1: 12-21   John 11: 20-27
Amos 8: 11, 12

QUINQUAGESIMA SUNDAY

INTROIT

BE thou my strong Rock, for an house of defense to save me. Thou art my Rock and my Fortress; therefore for thy Name's sake lead me and guide me.

Psalm. In thee, O Lord, do I put my trust; let me never be ashamed: deliver me in thy righteousness.

Gloria Patri

EPISTLE: I Corinthians 13: 1-13   GOSPEL: Luke 18: 31-43

SECONDARY LECTIONARY

I Corinthians 1: 21-31; Mark 10: 35-45; or John 11: 47-57; Jeremiah 8: 4-9

ASH WEDNESDAY. THE FIRST DAY OF LENT
INTROIT

I WILL cry unto God Most High, unto God that performeth all things for me. Yea, in the shadow of thy wings will I make my refuge, until these calamities be overpast.

Psalm. Be merciful unto me, O God, be merciful unto me; for my soul trusteth in thee.

Gloria Patri

EPISTLE: Joel 2: 12-19   GOSPEL: Matthew 6: 16-21

INVOCAVIT. THE FIRST SUNDAY IN LENT
INTROIT

HE shall call upon me, and I will answer him; I will deliver him and honor him. With long life will I satisfy him, and show him my salvation.

Psalm. He that dwelleth in the secret place of the Most High shall abide under the shadow of the Almighty.

Gloria Patri

EPISTLE: II Corinthians 6: 1-10   GOSPEL: Matthew 4: 1-11

SECONDARY LECTIONARY

Hebrews 4: 15, 16; Matthew 16: 21-26; or Luke 22: 39-46; Genesis 22: 1-14

REMINISCERE. THE SECOND SUNDAY IN LENT
INTROIT

REMEMBER, O Lord, thy tender mercies and thy loving kindnesses; for they have been ever of old. Let not mine enemies triumph over me. God of Israel, deliver us out of all our troubles.

Psalm. Unto thee, O Lord, do I lift up my soul; O my God, I trust in thee; let me not be ashamed.

Gloria Patri

EPISTLE: I Thessalonians 4: 1-7   GOSPEL: Matthew 15: 21-28

SECONDARY LECTIONARY

I John 2: 12-17; Luke 10: 17-20; or Luke 22: 54-62; Exodus 33: 17-23

OCULI. THE THIRD SUNDAY IN LENT

INTROIT

MINE eyes are ever toward the Lord; for he shall pluck my feet out of the net. Turn thee unto me, and have mercy upon me; for I am desolate and afflicted.

Psalm. Unto thee, O Lord, do I lift up my soul: O my God, I trust in thee; let me not be ashamed.

Gloria Patri

EPISTLE: Ephesians 5: 1-9   GOSPEL: Luke 11: 14-28

SECONDARY LECTIONARY

I Peter 1: 13-16; Luke 9: 51-56; or Luke 22: 63-71; Jeremiah 26: 1-15

LAETARE. THE FOURTH SUNDAY IN LENT

INTROIT

REJOICE ye with Jerusalem, and be glad with her, all ye that love her. Rejoice for joy with her, all ye that mourn for her.

Psalm. I was glad when they said unto me: Let us go into the house of the Lord.

Gloria Patri

EPISTLE: Romans 5: 1-11   GOSPEL: John 6: 1-15

SECONDARY LECTIONARY

II Corinthians 7: 4-10; John 6: 47-57; or Matthew 27: 15-31; Isaiah 52: 7-10

JUDICA. THE FIFTH SUNDAY IN LENT

INTROIT

JUDGE me, O God, and plead my cause against an ungodly nation. O deliver me from the deceitful and unjust man, for thou art the God of my strength.

Psalm. O send out thy light and thy truth: let them lead me; let them bring me unto thy holy hill.

Gloria Patri

EPISTLE: Hebrews 9: 11-15   GOSPEL: John 8: 46-59

SECONDARY LECTIONARY

I Peter 1: 17-25; John 13: 31-35; or Luke 23: 27-34;
Numbers 21: 4-9

PALMARUM. THE SIXTH SUNDAY IN LENT

INTROIT

LIFT up your heads, O ye gates; even lift them up, ye everlasting doors; and the King of glory shall come in.

Psalm. Who is this King of glory? The Lord of hosts, he is the King of glory.

Gloria Patri

EPISTLE: Philippians 2: 5-11   GOSPEL: Matthew 21: 1-9

SECONDARY LECTIONARY

Hebrews 12: 1-6   John 12: 1-8
Zechariah 9: 8-12

MONDAY IN HOLY WEEK

INTROIT

PLEAD my cause, O Lord, with them that strive with me; fight against them that fight against me. Take hold of shield and buckler, and stand up for mine help.

Psalm. Draw out also the spear, and stop the way against them that persecute me; say unto my soul, I am thy salvation.

Gloria Patri

EPISTLE: Isaiah 50: 5-10   GOSPEL: John 12: 1-23

TUESDAY IN HOLY WEEK

INTROIT

GOD forbid that I should glory, save in the cross of our Lord Jesus Christ. In him is salvation, life, and resurrection from the dead, by him we are redeemed and set at liberty.

Psalm. God be merciful unto us, and bless us, and cause his face to shine upon us.

Gloria Patri

EPISTLE: Jeremiah 11: 18-20   GOSPEL: John 12: 24-43

WEDNESDAY IN HOLY WEEK

INTROIT

AT the Name of Jesus every knee shall bow: of things in heaven, and things in earth, and things under the earth. For he became obedient unto death, even the death of the cross: wherefore he is Lord, to the glory of God the Father.

Psalm. Hear my prayer, O Lord, and let my cry come unto thee.

Gloria Patri

EPISTLE: Isaiah 62: 11—63: 7   GOSPEL: Luke 22: 1—23: 42

THURSDAY IN HOLY WEEK

INTROIT *the same as for* TUESDAY IN HOLY WEEK

EPISTLE: I Corinthians 11: 23-32   GOSPEL: John 13: 1-15

GOOD FRIDAY

INTROIT

SURELY he hath borne our griefs and carried our sorrows; he was wounded for our transgressions, he was bruised for our iniquities. All we like sheep have gone astray, and the Lord hath laid on him the iniquity of us all.

Psalm. Hear my prayer, O Lord, and let my cry come unto thee.

Gloria Patri

EPISTLE: Isaiah 52: 13—53: 12   GOSPEL: John 19: 1-42

EASTER DAY. THE RESURRECTION OF OUR LORD

INTROIT

WHEN I awake, I am still with thee. Hallelujah! Thou hast laid thine hand upon me. Hallelujah! Such knowledge is too wonderful for me; it is high, I cannot attain unto it. Hallelujah! Hallelujah!

Psalm. O Lord, thou hast searched me, and known me; thou knowest my down-sitting and mine uprising.

Gloria Patri

Or,

HE is risen, Hallelujah! Why seek ye the living among the dead? Hallelujah! Remember how he spake unto you, Hallelujah; the Son of Man must be crucified, and the third day rise again. Hallelujah! Hallelujah!

Psalm. Thou crownest him with glory and honor; thou madest him to have dominion over the works of thy hands.

Gloria Patri

EPISTLE: I Corinthians 5: 6-8   GOSPEL: Mark 16: 1-8

SECONDARY LECTIONARY

I Corinthians 15: 12-20   Matthew 28: 1-10
Psalm 118: 14-24

QUASIMODOGENITI. THE FIRST SUNDAY AFTER EASTER
INTROIT

As newborn babes, desire the sincere milk of the Word. Hear, O my people, and I will testify unto thee; O Israel, if thou wilt hearken unto me.

Psalm. Sing aloud unto God our strength, make a joyful noise unto the God of Jacob.

Gloria Patri

EPISTLE: I John 5: 4-12   GOSPEL: John 20: 19-31

SECONDARY LECTIONARY

I Peter 1: 3-9   John 21: 15-19
Genesis 32: 22-31

MISERICORDIAS DOMINI.
THE SECOND SUNDAY AFTER EASTER
INTROIT

THE earth is full of the goodness of the Lord; by the word of the Lord were the heavens made.

Psalm. Rejoice in the Lord, O ye righteous; for praise is comely for the upright.

Gloria Patri

EPISTLE: I Peter 2: 21-25   GOSPEL: John 10: 11-16

SECONDARY LECTIONARY

Ephesians 2: 4-10   John 14: 1-6
Psalm 23

JUBILATE. THE THIRD SUNDAY AFTER EASTER

INTROIT

MAKE a joyful noise unto God, all ye lands; sing forth the honor of his Name; make his praise glorious.

Psalm. Say unto God, How terrible art thou in thy works; through the greatness of thy power shall thine enemies submit themselves unto thee.

Gloria Patri

EPISTLE: I Peter 2: 11-20   GOSPEL: John 16: 16-23

SECONDARY LECTIONARY

I John 4: 9-14   John 12: 20-26

Isaiah 40: 26-31

CANTATE. THE FOURTH SUNDAY AFTER EASTER

INTROIT

O SING unto the Lord a new song, for he hath done marvellous things. The Lord hath made known his salvation; his righteousness hath he openly showed in the sight of the heathen.

Psalm. His right hand and his holy arm hath gotten him the victory.

Gloria Patri

EPISTLE: James 1: 16-21   GOSPEL: John 16: 5-15

SECONDARY LECTIONARY

II Timothy 2: 8-13   John 6: 60-69

Psalm 98

ROGATE. THE FIFTH SUNDAY AFTER EASTER

INTROIT

WITH the voice of singing declare ye, and tell this; utter it even to the end of the earth. Hallelujah! The Lord hath redeemed his servant Jacob. Hallelujah! Hallelujah!

Psalm. Make a joyful noise unto God, all ye lands; sing forth the honor of his Name; make his praise glorious.

Gloria Patri

EPISTLE: James 1: 22-27   GOSPEL: John 16: 23-30

SECONDARY LECTIONARY

I Timothy 2: 1-6   Luke 11: 5-13

Isaiah 55: 6-11

THE ASCENSION OF OUR LORD

INTROIT

YE men of Galilee, why stand ye gazing up into heaven? Hallelujah! This same Jesus, which is taken up from you into heaven, shall so come in like manner as ye have seen him go into heaven. Hallelujah! Hallelujah!

Psalm. O clap your hands, all ye people; shout unto God with the voice of triumph.

Gloria Patri

EPISTLE: Acts 1: 1-11   GOSPEL: Mark 16: 14-20

SECONDARY LECTIONARY

Colossians 3: 1-4; Luke 24: 50-53; or John 17: 11-26; Psalm 110: 1-4

EXAUDI. THE SUNDAY AFTER THE ASCENSION

INTROIT

HEAR, O Lord, when I cry with my voice. Hallelujah! When thou saidst, Seek ye my face, my heart said unto thee, Thy face, Lord, will I seek. Hide not thy face from me. Hallelujah! Hallelujah!

Psalm. The Lord is my Light, and my Salvation. Whom shall I fear?

Gloria Patri

EPISTLE: I Peter 4: 7-11   GOSPEL: John 15: 26—16: 4

SECONDARY LECTIONARY

Ephesians 1: 15-23   John 7: 33-39
Psalm 42

THE FESTIVAL OF PENTECOST. WHITSUNDAY

INTROIT

THE Spirit of the Lord filleth the world. Hallelujah! Let the righteous be glad; let them rejoice before God; yea, let them exceedingly rejoice. Hallelujah! Hallelujah!

Psalm. Let God arise, let his enemies be scattered; let them also that hate him flee before him.

Gloria Patri

EPISTLE: Acts 2: 1-13   GOSPEL: John 14: 23-31

SECONDARY LECTIONARY

Ephesians 2: 10-22   John 14: 15-21
Ezekiel 36: 22-28

513

THE FESTIVAL OF THE HOLY TRINITY

INTROIT

BLESSED be the Holy Trinity, and the undivided Unity. Let us give glory to him because he hath shown his mercy to us.

Psalm. O Lord, our Lord, how excellent is thy Name in all the earth.

Gloria Patri

Or,

HOLY, Holy, Holy, is the Lord of Hosts: of him, and through him, and to him, are all things.

Psalm. O Lord, our Lord, how excellent is thy Name in all the earth.

Gloria Patri

EPISTLE: Romans 11: 33-36   GOSPEL: John 3: 1-15

SECONDARY LECTIONARY

Ephesians 1: 3-14; or II Corinthians 13: 11-13; Matthew 28: 16-20; Isaiah 6: 1-8; or Numbers 6: 22-27

THE FIRST SUNDAY AFTER TRINITY

INTROIT

O LORD, I have trusted in thy mercy; my heart shall rejoice in thy salvation. I will sing unto the Lord, because he hath dealt bountifully with me.

Psalm. How long wilt thou forget me, O Lord; how long wilt thou hide thy face from me?

Gloria Patri

EPISTLE: I John 4: 16-21   GOSPEL: Luke 16: 19-31

SECONDARY LECTIONARY

Acts 4: 32-35   Matthew 13: 31-35
Deuteronomy 6: 4-13

THE SECOND SUNDAY AFTER TRINITY

INTROIT

THE Lord was my stay; he brought me forth also into a large place. He delivered me, because he delighted in me.

Psalm. I will love thee, O Lord, my Strength. The Lord is my Rock and my Fortress.

Gloria Patri

EPISTLE: I John 3: 13-18   GOSPEL: Luke 14: 16-24

SECONDARY LECTIONARY

Romans 10: 1-15   Matthew 9: 9-13

Proverbs 9: 1-10

THE THIRD SUNDAY AFTER TRINITY

INTROIT

TURN thee unto me, and have mercy upon me; for I am desolate and afflicted. Look upon mine affliction and my pain, and forgive all my sins.

Psalm. Unto thee, O Lord, do I lift up my soul. O my God, I trust in thee, let me not be ashamed.

Gloria Patri

EPISTLE: I Peter 5: 6-11   GOSPEL: Luke 15: 1-10

SECONDARY LECTIONARY

Acts 3: 1-16   Luke 15: 11-32

Isaiah 12

THE FOURTH SUNDAY AFTER TRINITY

INTROIT

THE Lord is my Light and my Salvation: whom shall I fear? The Lord is the Strength of my life: of whom shall I be afraid? When the wicked, even mine enemies and my foes, came upon me, they stumbled and fell.

Psalm. Though an host should encamp against me, my heart shall not fear.

Gloria Patri

EPISTLE: Romans 8: 18-23   GOSPEL: Luke 6: 36-42

SECONDARY LECTIONARY

Acts 4: 1-12   Matthew 5: 13-16

Isaiah 65: 17-19, 24, 25

THE FIFTH SUNDAY AFTER TRINITY

INTROIT

HEAR, O Lord, when I cry with my voice; thou hast been my help. Leave me not, neither forsake me, O God of my Salvation.

Psalm. The Lord is my Light and my Salvation; whom shall I fear?

Gloria Patri

EPISTLE: I Peter 3: 8-15   GOSPEL: Luke 5: 1-11

SECONDARY LECTIONARY

Acts 5: 34-42   Luke 9: 18-26

Lamentations 3: 22-32

THE SIXTH SUNDAY AFTER TRINITY

INTROIT

THE Lord is the strength of his people; he is the saving strength of his anointed. Save thy people, and bless thine inheritance; feed them also, and lift them up forever.

Psalm. Unto thee will I cry, O Lord, my Rock; be not silent unto me, lest, if thou be silent to me, I become like them that go down into the pit.

Gloria Patri

EPISTLE: Romans 6: 3-11   GOSPEL: Matthew 5: 20-26

SECONDARY LECTIONARY

Acts 8: 26-38   Matthew 21: 28-32

Psalm 1

THE SEVENTH SUNDAY AFTER TRINITY

INTROIT

O CLAP your hands, all ye people. Shout unto God with the voice of triumph.

Psalm. He shall subdue the people under us, and the nations under our feet.

Gloria Patri

EPISTLE: Romans 6: 19-23   GOSPEL: Matthew 9: 35-38

SECONDARY LECTIONARY

I Timothy 6: 6-12   Mark 4: 26-29

Isaiah 62: 6-12

THE EIGHTH SUNDAY AFTER TRINITY

INTROIT

WE have thought of thy loving kindness, O God, in the midst of thy temple. According to thy Name, O God, so is thy praise unto the ends of the earth; thy right hand is full of righteousness.

Psalm. Great is the Lord, and greatly to be praised, in the city of our God, in the mountain of his holiness.

Gloria Patri

EPISTLE: Romans 8: 12-17   GOSPEL: Matthew 7: 15-23

SECONDARY LECTIONARY

Acts 16: 16-32   Matthew 12: 46-50
Jeremiah 23: 16-19

THE NINTH SUNDAY AFTER TRINITY

INTROIT

BEHOLD, God is my Helper; the Lord is with them that uphold my soul. He shall reward evil unto mine enemies. Cut them off in thy truth, O Lord.

Psalm. Save me, O God, by thy Name, and judge me by thy strength.

Gloria Patri

EPISTLE: I Corinthians 10: 6-13   GOSPEL: Luke 15: 11-24

SECONDARY LECTIONARY

Acts 17: 16-34   Matthew 13: 44-46
Proverbs 16: 1-9

THE TENTH SUNDAY AFTER TRINITY

INTROIT

As for me, I will call upon God, and he shall hear my voice; he hath delivered my soul in peace from the battle that was against me. God shall hear and afflict them, even he that abideth of old. Cast thy burden upon the Lord, and he shall sustain thee.

Psalm. Give ear to my prayer, O God, and hide not thyself from my supplication.

Gloria Patri

EPISTLE: I Corinthians 12: 1-11   GOSPEL: Luke 19: 41-48

Acts 20: 17-38   Matthew 23: 34-39
Jeremiah 7: 1-11

THE ELEVENTH SUNDAY AFTER TRINITY

INTROIT

God is in his holy habitation; he is God who setteth the solitary in families. The God of Israel is he that giveth strength and power unto his people.

Psalm. Let God arise, let his enemies be scattered; let them also that hate him flee before him.

Gloria Patri

EPISTLE: I Corinthians 15: 1-10   GOSPEL: Luke 18: 9-14

Romans 8: 33-39   Luke 7: 36-50
Daniel 9: 15-18

THE TWELFTH SUNDAY AFTER TRINITY

INTROIT

MAKE haste, O God, to deliver me; make haste to help me, O Lord. Let them be ashamed and confounded that seek after my soul.

Psalm. Let them be turned backward, and put to confusion that desire my hurt.

Gloria Patri

EPISTLE: II Corinthians 3: 4-9   GOSPEL: Mark 7: 31-37

Acts 16: 9-15   John 8: 31-36
Isaiah 29: 18-21

THE THIRTEENTH SUNDAY AFTER TRINITY

INTROIT

HAVE respect, O Lord, unto thy covenant; O let not the oppressed return ashamed. Arise, O God, plead thine own cause, and forget not the voice of thine enemies.

Psalm. O God, why hast thou cast us off forever, why doth thine anger smoke against the sheep of thy pasture?

Gloria Patri

EPISTLE: Galatians 3: 15-22   GOSPEL: Luke 10: 23-37

I Peter 2: 1-10   Mark 12: 41-44
Zechariah 7: 4-10

THE FOURTEENTH SUNDAY AFTER TRINITY

INTROIT

BEHOLD, O God our Shield, and look upon the face of thine anointed; for a day in thy courts is better than a thousand.

Psalm. How amiable are thy tabernacles, O Lord of Hosts. My soul longeth, yea, even fainteth for the courts of the Lord.

Gloria Patri

EPISTLE: Galatians 5: 16-24   GOSPEL: Luke 17: 11-19

SECONDARY LECTIONARY
I Timothy 1: 12-17   John 5: 1-14
Psalm 50: 14-23

THE FIFTEENTH SUNDAY AFTER TRINITY

INTROIT

Bow down thine ear, O Lord, hear me; O thou, my God, save thy servant that trusteth in thee. Be merciful unto me, O Lord; for I cry unto thee daily.

Psalm. Rejoice the soul of thy servant; for unto thee, O Lord, do I lift up my soul.

Gloria Patri

EPISTLE: Galatians 5: 25—6: 10   GOSPEL: Matthew 6: 24-34

SECONDARY LECTIONARY
II Thessalonians 3: 6-13   John 11: 1-11
I Kings 17: 8-16

THE SIXTEENTH SUNDAY AFTER TRINITY

INTROIT

BE merciful unto me, O Lord, for I cry unto thee daily. For thou, Lord, art good, and ready to forgive, and plenteous in mercy unto all them that call upon thee.

Psalm. Bow down thine ear, O Lord, hear me; for I am poor and needy.

Gloria Patri

EPISTLE: Ephesians 3: 13-21   GOSPEL: Luke 7: 11-17

519

Hebrews 12: 18-24   Matthew 11: 25-30
Job 5: 17-26

THE SEVENTEENTH SUNDAY AFTER TRINITY

INTROIT

RIGHTEOUS art thou, O Lord, and upright are thy judgments. Deal with thy servant according to thy mercy.

Psalm. Blessed are the undefiled in the way, who walk in the law of the Lord.

Gloria Patri

EPISTLE: Ephesians 4: 1-6   GOSPEL: Luke 14: 1-11

SECONDARY LECTIONARY
Hebrews 4: 9-13   Matthew 12: 1-8
Psalm 75: 4-7

THE EIGHTEENTH SUNDAY AFTER TRINITY

INTROIT

REWARD them that wait for thee, O Lord, and let thy prophets be found faithful. Hear the prayer of thy servants and of thy people Israel.

Psalm. I was glad when they said unto me, Let us go into the house of the Lord.

Gloria Patri

EPISTLE: I Corinthians 1: 4-9   GOSPEL: Matthew 22: 34-46

SECONDARY LECTIONARY
James 2: 10-17   Mark 10: 17-27
II Chronicles 1: 7-12

THE NINETEENTH SUNDAY AFTER TRINITY

INTROIT

SAY unto my soul, I am thy Salvation. The righteous cry, and the Lord heareth. He delivereth them out of all their troubles, he is their God forever and ever.

Psalm. Give ear, O my people, to my law; incline your ears to the words of my mouth.

Gloria Patri

EPISTLE: Ephesians 4: 22-28   GOSPEL: Matthew 9: 1-8

James 5: 13-20   John 9: 24-41

Psalm 32: 1-7

THE TWENTIETH SUNDAY AFTER TRINITY

INTROIT

THE LORD our God is righteous in all his works which he doeth; for we obeyed not his voice. Give glory to thy Name, O Lord, and deal with us according to the multitude of thy mercies.

Psalm. Great is the Lord, and greatly to be praised in the city of our God, in the mountain of his holiness.

Gloria Patri

EPISTLE: Ephesians 5: 15-21   GOSPEL: Matthew 22: 1-14

SECONDARY LECTIONARY

Romans 14: 1-9   John 15: 1-8

Proverbs 2: 1-8

THE TWENTY-FIRST SUNDAY AFTER TRINITY

INTROIT

THE whole world is in thy power, O Lord, King Almighty; there is no man that can gainsay thee. For thou hast made heaven and earth, and all the wondrous things under the heaven: thou art Lord of all.

Psalm. Blessed are the undefiled in the way who walk in the law of the Lord.

Gloria Patri

EPISTLE: Ephesians 6: 10-17   GOSPEL: John 4: 46-54

SECONDARY LECTIONARY

Ephesians 6: 1-9   Mark 10: 13-16

II Samuel 7: 17-29

THE TWENTY-SECOND SUNDAY AFTER TRINITY

INTROIT

IF thou, Lord, shouldest mark iniquities, O Lord, who shall stand? But there is forgiveness with thee, that thou mayest be feared, O God of Israel.

Psalm. Out of the depths have I cried unto thee, O Lord. Lord, hear my voice.

Gloria Patri

EPISTLE: Philippians 1: 3-11   GOSPEL: Matthew 18: 23-35

SECONDARY LECTIONARY

Hebrews 13: 1-9   Luke 9: 57-62

Proverbs 24: 14-20

THE TWENTY-THIRD SUNDAY AFTER TRINITY

INTROIT

I KNOW the thoughts that I think toward you, saith the Lord: thoughts of peace, and not of evil. Then shall ye call upon me, and pray unto me, and I will hearken unto you; and I will turn your captivity, and gather you from all nations and from all places.

Psalm. Lord, thou hast been favorable unto thy land, thou hast brought back the captivity of Jacob.

Gloria Patri

EPISTLE: Philippians 3: 17-21   GOSPEL: Matthew 22: 15-22

SECONDARY LECTIONARY

I Timothy 4: 4-11   Matthew 10: 24-33

Psalm 85: 8-13

THE TWENTY-FOURTH SUNDAY AFTER TRINITY

INTROIT

O COME, let us worship and bow down, let us kneel before the Lord our Maker. For he is our God, and we are the people of his pasture, and the sheep of his hand.

Psalm. O come, let us sing unto the Lord, let us make a joyful noise to the Rock of our salvation.

Gloria Patri

EPISTLE: Colossians 1: 9-14   GOSPEL: Matthew 9: 18-26

SECONDARY LECTIONARY

I Thessalonians 5: 14-24   John 10: 23-30

Psalm 39: 5-14

THE TWENTY-FIFTH SUNDAY AFTER TRINITY

INTROIT

HAVE mercy upon me, O Lord, for I am in trouble; deliver me from the hand of mine enemies, and from them that persecute me. Let me not be ashamed, O Lord, for I have called upon thee.

Psalm. In thee, O Lord, do I put my trust, let me never be ashamed.

Gloria Patri

EPISTLE: Revelation 7: 13-17   GOSPEL: John 14: 1-6

SECONDARY LECTIONARY

Hebrews 10: 32-39   John 5: 19-29

Job 14: 1-5

THE TWENTY-SIXTH SUNDAY AFTER TRINITY

INTROIT

SAVE me, O God, by thy Name, and judge me by thy strength. Hear my prayer, O God; give ear to the words of my mouth.

Psalm. He shall reward evil to mine enemies. Cut them off in thy truth.

Gloria Patri

EPISTLE: Revelation 21: 1-7   GOSPEL: Matthew 25: 31-46

SECONDARY LECTIONARY

Revelation 2: 8-11   Luke 19: 11-27

Psalm 126

THE LAST SUNDAY AFTER TRINITY

The INTROIT, COLLECT, EPISTLE *and* GOSPEL, *here following, shall be used the* LAST SUNDAY AFTER TRINITY *of each year.*

INTROIT

I AM Alpha and Omega, the beginning and the ending, which was, and which is to come, the Almighty. Behold, the tabernacle of God is with men, and he will dwell with them, and they shall be his people, and God himself shall be with them, and be their God.

Psalm. Lift up your heads, O ye gates, and be ye lifted up, ye everlasting doors; and the King of Glory shall come in.

Gloria Patri

EPISTLE: I Thessalonians 5: 1-11   GOSPEL: Matthew 25: 1-13

SECONDARY LECTIONARY

Revelation 7: 9-17   Luke 12: 35-43

Isaiah 35: 3-10

THE FESTIVAL OF THE REFORMATION
October 31

The Sunday preceding this Festival may be observed as REFORMATION
SUNDAY, *except when October 31st falls on Saturday, in which event
the following day may be observed as* REFORMATION SUNDAY.

INTROIT

THE Lord of Hosts is with us, the God of Jacob is our refuge. Therefore will we not fear, though the earth be removed, and though
the mountains be carried into the midst of the sea.

Psalm. God is our refuge and strength, a very present help in
trouble.

Gloria Patri

EPISTLE: Galatians 2: 16-21 GOSPEL: John 8: 31-36

A DAY OF HUMILIATION AND PRAYER

INTROIT

HEAR, O heavens, and give ear, O earth, for the Lord hath spoken: I
have nourished and brought up children, and they have rebelled
against me. They have forsaken the Lord, they have provoked
the Holy One of Israel unto anger, they are gone away backward.

Psalm. If thou, Lord, shouldest mark iniquities, O Lord, who shall
stand?

Gloria Patri

EPISTLE: Revelation 3: 1-6 GOSPEL: Luke 15: 11-32

A DAY OF GENERAL OR SPECIAL THANKSGIVING

INTROIT

LET every thing that hath breath praise the Lord. Praise ye the Lord:
praise him for his mighty acts; praise him according to his excellent greatness.

Psalm. Praise ye the Lord. Praise God in his sanctuary; praise
him in the firmament of his power.

Gloria Patri

LESSONS. Deuteronomy 8: 1-20 Isaiah 26: 1-12
I Timothy 2: 1-8

524

Responsive Prayers

Litanies

Responsive Prayers — Litanies

1. WORSHIP

God is a Spirit, and they that worship him must worship him in spirit and in truth.

GLORY BE TO GOD ON HIGH.

God is light. If we walk in the light as he is in the light, we have fellowship one with another, and truly our fellowship in the Spirit is with the Father and his Son Jesus Christ.

GLORY BE TO GOD ON HIGH.

God is power. They that wait upon the Lord shall renew their strength. They shall mount up with wings as eagles. They shall run and not be weary. They shall walk and not faint.

GLORY BE TO GOD ON HIGH.

God is love. Everyone that loveth is born of God and knoweth God; and we know that we have passed from death unto life because we love.

GLORY BE TO GOD ON HIGH. AMEN.

2. PRAISE AND HARVEST

Let us praise God:

For the day, for the glory and warmth of the sun, for the stir of life, and for honest toil that wins food and rest.

GOD BE PRAISED FOR THE DAY.

For the earth, the sustainer of life; for the hills, the plains, and the dales; and for the beauty of meadows and fields, of flowers and of trees.

GOD BE PRAISED FOR THE EARTH.

For the sky, for the shifting clouds, and for the glory of sunrise and sunset.

GOD BE PRAISED FOR THE SKY.

For the sea, that yields and receives again the water without which life would die, and is wonderful in its stillness and more wonderful in its storm.

GOD BE PRAISED FOR THE SEA.

For the shelter and joy of our homes; for fathers and mothers who have provided for us; for brothers and sisters and all who share our common life; and for the large vision which prompts us to receive all men as brothers.

GOD BE PRAISED FOR OUR HOMES.

For friends who have exalted us by their trust, encouraged us by their love, and enlarged our lives by sharing with us their confidences and their dreams.

GOD BE PRAISED FOR OUR FRIENDS.

We bless thee for the deathless vision of a fairer day in which all men may work together as friends to make thy kingdom come on earth. May we see beyond the present to future days, and so live that we may become a worthy part of the divine society which is thy life expressing itself in the world of men.

THY KINGDOM COME, THY WILL BE DONE. AMEN.

For the Harvest Season add the following:

Almighty and everlasting God, who hast graciously given to us the fruits of the earth in their season, we yield thee humble and hearty thanks for these thy bounties, beseeching thee to give us grace rightly to use them to thy glory and the relief of those that need; through Jesus Christ our Lord.

AMEN.

3. THANKSGIVING

Almighty God, our heavenly Father, from whom cometh every good and perfect gift, we call to remembrance thy loving-kindness and thy tender mercies which have been ever of old, and with grateful hearts we would lift up to thee the voice of our thanksgiving.

For all the gifts which thou hast bestowed upon us; for the life thou hast given us, and the world in which we live,

WE PRAISE THEE, O GOD.

For the work we are enabled to do, and the truth we are permitted to learn; for whatever of good there has been in our past lives, and for all the hopes and aspirations which lead us on toward better things,

WE PRAISE THEE, O GOD.

For the order and constancy of nature; for the beauty and bounty of the world; for day and night, summer and winter, seed-time and harvest; for the varied gifts of loveliness and use which every season brings,

WE PRAISE THEE, O GOD.

For all the comforts and gladness of life; for our homes and all our home-blessings; for our friends and all pure pleasure; for the love, sympathy, and good will of men,

WE PRAISE THEE, O GOD.

For all the blessings of civilization, wise government and legislation; for education, and all the privileges we enjoy through literature, science, and art; for the help and counsel of those who are wiser and better than ourselves,

WE PRAISE THEE, O GOD.

For all true knowledge of thee and the world in which we live, and the life of truth and righteousness and divine communion to which thou hast called us; for prophets and apostles, and all earnest seekers after truth; for all lovers and helpers of mankind, and all godly and gifted men and women,

WE PRAISE THEE, O GOD.

For the gift of thy Son Jesus Christ, and all the helps and hopes which are ours as his disciples; for the presence and inspiration of thy Holy Spirit, for all the ministries of thy truth and grace,

WE PRAISE THEE, O GOD.

For communion with thee, the Father of our spirits; for the light and peace that are gained through trust and obedience, and the darkness and disquietude which befall us when we disobey thy laws and follow our lower desires and selfish passions,

WE PRAISE THEE, O GOD.

For the desire and power to help others; for every opportunity of serving our generation according to thy will, and manifesting the grace of Christ to men,

WE PRAISE THEE, O GOD.

For all the discipline of life; for the tasks and trials by which we are trained to patience, self-knowledge and self-conquest, and brought into closer sympathy with our suffering brethren; for troubles which have lifted us nearer to thee and drawn us into deeper fellowship with Jesus Christ,

WE PRAISE THEE, O GOD.

For the sacred and tender ties which bind us to the unseen world; for the faith which dispels the shadows of earth, and fills the saddest and the last moments of life with the light of an immortal hope,

WE PRAISE THEE, O GOD.

God of all grace and love, we have praised thee with our lips; grant that we may praise thee also in consecrated and faithful lives. And may the words of our mouth and the meditations of our heart be acceptable in thy sight, O Lord, our Strength and our Redeemer.

AMEN.

4. THE KINGDOM OF GOD

There were great voices in heaven, saying: The kingdoms of this world are become the kingdom of the Lord and of his Christ, and he shall reign for ever and ever.

Let us pray:

O God, who hast made all things by thy power, thou King and Ruler of the world, glorious in beauty and truth and love,

THINE IS THE KINGDOM AND THE POWER AND THE GLORY, FOR EVER AND EVER.

O God, who hast shown us the glory of thy kingdom in the majestic love of Jesus Christ,

THINE IS THE KINGDOM AND THE POWER AND THE GLORY, FOR EVER AND EVER.

O God, who art ever working in the world by thy mighty and creative Spirit, to manifest thy kingdom among men,

THINE IS THE KINGDOM AND THE POWER AND THE GLORY, FOR EVER AND EVER.

O God, more wonderful in thy perfection than all that we can ever desire or know,

THINE IS THE KINGDOM AND THE POWER AND THE GLORY, FOR EVER AND EVER.

O God, who hast made man that he should be the praise of thy glory,

THINE IS THE KINGDOM AND THE POWER AND THE GLORY, FOR EVER AND EVER.

O God, who hast given our wills that we may offer them to thee,

THINE IS THE KINGDOM AND THE POWER AND THE GLORY, FOR EVER AND EVER.

O God, whose blessed Son has revealed to us the joy of doing thy will,

> THINE IS THE KINGDOM AND THE POWER AND THE GLORY, FOR EVER AND EVER.

O God, whose kingdom is where thy will is done, and the service of whose will is perfect freedom,

> THINE IS THE KINGDOM AND THE POWER AND THE GLORY, FOR EVER AND EVER.

O God, whose will is power, and in the doing of whose will men are endued with power from on high,

> THINE IS THE KINGDOM AND THE POWER AND THE GLORY, FOR EVER AND EVER.

O God, who dost will that through the service of men in fellowship with thy will thine age-long purpose for all the peoples of the earth shall be fulfilled,

> THINE IS THE KINGDOM AND THE POWER AND THE GLORY, FOR EVER AND EVER.

O God, who hast set before us the great hope that thy kingdom shall be established upon earth, so rule our lives by thy Spirit that all our thoughts, desires, and acts, being made obedient unto thee, thy power, thy glory, and the mightiness of thy kingdom, may be made known unto men; grant this, O merciful Father, for Christ's sake, thy Son our Lord.

> AMEN.

5. THE COMMANDMENTS

God spake all these words, saying,

Thou shalt have no other gods before me.

> LORD, HAVE MERCY UPON US, AND INCLINE OUR HEARTS TO KEEP THIS LAW.

Thou shalt not make unto thee any graven image, or any likeness of any thing that is in heaven above, or that is in the earth beneath, or that is in the water under the earth; thou shalt not bow down thyself to them, nor serve them.

> LORD, HAVE MERCY UPON US, AND INCLINE OUR HEARTS TO KEEP THIS LAW.

Thou shalt not take the Name of the Lord thy God in vain; for the Lord will not hold him guiltless that taketh his Name in vain.

> LORD, HAVE MERCY UPON US, AND INCLINE OUR HEARTS TO KEEP THIS LAW.

Remember the sabbath day, to keep it holy. Six days shalt thou labor and do all thy work, but on the seventh day is the sabbath of the Lord thy God.

LORD, HAVE MERCY UPON US, AND INCLINE OUR HEARTS TO KEEP THIS LAW.

Honor thy father and thy mother, that thy days may be long upon the land which the Lord thy God giveth thee.

LORD, HAVE MERCY UPON US, AND INCLINE OUR HEARTS TO KEEP THIS LAW.

Thou shalt not kill.

LORD, HAVE MERCY UPON US, AND INCLINE OUR HEARTS TO KEEP THIS LAW.

Thou shalt not commit adultery.

LORD, HAVE MERCY UPON US, AND INCLINE OUR HEARTS TO KEEP THIS LAW.

Thou shalt not steal.

LORD, HAVE MERCY UPON US, AND INCLINE OUR HEARTS TO KEEP THIS LAW.

Thou shalt not bear false witness against thy neighbor.

LORD, HAVE MERCY UPON US, AND INCLINE OUR HEARTS TO KEEP THIS LAW.

Thou shalt not covet.

LORD, HAVE MERCY UPON US, AND INCLINE OUR HEARTS TO KEEP THIS LAW.

And Jesus said: Thou shalt love the Lord thy God with all thy heart, and with all thy soul, and with all thy mind, and with all thy strength. This is the first and great commandment.

LORD, HAVE MERCY UPON US, AND INCLINE OUR HEARTS TO KEEP THIS LAW.

And the second is like unto it: Thou shalt love thy neighbor as thyself.

LORD, HAVE MERCY UPON US, AND INCLINE OUR HEARTS TO KEEP THIS LAW.

A new commandment I give unto you, that ye love one another; as I have loved you, that ye also love one another. By this shall all men know that ye are my disciples, if ye have love one to another.

LORD, HAVE MERCY UPON US, AND WRITE ALL THESE THY LAWS IN OUR HEARTS, WE BESEECH THEE. AMEN.

6. PENITENCE

Bow down thine ear, O Lord, and hear us, for we are poor and needy. Rejoice the soul of thy servants, for thou art good, and ready to forgive, and plenteous in mercy unto all that call upon thee. Attend to the voice of our supplications, for the day of trouble is upon us.

WE BESEECH THEE TO HEAR US, GOOD LORD.

Have mercy upon us, O God, according to thy loving-kindness; according to the multitude of thy tender mercies blot out our transgressions. Wash us thoroughly from our iniquity and cleanse us from our sin.

WE BESEECH THEE TO HEAR US, GOOD LORD.

Create in us a clean heart, O God, and renew a right spirit within us. Cast us not away from thy presence, and take not thy Holy Spirit from us.

WE BESEECH THEE TO HEAR US, GOOD LORD.

Restore unto us the joy of thy salvation, and uphold us with thy free spirit. Then shall we teach transgressors thy ways, and sinners shall be converted unto thee.

WE BESEECH THEE TO HEAR US, GOOD LORD.

Thou desirest not sacrifice, else would I give it; thou delightest not in burnt offerings. The sacrifices of God are a broken spirit; a broken and a contrite heart, O God, thou wilt not despise.

HEAR US, GOOD LORD, AND GRANT US THY SALVATION.

Almighty and everlasting God, who dost forgive the sins of all them that are penitent, create and make in us new and contrite hearts, that we, repenting of our sins, may obtain of thee, the God of all mercy, perfect remission and forgiveness; through Jesus Christ our Lord.

AMEN.

7. CONFESSION

Most merciful Father, Spirit of purity and grace, whose salvation is never far from the contrite heart, be merciful unto us and pardon our iniquities of thought, word, and deed. May thy forgiveness kindle our wonder, banish our fear, and fill us with gratitude.

HEAR US, HEAVENLY FATHER.

Forgive our broken vows, the better purposes we have allowed to grow weak, the good resolutions we have not kept, and the pretenses we have made to hide from ourselves our unfaithful lives.

HEAR US, HEAVENLY FATHER.

Forgive our words of unjust anger and bitterness, our readiness to blame others and our want of thoughtfulness, patience, kindness, and sympathy.

HEAR US, HEAVENLY FATHER.

From the sins of evil passion which estrange our hearts from goodness and dim our vision of heavenly things, from all hardness of heart and impenitence of spirit, and from pride and self-sufficiency,

SAVE US, WE BESEECH THEE, HEAVENLY FATHER.

From secret faults and careless ways, from yielding to the temptations to which by nature we are exposed, and from going back to any sin of which we have repented,

SAVE US, WE BESEECH THEE, HEAVENLY FATHER.

Almighty God, our heavenly Father, who of thy great mercy hast promised forgiveness of sins to all them that with hearty repentance and true faith turn unto thee, have mercy upon us; pardon and deliver us from all our sins; confirm and strengthen us in all goodness; and bring us to everlasting life; through Jesus Christ our Lord.

AMEN.

8. THE CHURCH

O God the Father, from whom the whole family in heaven and earth is named;
O God the Son, given to be head over the Church;
O God the Holy Spirit, the bond of peace;
O Holy Trinity, eternal love,

HAVE MERCY UPON US.

By thy ministry of healing and forgiveness; by thy seeking and saving the lost; by thy words of eternal life,

HELP US, GOOD LORD.

By thy calling and training of the twelve apostles; by thy promise to build thy Church; by thy institution of the holy sacraments,

HELP US, GOOD LORD.

By the love shown in thy crucifixion; by the power of thy resurrection; by the glory of thine ascension, and by the indwelling of thy Holy Spirit,

HELP US, GOOD LORD.

That it may please thee to strengthen and enlarge thy holy Church in every land, and to unite all those who profess and call themselves Christians in faith and hope and charity,

WE BESEECH THEE, GOOD LORD.

That thy Church may strive not for her own safety, but for the world's salvation, seeking only thy kingdom and thy righteousness,

WE BESEECH THEE, GOOD LORD.

That thy Church may proclaim the gospel throughout the whole earth and make disciples of all nations,

WE BESEECH THEE, GOOD LORD.

That thou wilt grant to all rulers of the Church and ministers of thy Word and sacraments the spirit of wisdom, power, and love, and call many more to the work of thy ministry,

WE BESEECH THEE, GOOD LORD.

That thou wilt give to all thy people grace to understand and to believe thy Word, and to show forth their faith in their lives,

WE BESEECH THEE, GOOD LORD.

That we may reverently and rightly use thy sacraments and be strengthened in body and soul by thy heavenly grace,

WE BESEECH THEE, GOOD LORD.

That thou wilt remove from us all hatred, prejudice, and narrowness of thought; that we may receive and rejoice in all that thou revealest,

WE BESEECH THEE, GOOD LORD.

That thou wilt guide us in all perplexities of belief and conduct, that we may hold fast that which is true, and faithfully confess thee before men,

WE BESEECH THEE, GOOD LORD.

That regardless of the praise or contempt of the world, thy Church may worship and adore thee in spirit and in truth,

WE BESEECH THEE, GOOD LORD.

And as we pray for the Church universal, so let us pray for God's blessing on the Church in this place:

Here may the faithful find salvation, and the careless be awakened.

AMEN.

Here may the doubting find faith and the anxious be encouraged.

AMEN.

Here may the tempted find help and the sorrowful comfort.

AMEN.

Here may the weary find rest and the strong be renewed.

AMEN.

Here may the aged find consolation and the young be inspired.

AMEN.

Now unto him that is able to do exceeding abundantly above all that we ask or think, according to the power that worketh in us, unto him be glory in the Church and in Christ Jesus unto all generations for ever and ever.

AMEN.

9. THE MISSIONARY WORK OF THE CHURCH

Blessed be the Lord God for his tender mercy, whereby the dayspring from on high hath visited us,

TO GIVE LIGHT UNTO THEM THAT SIT IN DARKNESS AND IN THE SHADOW OF DEATH, AND TO GUIDE OUR FEET INTO THE WAY OF PEACE.

Jesus said: They shall come from the east and west, and from the north and south, and shall sit down in the kingdom of God.

THANKS BE TO THEE, O CHRIST, FOR THY HOLY GOSPEL.

Other sheep I have which are not of this fold; them also must I bring and they shall hear my voice; and they shall become one flock, one shepherd.

THANKS BE TO THEE, O CHRIST, FOR THY HOLY GOSPEL.

Go ye therefore, and make disciples of all the nations, baptizing them in the Name of the Father and of the Son and of the Holy Spirit, teaching them to observe all things, whatsoever I have commanded you.

THANKS BE TO THEE, O CHRIST, FOR THY HOLY GOSPEL.

Ye shall receive power, when the Holy Spirit is come upon you; and ye shall be my witnesses both in Jerusalem, and in all Judæa and Samaria, and unto the uttermost parts of the earth.

THANKS BE TO THEE, O CHRIST, FOR THY HOLY GOSPEL.

Thanks be to thee, most glorious God, Father, Son, and Holy Spirit, for the revelation of thyself in this our world, and for thy commission to thy Church to proclaim the gospel of Christ to every creature.

THANKS BE TO THEE, O GOD.

For the early disciples who were sent forth by Christ to proclaim the coming of the kingdom,

WE PRAISE THEE, O GOD.

536

For the apostles of the nations, who in obedience to his Word carried the gospel throughout the world,

WE PRAISE THEE, O GOD.

For those missionaries, known and unknown, who first brought the gospel to these shores,

WE PRAISE THEE, O GOD.

For all those who, in the ages of darkness, kept alive the light, and who, while all slumbered and slept, were faithful to their Lord's command,

WE PRAISE THEE, O GOD.

For all who at any time have recalled the Church to her great task of evangelizing the world,

WE PRAISE THEE, O GOD.

For those who have gone to the ends of the world with the joyful news, and have sought out the dark places of the earth to bring light to them that dwell in the shadow of death,

WE PRAISE THEE, O GOD.

For thy missionary servants who have joined the noble army of martyrs, and for all witnesses to the faith who have sealed their testimony with their blood,

WE PRAISE THEE, O GOD.

For the innumerable company who now praise thy Name out of every kindred and nation and tongue,

WE PRAISE THEE, O GOD.

O God, hasten the time when the gospel shall have been preached to all nations, thy kingdom shall have come on earth, and the whole world shall be filled with the knowledge of thy Name.

HEAR US, WE BESEECH THEE.

O thou, who art the light of the world, the desire of all nations, and the shepherd of our souls, let thy light shine in the darkness, that all the ends of the earth may see the salvation of our God. By the lifting up of thy cross gather the peoples to thine obedience, to whom alone belongeth the sceptre and the crown. Let thy sheep hear thy voice and be brought home to thy fold, so that there may be one flock, one shepherd; one holy kingdom of righteousness and peace; one God and Father of us all, above all, and through all, and in all.

AMEN.

10. THE NATION

Almighty God, the Father of mankind, who hast commanded us to make intercession for all men, hear us while we pray:

That it may please thee to bless the whole family of mankind from one end of the earth to the other; to destroy every form of tyranny and superstition; to give light to those who sit in darkness and in the shadow of death; to remember for good all rulers, and to bind all nations in unity, peace and concord,

WE BESEECH THEE TO HEAR US, O GOD.

That it may please thee to look with favor upon our country; to preserve to us the blessings of an equal and impartial freedom; to bring in upon us the righteousness of the kingdom of God, and so to control us by thy good Spirit that we may use our liberties only for thy glory and the welfare and progress of mankind,

WE BESEECH THEE TO HEAR US, O GOD.

That it may please thee to bless our President and all who bear office; to rule their hearts in thy faith, fear and love, that they may ever seek thy honor and glory, and that their example may be a power for goodness in the life of this nation,

WE BESEECH THEE TO HEAR US, O GOD.

That it may please thee to bless our law-makers in all their deliberations; to give each one a right understanding, a pure purpose and sound speech that cannot be condemned, and to enable them to rise above all self-seeking and party zeal into the large sentiments of public good and human brotherhood,

WE BESEECH THEE TO HEAR US, O GOD.

That it may please thee to purge our political life of every evil that would keep back the people from the highest measure of virtue and happiness; to subdue in this nation all unhallowed thirst for conquest and love of vainglory; and to inspire us with calmness and self-restraint, and the endeavor to accomplish thy will everywhere upon this earth,

WE BESEECH THEE TO HEAR US, O GOD.

That it may please thee to prosper the community in which we live and all its institutions; to bless every effort made in our midst to remove the causes of ignorance and crime; to raise the general level of comfort, and to give a higher standard to public and private life,

WE BESEECH THEE TO HEAR US, O GOD.

O God of our fathers, who from generation to generation hast watched over us in love, hear us now in hours of perplexity and need. Revive in all hearts a spirit of devotion to the public good, that strife and tumult may cease, and justice and truth be exalted. Enable the people of this nation and every nation to live in righteousness and good will, so that the coming of the kingdom of brotherhood and peace may be hastened, and thy will be done upon the earth; through Jesus Christ our Lord.

AMEN.

11. PEACE AND FELLOWSHIP AMONG THE NATIONS

Our heavenly Father, who hast declared that all the kingdoms of this world shall become the kingdom of thy Son, bless all the races of mankind, banishing from among them all hatred and enmity, purging them of all pride and vainglory, delivering them from all lust for power and greed for gain. Incline the hearts of all peoples to open their gates to the Lord of lords, and King of kings, that he may enter into their cities, their churches, and their homes, to dwell there and to govern all things by his Word and Spirit. So may justice, mercy, and peace prevail throughout the world, and thy Name be glorified; through Jesus Christ our Lord.

AMEN.

O God, the Lord of might and love, control the nations of mankind by thy gracious power, and make them to long for the reign of good will in the earth.

HEAR US, HEAVENLY FATHER.

Guide the hearts and minds of all who govern, that they may seek first thy kingdom, and bring forth justice for all nations, whether small or great.

HEAR US, HEAVENLY FATHER.

May the children of our own and every land grow up in hatred of war and in love of peace; and, renouncing all self-seeking, may they devote their lives to the service of Christ in the upbuilding of a righteous and peaceful world.

HEAR US, HEAVENLY FATHER.

Save us from the spirit which leads to strife, from the temper which refuses to forgive, from the ill will that has no wish to forget, and from lack of faith in thy power to change the hearts of men.

HEAR US, HEAVENLY FATHER.

Grant thy Holy Spirit to those who bear on their hearts the burden of the world's sin and pain; prosper their work for the welfare of human life, and inspire them with wise judgment, that they may build a brotherhood of nations in the fatherhood of God.

HEAR US, HEAVENLY FATHER, AND GRANT US PEACE. AMEN.

12. PEACE

O Christ, Son of the living God, have mercy upon us.
Thou that sittest at the right hand of the Father, have mercy upon us.
Arise, O Christ, and help us,
And deliver us for thy Name's sake.

AMEN.

O Christ, when thou didst open thine eyes on this fair earth, the angels greeted thee as the Prince of Peace and besought us to be of good will one toward another; but thy triumph is delayed and we are weary of war.

SAVE US AND HELP US, O LORD AND MASTER.

O Christ, the very earth groans with pain as the feet of armed men march across her mangled form.

SAVE US AND HELP US, O LORD AND MASTER.

O Christ, may the Church, whom thou didst love into life; not fail thee in her witness for the things for which thou didst live and die.

TEACH US TO DO THY HOLY WILL, O LORD AND MASTER.

O Christ, the people who are called by thy Name are separated from each other in thought and life; still our tumults, take away our vain imaginings, and grant to thy people at this time the courage to proclaim the gospel of forgiveness, and faithfully to maintain the ministry of reconciliation.

TEACH US TO DO THY HOLY WILL, O LORD AND MASTER.

O Christ, come to us in our sore need and save us; O God, plead thine own cause and give us help, for vain is the help of man.

SAVE US AND HELP US, O LORD AND MASTER.

O Christ of God, by thy birth in the stable, save us and help us;
By thy toil at the carpenter's bench, save us and help us;
By thy sinless life, save us and help us;
By thy cross and passion, save us and help us.

SAVE US AND HELP US, O LORD AND MASTER.

Then all shall join in the Lord's Prayer.

Our Father, who art in heaven, Hallowed be thy Name. Thy kingdom come. Thy will be done, on earth as it is in heaven. Give us this day our daily bread. And forgive us our debts, as we forgive our debtors. And lead us not into temptation, but deliver us from evil. For thine is the kingdom, and the power, and the glory, for ever. Amen.

13. JESUS—MASTER OF LIFE

O King of men, Master of our lives, entering into thy glory by the cross, to whom all authority is given, both in heaven and on earth, we acknowledge thy sovereignty over every realm of life. Come, O Lord, enter into thy kingdom; subdue the world by the might of thy love.

BLESSING AND HONOR, AND GLORY AND POWER, BE UNTO THEE, FOR EVER AND EVER.

O Son of Mary,

CONSECRATE OUR HOMES.

Son of David,

CLEANSE OUR NATIONAL LIFE.

Son of Man,

RULE THE AFFAIRS OF NATIONS.

Son of God,

GIVE US ETERNAL LIFE.

Jesus the Carpenter,

HALLOW OUR DAILY WORK.

Jesus the Christ,

DELIVER A WORLD WHICH WAITS FOR THEE.

Jesus the Saviour,

SAVE US FROM OURSELVES.

Jesus the Life-giver,

RENEW THY CHURCH.

Word of God,

PERFECT THY CREATION.

Lord exalted at the Father's side,

RAISE US TO LIVE WITH THEE IN GOD.

May the power and glory of thy love be known and adored to all the ends of the earth;

FOR THINE IS THE KINGDOM, AND THE POWER, AND THE GLORY, FOR EVER AND EVER.

Behold, O our God, our strivings after a truer and more abiding order. Grant us visions of the better things thou hast prepared for us. Scatter every excuse of frailty and unworthiness; consecrate us with a heavenly mission; open to us a clearer prospect of our work, and give us strength gladly to welcome and gratefully to fulfill it, in the power and for the sake of Jesus Christ our Saviour.

AMEN.

14. LABOR AND SOCIAL JUSTICE

O Son of God, once carpenter of Nazareth,
HAVE MERCY UPON US, GUIDE AND BLESS OUR DAILY TOIL.

Remember not our iniquities, nor the sins and oppressions of those who were before us, but spare us, good Lord; though we have defaced thine image in man, despoiled the works of thy hands, and made labor a curse through our sin,
SPARE US, GOOD LORD.

From greed and selfishness; from envy and covetousness; from pride and contempt; and from all uncharitableness,
GOOD LORD, DELIVER US.

From injustice, oppression, and slavery; from keeping back the price of labor; and from binding upon men burdens too grievous to be borne,
GOOD LORD, DELIVER US.

From the love of money, from trust in the uncertainty of riches, and from regarding a man's life as consisting in the abundance of things which he possesseth,
GOOD LORD, DELIVER US.

From bribery and corruption; from unjust dealing and dishonest practices; from taking unfair advantage and seeking unrighteous profit; from all trade in temptation and commerce in things harmful to body or soul,
GOOD LORD, DELIVER US.

From strife and contention; from the inequalities that breed unrest and discontent; from bitterness and distrust; from all denial of our common humanity and our brotherhood in Christ,
GOOD LORD, DELIVER US.

By thy humble birth; by thy cradling in the manger; by the poverty of thy home and the obscurity of thine early years,
GOOD LORD, DELIVER US.

By thy daily toil; by thy weariness, hunger and thirst; by thy ministering to the multitude; by thy journeyings to preach the glad tidings, when thou hadst not where to lay thy head,
GOOD LORD, DELIVER US.

We beseech thee to hear us, that thou wilt deliver thy holy Church universal from the worship of mammon, from bondage to the world, and from all complicity in social evil and silence at wrong;
WE BESEECH THEE TO HEAR US, GOOD LORD.

That thou wilt deliver all who are enslaved, overworked or burdened; protect all whose labor brings them into danger or leads them into temptation; and comfort those whose toil is monotonous, or without joy,

WE BESEECH THEE TO HEAR US, GOOD LORD.

That thou wilt bring near the day when men shall toil, not for their own gain, but for the common good; when all commerce shall be brotherly, all labor prayer, all work worship, and men shall rejoice in the things that their hands have made,

WE BESEECH THEE TO HEAR US, GOOD LORD.

That thou wilt hasten the coming of thy kingdom and its righteousness; put an end to international and industrial strife; establish true fellowship among men; and restore the apostolic order where no man shall regard aught of the things he possesseth as his own, but all things shall be for the service of his fellow men,

WE BESEECH THEE TO HEAR US, GOOD LORD.

Now the God of patience and comfort grant you to be of the same mind one with another, that with one accord ye may glorify the God and Father of our Lord Jesus Christ.

AMEN.

15. COMPASSION

Almighty Father, who in the afflictions of thy people art thyself afflicted, and art full of compassion and tender mercy, hear us as we pray for those who suffer, for those who bear the pains of childbirth or sickness, for the aged and the dying.

WE BESEECH THEE TO HEAR US, GOOD LORD.

For all who are hindered in the race of life through no fault of their own; for the defective and the delicate; and for those who have been maimed and disabled,

HEAR OUR PRAYER, GOOD LORD.

For those whose livelihood is insecure; for the hungry, the homeless, and the destitute; for those who are downtrodden and in despair,

HEAR OUR PRAYER, GOOD LORD.

For thy little children, whose surroundings hide from them thy love and thy beauty; for all the fatherless and motherless; and for the unwanted,

HEAR OUR PRAYER, GOOD LORD.

For those who have to bear their burdens alone; for those who are in doubt and anguish of soul; for those who suffer through their own wrongdoing,

HEAR OUR PRAYER, GOOD LORD.

For all who do not pray for themselves; for all who have not the consolation of the prayers of others; and for all whose anguish is unrelieved by the knowledge of thy love,

HEAR OUR PRAYER, GOOD LORD.

Almighty God, whose blessed Son Jesus Christ went about doing good and healing all manner of sickness and all manner of disease among the people, continue, we beseech thee, this his gracious work among us, especially in the hospitals and infirmaries here and in foreign lands; cheer, heal, and sanctify the sick; grant to the physicians, surgeons, and nurses wisdom and skill, sympathy and patience; and assist with thy blessing all who are seeking to prevent suffering and to further thy purposes of love; through Jesus Christ our Lord.

AMEN.

16. STRENGTH AND COMFORT

O Lord, who knowest our frame and rememberest that we are dust, pity those who are bearing pain and sorrow. Cheer those who are worn by constant care. Strengthen the faith of the dying and comfort the bereaved with thy compassion. Deliver the souls of those who are bound in the chain of their own misdeeds, and send thy peace and joy to all who are oppressed by the burden of the world's sin. Bringing all our sins and sorrows, we lay them before thee, in the Name of our Redeemer.

HEAVENLY FATHER, HEAR US.

Most holy and most merciful God, the strength of the weak, the rest of the weary, the comfort of the sorrowful, the Saviour of the sinful, and the refuge of thy children in every time of need, hear us while we pray for thy help.

HEAVENLY FATHER, HEAR US.

When our faith is growing weak, and our love is growing cold, and we are losing the vision of thy face, and the spiritual world is not real to us,

HEAVENLY FATHER, HELP US.

When we are tempted to mean and wicked ways, and sin grows less sinful in our sight; when duty is difficult and work is hard, and our burdens are heavy,

HEAVENLY FATHER, HELP US.

544

When the unknown future troubles us, and in our fears and anxieties we forget the eternal love and mercy; and when the last darkness shall close around us, and heart and flesh fail, and vain is the help of man,

HEAVENLY FATHER, HELP US.

O God, who knowest us to be set in the midst of so many and great dangers, that by reason of the frailty of our nature we cannot always stand upright, grant to us such strength and protection as may sustain us in all dangers and carry us through all trials.

HEAVENLY FATHER, HELP US.

O Lord, support us all the day long of this troublous life, until the shadows lengthen and the evening comes, and the busy world is hushed, and the fever of life is over, and our work is done. Then of thy tender mercy grant us a safe lodging, and a holy rest, and peace at the last; through Jesus Christ our Lord.

AMEN.

17. LIGHT AND GUIDANCE

O thou eternal Light, towards whose quickening dawn have moved the peoples that walked in darkness, rise with thy radiance upon the souls which here await thee.

By the visions of ancient seers who beheld thy power moving within the veil of earthly things,

TEACH US TO LIVE AS SEEING THE INVISIBLE.

By the voices of holy prophets who discerned the signs of their times and foretold the doom that follows wrong,

AROUSE US TO SEE AND OVERCOME THE EVILS OF TODAY.

By the mind that was in Christ Jesus, compassionate, free in thought, steadfast in purpose, stayed on thee,

AWAKEN IN US ALSO A GENEROUS MIND AND A BOLD VISION.

By the self-sacrifice of saints and apostles, martyrs and missionaries, who counted not the cost to themselves, if only they might testify to thy grace,

INSPIRE US TO FIND IN COMMON LIFE THE PATHS OF HIGH DE-VOTION.

By the joy and praise of the Church universal, by every prayer for light in shrines of whatsoever faith, in east or west or north or south,

KINDLE IN OUR HEARTS THE FAITH THAT SHALL BE A LIGHT UPON OUR WAY AND A SONG UPON OUR LIPS.

By the labors of all who show forth thy wonderful works, searching out thy law in nature, fashioning forms of beauty, skillful in industry, wise in statecraft, gentle in parenthood, gifted with insight,

ENLARGE ALL OUR BEING WITH THE FULLNESS OF THY DIVINE LIFE, THAT IN THY LIGHT WE MAY SEE LIGHT AND BECOME MINISTERS OF THY LOVE BROUGHT NEAR.

O God, Fountain of light and truth, give to thy Church a new vision and a new charity, new wisdom and understanding, that the eternal message of thy Son, no longer confused by the traditions of men, may be hailed as the good news of this age; through him who maketh all things new, Jesus Christ our Lord.

AMEN.

18. DEDICATION OF OFFERINGS

O God, who art the giver of every good and perfect gift,

PRAISE AND GLORY BE UNTO THEE.

In gratitude for all thy mercies, and in remembrance of thy never-failing grace,

WE OFFER THEE OUR GIFTS.

To the preaching of the good tidings of salvation,

WE DEDICATE OUR GIFTS.

To the teaching of Jesus' way of life,

WE DEDICATE OUR GIFTS.

To the healing of broken bodies and the soothing of fevered brows,

WE DEDICATE OUR GIFTS.

To the leading of every little child to the knowledge and love of Jesus,

WE DEDICATE OUR GIFTS.

To the caring for helpless age and the relief of all who look to us for help,

WE DEDICATE OUR GIFTS.

To the evangelization of the world and the building of the kingdom of God,

WE DEDICATE OUR WEALTH, OUR EFFORTS AND OUR LIVES.

Receive them, O God, and use them to thy glory;

FOR JESUS, OUR REDEEMER'S SAKE. AMEN.

19. YOUTH

The Lord Jesus said:

I have spoken unto you, that my joy might remain in you, and that your joy might be full.

PRAISE BE TO THEE, O LORD.

We rejoice in the exultation of all created things, in the echo of human hearts to all pure and lovely things, and we rejoice in thine ineffable garment of things all bright and glorious, O thou who art the Sun of Righteousness and the Light eternal.

PRAISE BE TO THEE, O LORD.

We rejoice in the example of thy life on earth, in thy sharing of our common joys, in thy loving and understanding the wonders of earth and sea and sky.

PRAISE BE TO THEE, O LORD.

We rejoice, O Lord, in the promise of life, youth, and the dawn of the unknown, in the hope and the assurance of fulfilment, and we beseech thee to preserve our youthful zeal fervent and pure.

CREATE IN US CLEAN HEARTS, O GOD.

We rejoice, O Lord, in the glory of manhood and womanhood, in the strength of wisdom and in the security of experience, and we beseech thee to sanctify our knowledge with power to do thy will.

GIRD US WITH THY POWER, O LORD.

We rejoice, O Lord, in the sweetness of companionship, in the joy of understanding hearts and in the faith of strong souls, and we beseech thee to interpret for us the wonder of human friendship.

BLESS, O LORD, OUR FRIENDSHIPS.

We rejoice, O Lord, in every measure of attainment, in the wholesome satisfaction of worthy accomplishment, and we beseech thee to stimulate in us a joy in the dignity of work.

BLESS, O LORD, OUR WORK.

We rejoice, O Lord, in the pleasures of art, of music and of literature, the enrichments of personality, and we beseech thee to restore unto us a full value of beauty.

TEACH US, O LORD, THE BEAUTY OF HOLINESS.

We rejoice, O Lord, in the sway and impulse of noble emotion, the laughter that alternates with tears, and we beseech thee to help us dispel every misunderstanding with good humor.

SANCTIFY, O LORD, THE HAPPY HOURS OF LIFE.

We rejoice in the calm assurance of thy presence, O Fountain and Light of life immortal, and we beseech thee to crown thy gifts with thine eternal peace.

AMEN, ALLELUIA! AMEN.

Comfort, we beseech thee, most gracious God, thy servants who are cast down and faint of heart amidst the sickness and sorrow of the world, and grant that by the power of thy Holy Spirit they also may be enabled to go upon their way rejoicing; through Jesus Christ our Lord.

AMEN.

Direct us, O Lord, in all our doings with thy most gracious favor, and further us with thy continual help, that in all our works begun, continued, and ended in thee, we may glorify thy holy Name, and finally by thy mercy attain unto everlasting life; through Jesus Christ our Lord.

AMEN.

20. HOME AND FAMILY

O God our heavenly Father, by whose wisdom mankind has been ordained to live in families, and by whose goodness our homes are established upon the foundations of love and fellowship, we beseech thee to accept our thanksgiving for all the blessings of home and family life.

WE BESEECH THEE TO HEAR US, HEAVENLY FATHER.

O Lord, we praise thee for our fathers, who in childhood guided us with the authority of love and shared with us their wisdom in the ways of life.

WE PRAISE THEE, O LORD.

For hours of happy comradeship which they have given to us and for hopes of high adventure which they have fulfilled,

WE PRAISE THEE, O LORD.

For all the ennobling influences that have come to us from their devotion to honor and virtue, piety and faith,

WE PRAISE THEE, O LORD.

Help us, we beseech thee, to walk in all the ways of life, ever worthy of the trust and hopes that they have placed in us.

WE BESEECH THEE TO HEAR US, HEAVENLY FATHER.

O Lord, we praise thee for our mothers, who have been devoted to us with a love like unto thine own.

WE PRAISE THEE, O LORD.

For the holy faith which fashioned our first thoughts of thee, patterned our first prayers and directed our infant feet to thy holy house,

WE PRAISE THEE, O LORD.

For the tender patience which ministered to all our needs, for the heart of compassion that rejoiced in our joy and carried the burden of our sorrow as her own,

WE PRAISE THEE, O LORD.

Grant, O heavenly Father, that the goodness of our mother's faith and love may ever be the guardian angel of our souls, and that we may fulfill in our lives her noblest dreams and her unselfish hopes.

WE BESEECH THEE TO HEAR US, HEAVENLY FATHER.

O Lord, we invoke thy blessing on the men and women who have toiled to build and warm our homes, to fashion our raiment, and to wrest from sea and land the food that nourishes us and our children.

WE BESEECH THEE TO HEAR US, O LORD.

We beseech thee to bless the men and women who teach the children and youth of our nation. Into their hands we daily commit the dearest that we have. Grant them, who are the helpers of the home and co-workers with thee, to bring forth from the life of the young those noble impulses of character and ability which thou hast placed in them.

WE BESEECH THEE TO HEAR US, O LORD.

Be ever present in our homes, O Lord, the unseen guest at every table, the silent listener to every conversation. Grant that the spirit of thy Son, our Elder Brother, Jesus Christ, may abide with us and ennoble all our relationships and sanctify all our tasks.

HEAR OUR PRAYER, O LORD.

Sustain us in all the needs of life, bless our labor, gladden our leisure, rejoice with us in our laughter, comfort us in our tears, and grant that through all the trials and anguish of our mortal days we may live with such triumphant faith, that we may be counted worthy to be joined at last with all our loved ones in the eternal fellowship of thy heavenly home; through Jesus Christ our Lord.

AMEN.

21. CHURCH ANNIVERSARY

Almighty and everlasting God, we rejoice before thee in the wondrous providence that has brought us to this day.

For the manifold blessings thou hast bestowed upon us,

WE PRAISE THEE, O LORD.

For Jesus Christ, the cornerstone of the Church, for his life which is the light of the world, for his cross by which we are saved, for his resurrection whereby we know that life is eternal, for his words of truth and for his love by which the ages are redeemed,

WE PRAISE THEE, O LORD.

For the Church which our fathers established and nurtured with sacrifice and devotion; for the blessed heritage they have given to us, their children; for courageous faith, for freedom and enlightenment and the vision that sees beyond the years,

WE PRAISE THEE, O LORD.

For the blessed company of those who have gone before us in the way of salvation: for pastors who have served their generation with devotion and vision; for men of piety and zeal who have given to the Church the labors of their hearts and hands and minds; for devout and faithful women whose devotion to thy house has made their lives beautiful; for all the sacred and hallowed memories enshrined in this church,

WE PRAISE THEE, O LORD.

For the congregation gathered here this day; for the bond of fellowship which is ours in Christ; for the comradeship of labor and service which we enjoy in thy Church; for the union of heart and mind which comes to us as we seek to do thy holy will,

WE PRAISE THEE, O LORD.

Grant that we thy people may be baptized anew this day with the cleansing fire of the Holy Spirit. Kindle in us a vision of thy righteous kingdom. Anoint us with power to do great things for thee. Stir our hearts to serve our generation with truth and love, so that thy kingdom may come and thy will be done.

HEAR OUR PRAYER, O LORD.

We praise thee, O God, for the endless renewal of life. Open our eyes to receive new light, and our ears to hear the voices that are calling us to make the world new by love.

HEAR OUR PRAYER, O LORD.

Grant that thy Church may be delivered from traditions which have lost their life, from usage which has lost its spirit, from institutions which no longer give life and power to their generation; that the Church may ever shine as a light in the world and be as a city set on a hill.

HEAR OUR PRAYER, O LORD.

O eternal God, who didst send thy Holy Spirit upon the apostles on the day of Pentecost, we pray that as thou didst strengthen their hearts with daring and fortitude, so thou wouldst confirm in us their faithful labors, their high vision, their holy purpose. Grant us so to live, that the generations to come may find their memorial not alone in graven tablets, but may read it in the living record of an active faith, an unswerving loyalty to truth, a self-forgetting service of mankind. Be this the gift of thy grace bestowed upon us; be this the memorial of the just, transmitted to their children's children through the long centuries to come: and thine shall be the kingdom and the power and the glory; through Jesus Christ our Lord, who with thee and the Holy Spirit liveth and reigneth, one God, world without end.

AMEN.

22. COMMEMORATION

Almighty and everlasting God, before whom stand the spirits of the living and the dead; Light of lights, Fountain of wisdom and goodness, who livest in all pure and humble and gracious souls.

For all who have witnessed a good confession for thy glory and the welfare of the world; for patriarchs, prophets, and apostles; for the wise of every land and nation, and all teachers of mankind,

WE PRAISE THEE, O GOD, AND BLESS THY NAME.

For the martyrs of our holy faith, the faithful witnesses to Christ of whom the world was not worthy, and for all who have resisted falsehood and wrong unto suffering or death,

WE PRAISE THEE, O GOD, AND BLESS THY NAME.

For all who have labored and suffered for freedom, good government, just laws, and the sanctity of the home; and for all who have given their lives for their country,

WE PRAISE THEE, O GOD, AND BLESS THY NAME.

For all who have sought to bless men by their service and life, and to lighten the dark places of the earth,

WE PRAISE THEE, O GOD, AND BLESS THY NAME.

For those who have been tender and true and brave in all times and places, and for all who have been one with thee in the communion of Christ's spirit and in the strength of his love,

WE PRAISE THEE, O GOD, AND BLESS THY NAME.

For the dear friends and kindred, ministering in the spiritual world, whose faces we see no more, but whose love is with us for ever,

WE PRAISE THEE, O GOD, AND BLESS THY NAME.

For the teachers and companions of our childhood and youth, and for the members of our household of faith who worship thee in heaven,

WE PRAISE THEE, O GOD, AND BLESS THY NAME.

For the grace which was given to all these, and for the trust and hope in which they lived and died,

WE PRAISE THEE, O GOD, AND BLESS THY NAME.

And that we may hold them in continual remembrance, that the sanctity of their wisdom and goodness may rest upon our earthly days, and that we may prepare ourselves to follow them in their upward way,

WE BESEECH THEE TO HEAR US, O GOD.

That we may ever think of them as with thee, and be sure that where they are, there we may be also,

WE BESEECH THEE TO HEAR US, O GOD.

That we may have a hope beyond this world for all thy children, even for wanderers who must be sought and brought home; that we may be comforted and sustained by the promise of a time when none shall be a stranger and an exile from thy kingdom and household,

WE BESEECH THEE TO HEAR US, O GOD.

In the communion of the Holy Spirit, with the faithful and the saintly in heaven, with the redeemed in all ages, with our beloved who dwell in thy presence and peace, we, who still serve and suffer on earth, unite in ascribing:

THANKSGIVING, GLORY, HONOR, AND POWER UNTO THEE, O LORD OUR GOD.

Glory be to the Father, and to the Son, and to the Holy Spirit,

AS IT WAS IN THE BEGINNING, IS NOW AND EVER SHALL BE, WORLD WITHOUT END. AMEN.

Responsive Readings

The organizing principle of this series of scriptural responsive readings is a modern calendar, modeled on the historic ecclesiastical year. It should be noted that the readings are chosen largely with reference to their devotional rather than their didactic values. They are in no sense thought of as a substitute for, or even a supplement to, the Lord's Day pericopal readings. The didactic selections may be read more effectively in unison.

The text used in these responsive readings is prevailingly the Authorized King James Version, 1611, with occasional use of the Revised Version, 1881, and the American Standard Edition of the Revised Bible, 1901. The last-named edition is used by permission of the copyright owner, The International Council of Religious Education.

Semester of Our Lord

Advent to Pentecost

I. ADVENT

Selection 1

The Light Everlasting

Arise, shine; for thy light is come, and the glory of the Lord is risen upon thee.

For, behold, the darkness shall cover the earth, and gross darkness the people: but the Lord shall arise upon thee, and his glory shall be seen upon thee.

The Gentiles shall come to thy light, and kings to the brightness of thy rising.

Lift up thine eyes round about, and see: they all gather themselves together, they come unto thee: thy sons shall come from far, and thy daughters shall be nursed at thy side.

Then shalt thou see, and flow together, and thine heart shall fear, and be enlarged; because the abundance of the sea shall be converted unto thee, the forces of the Gentiles shall come unto thee.

For brass I will bring gold, and for iron I will bring silver, and for wood brass, and for stones iron.

I will also make thy officers peace, and thine exactors righteousness.

Violence shall no more be heard in thy land, wasting nor destruction within thy borders; but thou shalt call thy walls Salvation, and thy gates Praise.

The sun shall be no more thy light by day; neither for brightness shall the moon give light unto thee: but the Lord shall be unto thee an everlasting light, and thy God thy glory.

Thy sun shall no more go down, neither shall thy moon withdraw itself: for the Lord shall be thine everlasting light, and the days of thy mourning shall be ended.

Thy people also shall be all righteous: they shall inherit the land forever, the branch of my planting, the work of my hands, that I may be glorified.

A little one shall become a thousand, and a small one a strong nation: I, the Lord, will hasten it in its time.

Selection 2

The Way of Holiness

The wilderness and the dry land shall be glad; and the desert shall rejoice, and blossom as the rose.

It shall blossom abundantly, and rejoice even with joy and singing;

The glory of Lebanon shall be given unto it, the excellency of Carmel and Sharon:

They shall see the glory of the Lord, the excellency of our God.

Strengthen ye the weak hands, and confirm the feeble knees.

Say to them that are of a fearful heart, Be strong, fear not;

Behold, your God will come with vengeance, even God with a recompense; he will come and save you.

Then the eyes of the blind shall be opened, and the ears of the deaf shall be unstopped.

Then shall the lame man leap as a hart, and the tongue of the dumb shall sing;

For in the wilderness shall waters break out, and streams in the desert.

And the glowing sand shall become a pool, and the thirsty ground springs of water:

In the habitation of jackals, where they lay, shall be grass with reeds and rushes.

And a highway shall be there, and a way, and it shall be called The way of holiness;

The unclean shall not pass over it; but it shall be for the redeemed:

The wayfaring men, though fools, shall not err therein.

No lion shall be there, nor shall any ravenous beast go up thereon;

They shall not be found there; but the redeemed shall walk there:

And the ransomed of the Lord shall return, and come with singing unto Zion;

And everlasting joy shall be upon their heads:

They shall obtain gladness and joy, and sorrow and sighing shall flee away.

Selection 3

Divine Assurance of Comfort

Comfort ye, comfort ye my people, saith your God.

Speak ye comfortably to Jerusalem,

And cry unto her, that her warfare is accomplished, that her iniquity is pardoned:

For she hath received of the Lord's hand double for all her sins.

The voice of him that crieth in the wilderness, Prepare ye the way of the Lord,

Make straight in the desert a highway for our God.

Every valley shall be exalted, and every mountain and hill shall be made low:

And the crooked shall be made straight, and the rough places plain:

And the glory of the Lord shall be revealed, and all flesh shall see it together:

For the mouth of the Lord hath spoken it.

The voice said, Cry.

And he said, What shall I cry?

All flesh is grass, and all the goodliness thereof is as the flower of the field: the grass withereth, the flower fadeth: because the spirit of the Lord bloweth upon it:

Surely the people is grass.

The grass withereth, the flower fadeth:

But the word of our God shall stand forever.

O Zion, that bringest good tidings, get thee up into the high mountain;

O Jerusalem, that bringest good tidings, lift up thy voice with strength; lift it up, be not afraid; say unto the cities of Judah, Behold your God!

Behold, the Lord God will come with strong hand, and his arm shall rule for him:

Behold, his reward is with him, and his work before him.

He shall feed his flock like a shepherd:

He shall gather the lambs with his arm, and carry them in his bosom, and shall gently lead those that are with young.

Why sayest thou, O Jacob, and speakest, O Israel, My way is hid from the Lord, and my judgment is passed over from my God?

Hast thou not known? hast

thou not heard, that the everlasting God, the Lord, the Creator of the ends of the earth, fainteth not, neither is weary? there is no searching of his understanding.

He giveth power to the faint; and to them that have no might he increaseth strength.

Even the youths shall faint and be weary, and the young men shall utterly fall:

But they that wait upon the Lord shall renew their strength; they shall mount up with wings as eagles;

They shall run, and not be weary; and they shall walk, and not faint.

Selection 4

The Great Invitation

Ho, everyone that thirsteth, come ye to the waters, and he that hath no money; come ye, buy, and eat;

Yea, come, buy wine and milk without money and without price.

Wherefore do ye spend money for that which is not bread? and your labor for that which satisfieth not?

Hearken diligently unto me, and eat ye that which is good, and let your soul delight itself in fatness.

Incline your ear, and come unto me; hear, and your soul shall live; and I will make an everlasting covenant with you, even the sure mercies of David.

Behold, I have given him for a witness to the peoples, a leader and commander to the peoples.

Behold, thou shalt call a nation that thou knowest not; and a nation that knew thee not shall run unto thee,

Because of the Lord thy God, and for thy Holy One of Israel; for he hath glorified thee.

Seek ye the Lord while he may be found, call ye upon him while he is near:

Let the wicked forsake his way, and the unrighteous man his thoughts:

And let him return unto the Lord, and he will have mercy upon him;

And to our God, for he will abundantly pardon.

For my thoughts are not your thoughts,

Neither are your ways my ways, saith the Lord.

For as the heavens are higher than the earth,

So are my ways higher than your ways, and my thoughts than your thoughts.

For as the rain cometh down, and the snow from heaven, and returneth not thither, but watereth the earth,

And maketh it bring forth and bud, that it may give seed to the sower, and bread to the eater:

So shall my word be that goeth forth out of my mouth: it shall not return unto me void, but it shall accomplish that which I please,

And it shall prosper in the thing whereto I sent it.

For ye shall go out with joy, and be led forth with peace: the mountains and the hills shall break forth before you into singing,

And all the trees of the field shall clap their hands.

Instead of the thorn shall come up the fir-tree,

And instead of the brier shall come up the myrtle-tree:

And it shall be to the Lord for a name,

For an everlasting sign that shall not be cut off.

Selection 5

The Messiah

Behold my servant, whom I uphold; mine elect, in whom my soul delighteth; I have put my spirit upon him: he shall bring forth judgment to the Gentiles.

He shall not cry, nor lift up, nor cause his voice to be heard in the street.

A bruised reed shall he not break, and the smoking flax shall he not quench: he shall bring forth judgment unto truth.

He shall not fail nor be discouraged, till he have set judgment in the earth: and the isles shall wait for his law.

Thus saith God the Lord, he that created the heavens, and stretched them out; he that spread forth the earth, and that which cometh out of it;

He that giveth breath unto the people upon it, and spirit to them that walk therein:

I the Lord have called thee in righteousness, and will hold thine hand, and will keep thee, and give thee for a covenant of the people, for a light of the Gentiles;

To open the blind eyes, to bring out the prisoners from the prison, and them that sit in darkness out of the prison house.

I will bring the blind by a way that they knew not;

I will lead them in paths that they have not known:

I will make darkness light before them, and crooked things straight.

These things will I do unto them, and not forsake them.

I am the Lord: that is my name: and my glory will I not give to another, neither my praise to graven images.

Behold, the former things

are come to pass, and new things do I declare: before they spring forth I tell you of them.

Sing unto the Lord a new song, and his praise from the end of the earth, ye that go down to the sea, and all that is therein; the isles, and the inhabitants thereof.

Let the wilderness and the cities thereof lift up their voice, the villages that Kedar doth inhabit:

Let the inhabitants of the rock sing, let them shout from the top of the mountains.

Let them give glory unto the Lord, and declare his praise in the islands.

Selection 6

The Messiah's Reign

Behold, the days come, saith the Lord, that I will raise unto David a righteous Branch.

And he shall reign as king and deal wisely, and shall execute justice and righteousness in the land.

And there shall come forth a shoot out of the stock of Jesse,

And a Branch out of his roots shall bear fruit:

And the Spirit of the Lord shall rest upon him,

The spirit of wisdom and understanding,

The spirit of counsel and might, the spirit of knowledge and of the fear of the Lord;

And shall make him of quick understanding in the fear of the Lord:

And he shall not judge after the sight of his eyes, neither reprove after the hearing of his ears:

But with righteousness shall

he judge the poor, and reprove with equity for the meek of the earth:

And he shall smite the earth with the rod of his mouth, and with the breath of his lips shall he slay the wicked.

And righteousness shall be the girdle of his loins, and faithfulness the girdle of his reins.

The wolf also shall dwell with the lamb, and the leopard shall lie down with the kid;

And the calf and the young lion and the fatling together; and a little child shall lead them.

They shall not hurt nor destroy in all my holy mountain:

For the earth shall be full of the knowledge of the Lord, as the waters cover the sea.

II. CHRISTMASTIDE TO EPIPHANY

Selection 7

The Prince of Peace

The people that walked in darkness have seen a great light:

They that dwell in the land of the shadow of death, upon them hath the light shined.

For unto us a child is born, unto us a son is given:

And the government shall be upon his shoulder:

And his name shall be called Wonderful, Counsellor, Mighty God, Everlasting Father, Prince of Peace.

Of the increase of his government and peace there shall be no end, upon the throne of David, and upon his kingdom,

To order it, and to establish it with judgment and with justice from henceforth even for ever.

The zeal of the Lord of hosts will perform this.

Selection 8

The Triumphant Saviour

In the beginning was the Word, and the Word was with God, and the Word was God.

The same was in the beginning with God.

And the Word was made flesh, and dwelt among us, and we beheld his glory,

The glory as of the only begotten of the Father, full of grace and truth.

For God so loved the world, that he gave his only begotten Son,

That whosoever believeth on him should not perish, but have everlasting life.

And thou shalt call his name Jesus; for it is he that shall save his people from their sins.

Wherefore God also hath exalted him, and given him a name which is above every name:

That at the name of Jesus every knee should bow, of things in heaven, and things in earth, and things under the earth;

And that every tongue should confess that Jesus Christ is Lord, to the glory of God the Father.

Selection 9

The Last Day of the Year

Lord, thou hast been our dwelling place in all generations.

Before the mountains were brought forth, or ever thou hadst formed the earth and the world, even from everlasting to everlasting, thou art God.

Thou turnest man to destruction; and sayest, Return, ye children of men.

For a thousand years in thy sight are but as yesterday when it is past, and as a watch in the night.

Thou carriest them away as with a flood; they are as a sleep:

In the morning they are like grass which groweth up.

In the morning it flourisheth, and groweth up; in the evening it is cut down, and withereth.

For we are consumed by thine anger, and by thy wrath are we troubled.

Thou hast set our iniquities before thee, our secret sins in the light of thy countenance.

For all our days are passed away in thy wrath; we spend our years as a tale that is told.

The days of our years are three-score years and ten; and if by reason of strength they be four-score years, yet is their strength labor and sorrow; for it is soon cut off, and we fly away.

Who knoweth the power of

thine anger? Even according to thy fear, so is thy wrath.

So teach us to number our days, that we may apply our hearts unto wisdom.

Return, O Lord, how long? And let it repent thee concerning thy servants.

O satisfy us early with thy mercy; that we may rejoice and be glad all of our days.

Make us glad according to the days wherein thou hast afflicted us, and the years wherein we have seen evil.

Let thy work appear unto thy servants, and thy glory unto their children.

And let the favor of the Lord our God be upon us;

And establish thou the work of our hands upon us;

Yea, the work of our hands establish thou it.

Selection 10

The New Year

He that dwelleth in the secret place of the Most High shall abide under the shadow of the Almighty.

I will say of the Lord, He is my refuge and my fortress: my God; in him will I trust.

Surely he will deliver thee from the snare of the fowler, and from the noisome pestilence.

He will cover thee with his feathers, and under his wings shalt thou trust:

His truth shall be thy shield and buckler.

Thou shalt not be afraid for the terror by night; nor for the arrow that flieth by day;

Nor for the pestilence that walketh in darkness; nor for the destruction that wasteth at noonday.

A thousand shall fall at thy side, and ten thousand at thy right hand; but it shall not come nigh thee.

Only with thine eyes shalt thou behold and see the reward of the wicked.

Because thou hast made the Lord, which is my refuge, even the Most High, thy habitation;

There shall no evil befall thee, neither shall any plague come nigh thy dwelling.

For he shall give his angels charge over thee, to keep thee in all thy ways.

They shall bear thee up in their hands, lest thou dash thy foot against a stone.

Thou shalt tread upon the lion and adder: the young lion and the dragon shalt thou trample under feet.

Because he hath set his love upon me, therefore will I deliver him:

I will set him on high, **because he hath known my name.**

He shall call upon me, and I will answer him:

I will be with him in trouble;

I will deliver him, and honor him.

With long life will I satisfy him, and show him my salvation.

Selection 11

The Triumph of the Gospel

I saw a new heaven and a new earth: for the first heaven and the first earth were passed away; and there was no more sea.

And I saw the holy city, new Jerusalem, coming down from God out of heaven, prepared as a bride adorned for her husband.

I heard a great voice out of heaven saying, Behold, the tabernacle of God is with men, and he will dwell with them, and they shall be his people.

And God himself shall be with them, and be their God; and God shall wipe away all tears from their eyes.

There shall be no more death, neither sorrow, nor crying, neither shall there be any more pain:

For the former things are **passed away. And he that sat upon the throne said, Behold, I make all things new.**

He said unto me, Write: for these words are true and faithful. I will give unto him that is athirst of the fountain of the water of life freely.

He that overcometh shall inherit all things; and I will be his God, and he shall be my son.

He showed me a pure river of water of life, clear as crystal, proceeding out of the throne of God and of the Lamb.

In the midst of the street of it, and on either side of the river, was there the tree of life; and the leaves of the tree were for the healing of the nations.

And there shall be no more curse: but the throne of God and of the Lamb shall be in it;

And his servants shall serve him: and they shall see his face; and his name shall be in their foreheads.

There shall be no night there; and they need no candle, neither light of the sun;

For the Lord giveth them light: and they shall reign for ever and ever.

My reward is with me, to give every man according as his work shall be. I am Alpha and Omega, the beginning and the end, the first and the last.

Blessed are they that do his commandments, that they may have right to the tree of life, and may enter in through the gates into the city.

III. EPIPHANY

Selection 12

The Divine Epiphany

Blessed be the Lord God of Israel; for he hath visited and redeemed his people,

And hath raised up a horn of salvation for us in the house of his servant David;

As he spake by the mouth of his holy prophets, which have been since the world began:

That we should be saved from our enemies, and from the hand of all that hate us;

To perform the mercy promised to our fathers, and to remember his holy covenant;

The oath which he sware to our father Abraham, that he would grant unto us,

That we being delivered out of the hand of our enemies might serve him without fear,

In holiness and righteousness before him, all the days of our life.

And thou, child, shalt be called the prophet of the Highest:

For thou shalt go before the face of the Lord to prepare his ways;

To give knowledge of salvation unto his people by the remission of their sins,

Through the tender mercy of our God; whereby the dayspring from on high hath visited us,

To give light to them that sit in darkness and in the shadow of death,

To guide our feet into the way of peace.

Lord, now lettest thou thy servant depart in peace, according to thy word;

For mine eyes have seen thy salvation,

Which thou hast prepared before the face of all peoples;

A light to lighten the Gentiles, and the glory of thy people Israel.

Selection 13

The Righteous Judge

O sing unto the Lord a new song: sing unto the Lord, all the earth.

Sing unto the Lord, bless his name; show forth his salvation from day to day.

Declare his glory among the nations, his wonders among all people.

For the Lord is great, and greatly to be praised: he is to be feared above all gods.

For all the gods of the nations are idols: but the Lord made the heavens.

Honor and majesty are before him: strength and beauty are in his sanctuary.

Give unto the Lord, O ye kindreds of the people, give unto the Lord glory and strength.

Give unto the Lord the glory due unto his name:

bring an offering, and come into his courts.

O worship the Lord in the beauty of holiness: fear before him, all the earth.

Say among the nations that the Lord reigneth:

The world also shall be established that it shall not be moved:

He shall judge the people righteously.

Let the heavens rejoice, and let the earth be glad; let the sea roar, and the fulness thereof.

Let the field be joyful, and all that is therein: then shall all the trees of the wood rejoice before the Lord:

For he cometh, for he cometh to judge the earth:

He shall judge the world with righteousness, and the people with his truth.

Selection 14

The Mission of the Messiah

The Spirit of the Lord God is upon me; because the Lord hath anointed me to preach good tidings unto the meek;

He hath sent me to bind up the broken-hearted,

To proclaim liberty to the captives, and the opening of the prison to them that are bound;

To proclaim the acceptable year of the Lord, and the day of vengeance of our God;

To comfort all that mourn; to appoint unto them that mourn in Zion, to give unto them beauty for ashes,

The oil of joy for mourning, the garment of praise for the spirit of heaviness;

That they may be called trees of righteousness,

The planting of the Lord, that he may be glorified.

Yea, saith the Lord, It is a light thing that thou shouldst be my servant to raise up the tribes of Jacob, and to restore the preserved of Israel:

I will also give thee for a light to the Gentiles, that thou mayest be my salvation unto the end of the earth.

Thus saith the Lord, In an acceptable time have I heard thee, and in a day of salvation have I helped thee:

And I will preserve thee, and give thee for a covenant of the people,

That thou mayest say to the prisoners, Go forth; to them that are in darkness, Show yourselves.

They shall feed in the ways, and their pastures shall be in all high places.

They shall not hunger nor thirst; neither shall the heat nor the sun smite them:

For he that hath mercy on them shall lead them, even by the springs of water shall he guide them.

And I will make all my mountains a way, and my highways shall be exalted.

Behold, these shall come from far: and lo, these from the north and from the west; and these from the land of Sinim.

Sing, O heavens; and be joyful, O earth; and break forth into singing, O mountains:

For the Lord hath comforted his people, and will have mercy upon his afflicted.

Selection 15

The Hope of the Kingdom

Hearken unto me, my people; and give ear unto me, O my nation:

For a law shall proceed from me, and I will make my judgment to rest for a light of the people.

My righteousness is near; my salvation is gone forth, and mine arms shall judge the people;

The isles shall wait for me, and on mine arm shall they trust.

Lift up your eyes to the heavens, and look upon the earth beneath:

For the heavens shall vanish away like smoke, and the earth shall wax old like a garment,

And they that dwell therein shall die in like manner:

But my salvation shall be forever, and my righteousness shall not be abolished.

Hearken unto me, ye that know righteousness, the people in whose heart is my law;

Fear ye not the reproach of men, neither be ye afraid of their revilings.

For the moth shall eat them up like a garment, and the worm shall eat them like wool:

But my righteousness shall be for ever, and my salvation unto all generations.

Awake, awake, put on strength, O arm of the Lord;

Awake, as in the ancient days, in the generations of old.

And the ransomed of the Lord shall return, and come with singing unto Zion;

And everlasting joy shall be upon their heads:

They shall obtain gladness and joy; and sorrow and mourning shall flee away.

I, even I, am he that comforteth you:

Who art thou, that thou shouldst be afraid of a man that shall die, and of the son of man that shall be made as grass;

And forgettest the Lord thy maker, that hath stretched forth the heavens, and laid the foundations of the earth;

And fearest continually every day because of the fury of the oppressor, as if he were ready to destroy?

And where is the fury of the oppressor?

The captive exile hasteneth

that he may be loosed, and that he should not die in the pit, nor that his bread should fail.

But I am the Lord thy God, that divided the sea, whose waves roared:

The Lord of hosts is his name.

And I have put my words in thy mouth, and have covered thee in the shadow of my hand,

That I may plant the heavens and lay the foundations of the earth,

And say unto Zion, Thou art my people.

Selection 16

Fulness of Praise

God be merciful unto us, and bless us; and cause his face to shine upon us;

That thy way may be known upon earth, thy saving health among all nations.

Let the people praise thee, O God; let all the people praise thee.

O let the nations be glad and sing for joy:

For thou shalt judge the people righteously, and govern the nations upon earth.

Let the people praise thee, O God; let all the people praise thee.

Then shall the earth yield her increase; and God, even our own God, shall bless us.

God shall bless us; and all the ends of the earth shall fear him.

Selection 17

The Reign of the Messiah

Give the king thy judgments, O God, and thy righteousness unto the king's son.

He shall judge thy people with righteousness, and thy poor with judgment.

The mountain shall bring peace to the people, and the little hills, by righteousness.

He will judge the poor of the people,

He will save the children of the needy, and will break in pieces the oppressor.

They shall fear thee as long as the sun and moon endure, throughout all generations.

He shall come down like rain

upon the mown grass, as showers that water the earth.

In his days shall the righteous flourish; and abundance of peace so long as the moon endureth.

He shall have dominion also from sea to sea, and from the river unto the ends of the earth.

Yea, all kings shall fall down before him: all nations shall serve him.

For he will deliver the needy when he crieth; the poor also, and him that hath no helper.

He will spare the poor and needy, and will save the souls of the needy.

He will redeem their soul from deceit and violence; and precious will their blood be in his sight.

He shall live, and to him shall be given of the gold of Sheba:

Prayer also shall be made for him continually; and daily shall he be praised.

There shall be abundance of grain in the earth upon the top of the mountains;

The fruit thereof shall shake like Lebanon; and they of the city shall flourish like grass of the earth.

His name shall endure forever: his name shall be continued as long as the sun: and men shall be blessed in him: all nations shall call him blessed.

Blessed be the Lord God, the God of Israel, who only doeth wondrous things:

Unison: **And blessed be his glorious name forever; and let the whole earth be filled with his glory, Amen, and Amen.**

Selection 18
Missions

God that made the world and all things therein, seeing that he is Lord of heaven and earth, dwelleth not in temples made with hands;

Neither is worshipped with men's hands, as though he needed anything,

Seeing he giveth to all life, and breath, and all things;

And hath made of one blood all nations of men for to dwell on the face of the earth,

And hath determined their appointed seasons, and the bounds of their habitation;

That they should seek the Lord, if haply they might feel after him and find him,

Though he is not far from each one of us:

For in him we live, and move, and have our being.

There is no difference between the Jew and Greek: for the same Lord over all is rich unto all that call upon him.

For whosoever shall call upon the name of the Lord shall be saved.

How then shall they call on him in whom they have not believed?

And how shall they believe in him of whom they have not heard?

And how shall they hear without a preacher?

And how shall they preach, except they be sent?

As it is written, How beautiful are the feet of them that preach the gospel of peace,

And bring glad tidings of good things!

The harvest truly is plenteous but the laborers are few;

Pray ye therefore the Lord of the harvest, that he will send forth laborers into his harvest.

And Jesus came and spake unto them, saying:

All power is given unto me in heaven and in earth.

Go ye therefore, and teach all nations,

Baptizing them in the name of the Father, and of the Son, and of the Holy Spirit:

Teaching them to observe all things whatsoever I have commanded you:

And, lo, I am with you always, even unto the end of the world.

IV. LENT

Selection 19

Sin and Repentance

Have mercy upon me, O God, according to thy lovingkindness:

According unto the multitude of thy tender mercies blot out my transgressions.

Wash me thoroughly from mine iniquity, and cleanse me from my sin.

For I acknowledge my transgressions: and my sin is ever before me.

571

Against thee, thee only, have I sinned, and done this evil in thy sight:

That thou mightest be justified when thou speakest, and be clear when thou judgest.

Behold, I was shapen in iniquity; and in sin did my mother conceive me.

Behold, thou desirest truth in the inward parts; and in the hidden part thou shalt make me to know wisdom.

Purge me with hyssop, and I shall be clean:

Wash me, and I shall be whiter than snow.

Make me to hear joy and gladness; that the bones which thou hast broken may rejoice.

Hide thy face from my sins, and blot out all mine iniquities.

Create in me a clean heart, O God; and renew a right spirit within me.

Cast me not away from thy presence; and take not thy Holy Spirit from me.

Restore unto me the joy of thy salvation; and uphold me with thy free spirit.

Then will I teach transgressors thy ways; and sinners shall be converted unto thee.

Deliver me from bloodguiltiness, O God, thou God of my salvation:

And my tongue shall sing aloud of thy righteousness.

O Lord, open thou my lips;

And my mouth shall show forth thy praise.

For thou desirest not sacrifice; else would I give it:

Thou delightest not in burnt offerings.

The sacrifices of God are a broken spirit:

A broken and a contrite heart, O God, thou wilt not despise.

Selection 20

Social Repentance

Hear, O heavens, and give ear, O earth, for the Lord hath spoken.

Hear the word of the Lord; and give ear unto the law of our God.

To what purpose is the multitude of your sacrifices unto me? saith the Lord: I am full of the burnt offerings of rams and the fat of fed beasts;

And I delight not in the

blood of bullocks, or of lambs, or of he goats.

When ye come to appear before me, who hath required this at your hand, to tread my courts?

Bring no more vain oblations; incense is an abomination unto me;

The new moons and sabbaths, the calling of assemblies, I cannot away with;

It is iniquity, even the solemn meeting.

Your new moons and your appointed feasts my soul hateth;

They are a trouble unto me; I am weary to bear them.

And when ye spread forth your hands, I will hide mine eyes from you:

Yea, when ye make many prayers, I will not hear: your hands are full of blood.

Wash you, make you clean;

put away the evil of your doings from before mine eyes;

Cease to do evil; learn to do well.

Seek judgment, relieve the oppressed, judge the fatherless, plead for the widow.

Come now and let us reason together, saith the Lord: Though your sins be as scarlet, they shall be as white as snow;

Though they be red like crimson, they shall be as wool.

Wherewith shall I come before the Lord, and bow myself before the high God?

Shall I come before him with burnt offerings? He hath showed thee, O man, what is good;

And what doth the Lord require of thee, but to do justly, and to love mercy, and to walk humbly with thy God?

Selection 21

Prayer for Protection, Guidance and Pardon

Unto thee, O Lord, do I lift up my soul.

O my God, I trust in thee: let me not be put to shame.

Show we thy ways, O Lord; teach me thy paths. Lead me in thy truth, and teach me:

For thou art the God of my salvation; on thee do I wait all the day.

Remember, O Lord, thy tender mercies and thy lovingkindnesses;

For they have been ever of old.

573

Remember not the sins of my youth, nor my transgressions:

According to thy mercy remember thou me for thy goodness' sake, O Lord.

Good and upright is the Lord:

Therefore will he teach sinners in the way.

The meek will he guide in judgment:

And the meek will he teach his way.

All the paths of the Lord are mercy and truth unto such as keep his covenant and his testimonies.

For thy name's sake, O Lord, pardon mine iniquity; for it is great.

O keep my soul, and deliver me: let me not be ashamed; for I put my trust in thee.

Let integrity and uprightness preserve me; for I wait for thee.

Selection 22
The Blessedness of Forgiveness

Blessed is he whose transgression is forgiven, whose sin is covered.

Blessed is the man unto whom the Lord imputeth not iniquity, and in whose spirit there is no guile.

I acknowledged my sin unto thee, and mine iniquity have I not hid.

I said, I will confess my transgressions unto the Lord; and thou forgavest the iniquity of my sin.

For this shall every one that is godly pray unto thee in a time when thou mayest be found:

Surely in the floods of great waters they shall not come nigh unto him.

Thou art my hiding place; thou shalt preserve me from trouble;

Thou shalt compass me about with songs of deliverance.

I will instruct thee and teach thee in the way which thou shalt go:

I will guide thee with mine eye.

Many sorrows shall be to the wicked:

But he that trusteth in the Lord, mercy shall compass him about.

Be glad in the Lord, and rejoice, ye righteous:

And shout for joy, all ye that are upright in heart.

Selection 23
Obedience the Best Sacrifice

I waited patiently for the Lord;

And he inclined unto me, and heard my cry.

He brought me up also out of an horrible pit, out of the miry clay,

And set my feet upon a rock, and established my goings.

And he hath put a new song in my mouth, even praise unto our God:

Many shall see it, and fear, and shall trust in the Lord.

Blessed is the man that maketh the Lord his trust,

And respecteth not the proud, nor such as turn aside to lies.

Many, O Lord my God, are thy wonderful works which thou hast done, and thy thoughts which are to us-ward:

They cannot be reckoned up in order unto thee: if I would declare and speak of them, they are more than can be numbered.

Sacrifice and offering thou didst not desire; mine ears hast thou opened:

Burnt offering and sin offering hast thou not required.

Then said I, Lo, I come: in the volume of the book it is written of me,

I delight to do thy will, O my God: yea, thy law is within my heart.

I have preached righteousness in the great congregation:

Lo, I have not refrained my lips, O Lord, thou knowest.

I have not hid thy righteousness within my heart;

I have declared thy faithfulness and thy salvation:

I have not concealed thy lovingkindness and thy truth from the great congregation.

Withhold not thou thy tender mercies from me, O Lord:

Let thy lovingkindness and thy truth continually preserve me.

For innumerable evils have compassed me about: mine iniquities have taken hold upon me, so that I am not able to look up;

They are more than the hairs of mine head; therefore my heart faileth me.

Be pleased, O Lord, to deliver me: O Lord, make haste to help me.

Let all those that seek thee rejoice and be glad in thee:

Let such as love thy salvation say continually, The Lord be magnified.

But I am poor and needy: yet the Lord thinketh upon me:

Thou art my help and my deliverer; make no tarrying, O my God.

Selection 24

Out of the Depths

Out of the depths have I cried unto thee, O Lord. Lord, hear my voice:

Let thine ears be attentive to the voice of my supplications.

If thou, Lord, shouldest mark iniquities, O Lord, who shall stand?

But there is forgiveness with thee, that thou mayest be feared.

I wait for the Lord, my soul doth wait,

And in his word do I hope.

My soul waiteth for the Lord more than they that watch for the morning:

Yea, more than they that watch for the morning.

Let Israel hope in the Lord:

For with the Lord there is mercy,

And with him is plenteous redemption.

And he shall redeem Israel from all his iniquities.

Thy mercy, O Lord, is in the heavens; and thy faithfulness reacheth unto the skies.

Thy righteousness is like the great mountains; thy judgments are a great deep:

O Lord, thou preservest man and beast.

How excellent is thy lovingkindness, O God! Therefore the children of men put their trust under the shadow of thy wings.

They shall be abundantly satisfied with the fatness of thy house;

And thou shalt make them drink of the river of thy pleasures.

For with thee is the fountain of life: in thy light shall we see light.

O continue thy lovingkindness unto them that know thee; and thy righteousness to the upright in heart.

Selection 25

The Eternal Presence

O Lord, thou hast searched me, and known me.

Thou knowest my downsitting and mine uprising, thou understandest my thought afar off.

Thou searchest out my path and my lying down, and art acquainted with all my ways.

For there is not a word in my tongue, but, lo, O Lord, thou knowest it altogether.

Thou hast beset me behind and before, and laid thine hand upon me.

Such knowledge is too wonderful for me; it is high, I cannot attain unto it.

Whither shall I go from thy spirit? or whither shall I flee from thy presence?

If I ascend up into heaven, thou art there: if I make my bed in hell, behold, thou art there.

If I take the wings of the morning, and dwell in the uttermost parts of the sea;

Even there shall thy hand lead me, and thy right hand shall hold me.

If I say, Surely the darkness shall cover me; even the night shall be light about me.

Yea, the darkness hideth not from thee; but the night shineth as the day:

The darkness and the light are both alike to thee.

How precious also are thy thoughts unto me, O God! how great is the sum of them!

If I should count them, they are more in number than the sand:

When I awake, I am still with thee.

Search me, O God, and know my heart: try me, and know my thoughts:

And see if there be any wicked way in me, and lead me in the way everlasting.

Selection 26

The Satisfying God

Hear my cry, O God; attend unto my prayer.

From the end of the earth will I call unto thee, when my heart is overwhelmed:

Lead me to the rock that is higher than I.

For thou hast been a shelter for me, a strong tower from the enemy.

I will abide in thy tabernacle for ever:

I will trust in the covert of thy wings.

It is of the Lord's mercies that we are not consumed, because his compassions fail not.

They are new every morning: great is thy faithfulness.

The Lord is my portion, saith my soul; therefore will I hope in him.

The Lord is good unto them that wait for him, to the soul that seeketh him.

It is good that a man should hope and quietly wait for the salvation of the Lord.

I will give thanks unto thee, O Lord;

For though thou wast angry with me, thine anger is turned away, and thou comfortest me.

Behold, God is my salvation; I will trust and will not be afraid:

For the Lord is my strength and my song; he also is become my salvation.

Therefore with joy shall ye draw water out of the wells of salvation.

Give thanks unto the Lord, call upon his name, declare his doings among the peoples, make mention that his name is exalted.

Sing unto the Lord; for he hath done excellent things: let this be known in all the earth.

Cry aloud and shout, thou inhabitant of Zion:

For great in the midst of thee is the Holy One of Israel.

Selection 27

The Mind of Christ

If there be any consolation in Christ, and if any comfort of love, if any fellowship of the Spirit, if any tender mercies and compassions, fulfil ye my joy,

That ye be of the same mind, having the same love, being of one accord, of one mind;

Let nothing be done through strife or vainglory; but in lowliness of mind let each esteem the other better than himself.

Look not every man to his own things, but every man also to the things of others.

Let this mind be in you, which was also in Christ Jesus:

Who, being in the form of

578

God, thought it not a thing to be grasped to be equal with God:

But made himself of no reputation, and took upon him the form of a servant, and was made in the likeness of men:

And being found in fashion as a man, he humbled himself, and became obedient unto death, even the death of the cross.

Wherefore God also hath highly exalted him, and given him a name which is above every name:

Unison: That at the name of Jesus every knee should bow, of things in heaven, and things in earth, and things under the earth; and that every tongue should confess that Jesus Christ is Lord, to the glory of God the Father.

Selection 28

Palm Sunday

The earth is the Lord's, and the fulness thereof; the world, and they that dwell therein.

For he hath founded it upon the seas, and established it upon the floods.

Who shall ascend into the hill of the Lord? and who shall stand in his holy place?

He that hath clean hands, and a pure heart; who hath not lifted up his soul unto vanity, nor sworn deceitfully.

He shall receive a blessing from the Lord, and righteousness from the God of his salvation.

This is the generation of them that seek him, that seek thy face, O Jacob.

Lift up your heads, O ye gates; and be ye lifted up, ye everlasting doors;

And the King of glory shall come in.

Who is this King of glory?

The Lord strong and mighty, the Lord mighty in battle.

Lift up your heads, O ye gates; even lift them up, ye everlasting doors;

And the King of glory shall come in.

Who is this King of glory?

The Lord of hosts, he is the King of glory.

Selection 29

The Triumphant Messiah

Rejoice greatly, O daughter of Zion; shout, O daughter of Jerusalem: behold, thy king cometh unto thee:

He is just, and having salvation; lowly, and riding upon an ass, and upon a colt, the foal of an ass.

And I will cut off the chariot from Ephraim, and the horse from Jerusalem, and the battle bow shall be cut off:

And he shall speak peace unto the nations: and his dominion shall be from sea even to sea, and from the river even to the ends of the earth.

Thou art fairer than the children of men: grace is poured into thy lips: therefore God hath blessed thee for ever.

Gird thy sword upon thy thigh, O Most Mighty, with thy glory and thy majesty.

In thy majesty ride prosperously, because of truth and meekness and righteousness.

Thy throne, O God, is forever and ever: the scepter of thy kingdom is a scepter of righteousness.

O Zion, that bringest good tidings, get thee up into the high mountain;

O Jerusalem, that bringest good tidings, lift up thy voice with strength;

Lift it up, be not afraid; say unto the cities of Judah, behold your God!

Unison: **How beautiful upon the mountains are the feet of him that bringeth good tidings, that publisheth peace; that bringeth good tidings of good, that publisheth salvation; that saith unto Zion, Thy God reigneth!**

Selection 30

The Triumph of the Cross

Who hath believed our report? and to whom hath the arm of the Lord been revealed?

For he shall grow up before him as a tender plant, and as a root out of a dry ground:

He hath no form nor comeliness that we should regard him,

And no beauty that we should desire him.

He is despised and rejected of

men; a man of sorrows and acquainted with grief:

And we hid as it were our faces from him; he was despised, and we esteemed him not.

Surely he hath borne our griefs, and carried our sorrows:

Yet we did esteem him stricken, smitten of God and afflicted.

But he was wounded for our transgressions, he was bruised for our iniquities:

The chastisement of our peace was upon him; and with his stripes we are healed.

All we like sheep have gone astray; we have turned every one to his own way;

And the Lord hath laid on him the inquity of us all.

Therefore will I divide him a portion with the great, and he shall divide the spoil with the strong; because he hath poured out his soul unto death:

And he was numbered with the transgressors; and he bore the sin of many, and made intercession for the transgressors.

Therefore, being justified by faith, we have peace with God through our Lord Jesus Christ:

By whom also we have access by faith into this grace wherein we stand, and rejoice in hope of the glory of God.

And not only so, but we glory in tribulations also: knowing that tribulation worketh patience;

And patience, experience; and experience, hope:

And hope maketh not ashamed; because the love of God is shed abroad in our hearts by the Holy Ghost which is given unto us.

For when we were yet without strength, in due time Christ died for the ungodly.

For scarcely for a righteous man will one die: yet peradventure for a good man some would even dare to die.

But God commendeth his love toward us, in that, while we were yet sinners, Christ died for us.

Selection 31

The Faithfulness of God

But now thus saith the Lord that created thee, O Jacob, and he that formed thee, O Israel,

Fear not: for I have redeemed thee, I have called thee by thy name; thou art mine.

When thou passest through the waters, I will be with thee;

And through the rivers, they shall not overflow thee;

When thou walkest through the fire, thou shalt not be burned; neither shall the flame kindle upon thee.

For I am the Lord thy God, the Holy One of Israel, thy Saviour.

For a small moment have I forsaken thee; but with great mercies will I gather thee.

In a little wrath I hid my face from thee for a moment;

But with everlasting kindness will I have mercy on thee, saith the Lord thy Redeemer.

For this is as the waters of Noah unto me:

For as I have sworn that the waters of Noah shall no more go over the earth;

So have I sworn that I will not be wroth with thee, nor rebuke thee.

For the mountains shall depart, and the hills be removed;

But my lovingkindness shall not depart from thee, neither shall my covenant of peace be removed, saith the Lord that hath mercy on thee.

V. EASTERTIDE

Selection 32

The Glory of the Resurrection

Now is Christ risen from the dead, and become the first-fruits of them that slept.

For since by man came death, by man came also the resurrection of the dead.

For as in Adam all die, even so in Christ shall all be made alive.

But some man will say, How are the dead raised up? and with what body do they come?

All flesh is not the same flesh: but there is one kind of flesh of men, another flesh of beasts, another of fishes, and another of birds.

There are also celestial bodies, and bodies terrestrial: but the glory of the celestial is one, and the glory of the terrestrial is another.

There is one glory of the sun, and another glory of the moon, and another glory of the stars:

For one star differeth from another star in glory.

So also is the resurrection of the dead. It is sown in corruption; it is raised in incorruption:

It is sown in dishonor; it is raised in glory: it is sown in weakness; it is raised in power:

It is sown a natural body; it is raised a spiritual body. There is a natural body, and there is a spiritual body.

So it is written, The first man Adam was made a living soul; the last Adam was made a life-giving spirit.

Behold, I show you a mystery:

we shall not all sleep, but we shall all be changed.

For this corruptible must put on incorruption, and this mortal must put on immortality.

Thanks be to God, who giveth us the victory through our Lord Jesus Christ.

Unison: **Therefore, my beloved brethren, be ye steadfast, unmovable, always abounding in the work of the Lord, forasmuch as ye know that your labor is not in vain in the Lord.**

Selection 33
The Risen Life

If ye then be risen with Christ, seek those things which are above, where Christ sitteth on the right hand of God.

Set your affection on things above, not on things on the earth. For ye are dead, and your life is hid with Christ in God.

When Christ, who is our life, shall appear, then shall ye also appear with him in glory.

Mortify therefore your members which are upon the earth, for the sake of which things the wrath of God cometh on the children of disobedience; in the which ye once walked, when ye lived in these things.

Ye have put off the old man with his deeds; and ye have put on the new man, which is renewed in knowledge after the image of him that created him: for Christ is all, and in all.

Put on therefore, as the elect of God, holy and beloved, hearts of compassion, kindness, humbleness of mind, meekness, long-suffering;

Forbearing one another, and forgiving one another, if any man have a quarrel against any: even as Christ forgave you, so also do ye.

And above all these things put on love, which is the bond of perfectness.

Let the peace of God rule in your hearts, to the which also ye are called in one body; and be ye thankful.

Let the word of Christ dwell in you richly in all wisdom;

Teaching and admonishing one another in psalms and hymns and spiritual songs, singing with grace in your hearts to the Lord.

Whatsoever ye do, in word or deed, do all in the name of the Lord Jesus. giving thanks to God and the Father by him.

Selection 34

The Triumph of Faith

There is therefore now no condemnation to them that are in Christ Jesus.

For the law of the Spirit of life in Christ Jesus made me free from the law of sin and of death.

For what the law could not do, in that it was weak through the flesh,

God, sending his own Son in the likeness of sinful flesh, and for sin, condemned sin in the flesh:

That the ordinance of the law might be fulfilled in us, who walk not after the flesh, but after the Spirit.

For they that are after the flesh mind the things of the flesh;

But they that are after the Spirit, the things of the Spirit.

For the mind of the flesh is death; but the mind of the Spirit is life and peace:

Because the mind of the flesh is enmity against God;

For it is not subject to the law of God, neither indeed can it be:

And they that are in the flesh cannot please God.

But ye are not in the flesh but in the Spirit, if so be that the Spirit of God dwelleth in you.

But if any man hath not the Spirit of Christ, he is none of his.

And if Christ is in you, the body is dead because of sin; but the spirit is life because of righteousness.

But if the Spirit of him that raised up Jesus from the dead dwelleth in you,

He that raised up Christ Jesus from the dead shall give life also to your mortal bodies through his Spirit that dwelleth in you.

So then, brethren, we are debtors, not to the flesh, to live after the flesh:

For if ye live after the flesh, ye must die; but if by the Spirit ye put to death the deeds of the body, ye shall live.

For as many as are led by the Spirit of God, these are the sons of God.

For ye received not the spirit of bondage again unto fear;

But ye received the spirit of adoption, whereby we cry, Abba, Father.

The Spirit himself beareth witness with our spirit, that we are children of God:

And if children, then heirs; heirs of God, and joint-heirs with Christ;

If so be that we suffer with him, that we may be also glorified with him.

Selection 35

The Experience of Immortality

The Lord is the portion of mine inheritance and of my cup: thou maintainest my lot.

The lines are fallen unto me in pleasant places; yea, I have a goodly heritage.

I have set the Lord always before me: because he is at my right hand, I shall not be moved.

Therefore my heart is glad, and my glory rejoiceth: my flesh also shall dwell in safety.

For thou wilt not leave my soul in hell; neither wilt thou suffer thine holy one to see corruption.

Thou wilt show me the path of life: in thy presence is fulness of joy; in thy right hand there are pleasures for evermore.

Blessed be the God and Father of our Lord Jesus Christ,

Who according to his great mercy begat us again unto a living hope by the resurrection of Jesus Christ from the dead,

Unto an inheritance incorruptible, and undefiled, and that fadeth not away, reserved in heaven for you,

Who by the power of God are guarded through faith unto a salvation ready to be revealed in the last time.

Wherein ye greatly rejoice, though now for a little while, if need be, ye have been put to grief in manifold trials,

That the proof of your faith, being more precious than gold that perisheth though it is proved by fire,

May be found unto praise and

glory and honor at the revelation of Jesus Christ:

Whom not having seen ye love;

On whom, though now ye see him not, yet believing, ye rejoice greatly with joy unspeakable and full of glory:

Receiving the end of your faith, even the salvation of your souls.

Wherefore we faint not; but though our outward man is decaying, yet our inward man is renewed day by day.

For our light affliction,

which is for the moment, worketh for us more and more exceedingly an eternal weight of glory;

While we look not at the things which are seen, but at the things which are not seen:

For the things which are seen are temporal; but the things which are not seen are eternal.

For we know that if the earthly house of our tabernacle be dissolved,

We have a building from God, a house not made with hands, eternal, in the heavens.

Selection 36
Hope for the Triumph of Righteousness

O sing unto the Lord a new song; for he hath done marvelous things: his right hand, and his holy arm, hath gotten him the victory.

The Lord hath made known his salvation: his righteousness hath he openly showed in the sight of the heathen.

He hath remembered his mercy and his truth toward the house of Israel:

All the ends of the earth have seen the salvation of our God.

Make a joyful noise unto the Lord, all the earth: make a loud noise, and rejoice, and sing praise.

Sing unto the Lord with the harp; with the harp, and the voice of a psalm.

With trumpets and sound of cornet make a joyful noise before the Lord, the King.

Let the sea roar, and the fulness thereof; the world, and they that dwell therein.

Let the floods clap their hands: let the hills be joyful together before the Lord;

For he cometh to judge the earth: with righteousness shall he judge the world, and the people with equity.

Selection 37

Gratitude for God's Everlasting Mercy

O give thanks unto the Lord; for he is good:

Because his mercy endureth forever.

Let them now that fear the Lord say,

That his mercy endureth forever.

I called upon the Lord in distress:

The Lord answered me, and set me in a large place.

The Lord is on my side; I will not fear:

What can man do unto me?

It is better to trust in the Lord than to put confidence in man.

It is better to trust in the Lord than to put confidence in princes.

The Lord is my strength and song,

And is become my salvation.

The voice of rejoicing and salvation is in the tabernacles of the righteous:

The right hand of the Lord doeth valiantly.

I shall not die, but live,

And declare the works of the Lord.

The Lord hath chastened me sore:

But he hath not given me over unto death.

Open to me the gates of righteousness:

I will go into them, and I will praise the Lord:

I will praise thee: for thou hast heard me,

And art become my salvation.

This is the day which the Lord hath made;

We will rejoice and be glad in it.

Save now, I beseech thee, O Lord:

O Lord, I beseech thee, send now prosperity.

Blessed be he that cometh in the name of the Lord:

We have blessed you out of the house of the Lord.

Thou art my God, and I will praise thee:

Thou art my God, I will exalt thee.

O give thanks unto the Lord; for he is good:

For his mercy endureth forever.

Selection 38
The Meaning of the Ascension

So then the Lord Jesus, after he had spoken unto them, was received up into heaven, and sat down at the right hand of God.

Wherefore also God highly exalted him, and gave unto him the name which is above every name;

That in the name of Jesus every knee should bow, of things in heaven, and things on earth, and things under the earth;

And that every tongue should confess that Jesus Christ is Lord, to the glory of God the Father.

Ye are witnesses of these things. And behold, I send forth the promise of my Father upon you:

But tarry ye in the city, until ye be clothed with power from on high.

Ye shall receive power, when the Holy Spirit is come upon you:

And ye shall be my witnesses both in Jerusalem, and in all Judea and Samaria, and unto the uttermost parts of the earth.

Grace to you and peace, from him who is and who was and who is to come; and from the seven Spirits that are before his throne;

And from Jesus Christ, who is the faithful witness, the first born of the dead, and the ruler of the kings of the earth.

Unto him that loved us, and loosed us from our sins by his blood; and he made us to be a kingdom, to be priests unto his God and Father;

To him be the glory and the dominion for ever and ever. Amen.

VI. PENTECOST

Selection 39
Pentecost in Prophecy

Turn ye even to me with all your heart, and with fasting, and with weeping, and with mourning, saith the Lord.

And rend your heart, and not your garments, and turn unto the Lord your God;

For he is gracious and merciful, slow to anger, and of great kindness, and repenteth him of the evil.

Blow the trumpet in Zion, sanctify a fast, call a solemn assembly:

Gather the people, sanctify the congregation, assemble the elders, gather the children.

Let the priests, the ministers of the Lord, weep between the porch and the altar;

And let them say, Spare thy people, O Lord.

Then will the Lord be jealous for his land, and pity his people.

Fear not, O land; be glad and rejoice: for the Lord will do great things.

And ye shall know that I am in the midst of Israel, and that I am the Lord your God, and

none else: and my people shall never be ashamed.

And it shall come to pass afterward, that I will pour out my Spirit upon all flesh;

And your sons and your daughters shall prophesy, your old men shall dream dreams, your young men shall see visions:

And also upon the servants and upon the handmaids in those days will I pour out my Spirit.

And it shall come to pass, that whosoever shall call on the name of the Lord shall be delivered.

Selection 40

Pentecost, the Birthday of the Christian Church

And when the day of Pentecost was now come, they were all together in one place.

And suddenly there came from heaven a sound as of the rushing of a mighty wind, and it filled all the house where they were sitting.

And there appeared unto them tongues parting asunder, like as of fire; and it sat upon each one of them.

Now there are diversities of gifts, but the same Spirit.

And there are diversities of ministrations, but the same Lord.

And there are diversities of workings, but the same God, who worketh all things in all.

There is one body, and one Spirit, even as also ye were called in one hope of your calling;

One Lord, one faith, one baptism, one God and Father of all, who is over all, and through all, and in all.

But unto each one of us was the grace given according to the measure of the gift of Christ.

Wherefore he saith, When he ascended on high, he led

captivity captive, and gave gifts unto men.

(Now this, that he ascended, what is it but that he also descended into the lower parts of the earth?

He that descended is the same also that ascended far above all the heavens, that he might fill all things.)

And he gave some to be apostles; and some to be prophets; and some, evangelists; and some, pastors and teachers;

For the perfecting of the saints, for the work of the ministry, for the edifying of the body of Christ:

Till we all come into the unity of the faith, and of the knowledge of the Son of God, unto a perfect man,

Unto the measure of the stature of the fulness of Christ:

That we henceforth be no more children, tossed to and fro, and carried about with every wind of doctrine, by the sleight of men, and cunning craftiness, whereby they lie in wait to deceive;

But speaking the truth in love, may grow up into him in all things, who is the head, even Christ:

From whom the whole body fitly joined together, and compacted by that which every joint supplieth,

According to the effectual working in the measure of every part, maketh increase of the body unto the edifying of itself in love.

Semester of the Church

Trinity Sunday to Advent

VII. TRINITY SEASON

Selection 41

Adoration of God

Holy, holy, holy, is the Lord of hosts: the whole earth is full of his glory.

All glory be to thee, O Lord most high.

Holy, holy, holy, is the Lord God Almighty, who was, and who is, and who is to come.

All glory be to thee, O Lord most high.

Great and marvelous are thy works, Lord God Almighty; just and true are thy ways, thou King of saints.

All glory be to thee, O Lord most high.

Who shall not fear thee, O Lord, and glorify thy name? for thou only art holy: for all nations shall come and worship before thee; for thy judgments are made manifest.

All glory be to thee, O Lord most high.

Worthy is the Lamb that was slain to receive power, and riches, and wisdom, and might, and honor, and glory, and blessing.

For through him we both have access by one Spirit unto the Father.

But when the Comforter is come, whom I will send unto you from the Father, even the Spirit of truth, who proceedeth from the Father, he shall testify of me:

Glory be to thee, O Lord most high.

And ye also shall bear witness, because ye have been with me from the beginning.

Glory be to thee, O Lord most high.

There is one body, and one Spirit, even as ye are called in one hope of your calling;

So then ye are no more strangers and sojourners, but ye are fellow-citizens with the saints, and of the household of God,

Being built on the foundation of the apostles and prophets, Christ Jesus himself being the chief cornerstone;

In whom all the building, fitly framed together, groweth into an holy temple in the Lord;

In whom ye also are builded together for an habitation of God through the Spirit.

All glory be to thee, O Lord most high.

Selection 42

Call to Worship

O come, let us sing unto the Lord:

Let us make a joyful noise to the rock of our salvation.

Let us come before his presence

with thanksgiving, and make a joyful noise unto him with psalms.

For the Lord is a great God, and a great King above all gods.

In his hand are the deep places of the earth: the strength of the hills is his also.

The sea is his, and he made it: and his hands formed the dry land.

O come, let us worship and bow down; let us kneel before the Lord our maker.

For he is our God; and we are the people of his pasture, and the sheep of his hand.

Part 2

The Lord is my shepherd; I shall not want.

He maketh me to lie down in green pastures;

He leadeth me beside the still waters; he restoreth my soul.

He leadeth me in the paths of righteousness for his name's sake.

Yea, though I walk through the valley of the shadow of death, I will fear no evil; for thou art with me;

Thy rod and thy staff, they comfort me.

Thou preparest a table before me in the presence of mine enemies;

Thou anointest my head with oil; my cup runneth over.

Surely goodness and mercy shall follow me all the days of my life;

And I shall dwell in the house of the Lord forever.

Selection 43

Christian Worship

I was glad when they said unto me, Let us go unto the house of the Lord.

Our feet are standing within thy gates, O Jerusalem.

Jerusalem is builded as a city that is compact together:

Whither the tribes go up, the tribes of the Lord,

Unto the testimony of Israel, to give thanks unto the name of the Lord.

For there are set thrones of judgment, the thrones of the house of David.

Pray for the peace of Jerusalem: they shall prosper that love thee.

Peace be within thy walls, and prosperity within thy palaces.

For my brethren and companions' sakes, I will now say, Peace be within thee.

Because of the house of the Lord our God I will seek thy good.

Part 2

But ye are come unto mount Zion, and unto the city of the living God, the heavenly Jerusalem,

And to innumerable hosts of angels, to the general assembly and church of the first-born who are enrolled in heaven.

And to God, the Judge of all, and to the spirits of just men made perfect, and to Jesus the mediator of a new covenant.

And to the blood of sprinkling that speaketh better than that of Abel.

Having, therefore, brethren, boldness to enter into the holy place by the blood of Jesus, by the way which he dedicated for us,

A new and living way, through the veil, that is to say, his flesh;

And having a great priest over the house of God,

Let us draw near with a true heart in fulness of faith, having our hearts sprinkled from an evil conscience;

And having our body washed with pure water,

Let us hold fast the confession of our hope that it waver not;

For he is faithful that promised:

And let us consider one another to provoke unto love and good works; not forsaking our own assembling together,

And be filled with the Spirit;

Speaking one to another in psalms and hymns and spiritual songs,

Singing and making melody with your heart to the Lord;

Giving thanks always for all things in the name of our Lord Jesus Christ to God, even the Father.

Selection 44

True Worship

Holy, holy, holy, is the Lord of hosts:

The whole earth is full of his glory.

The Lord is in his holy temple:

Let all the earth keep silence before him.

Thus saith the Lord, Heaven is my throne, and the earth is my footstool:

But to this man will I look, even to him that is poor and of a contrite spirit, and that trembleth at my word.

For thus saith the high and lofty One that inhabiteth eternity, whose name is Holy: I dwell in the high and holy place,

With him also that is of a contrite and humble spirit,

To revive the spirit of the humble,

And to revive the heart of the contrite.

Wherewith shall I come before the Lord, and bow myself before the high God?

Shall I come before him with burnt-offerings, with calves a year old?

Will the Lord be pleased with thousands of rams, or with ten thousands of rivers of oil?

Shall I give my firstborn for my transgression, the fruit of my body for the sin of my soul?

He hath showed thee, O man, what is good; and what doth the Lord require of thee,

But to do justly, and to love mercy, and to walk humbly with thy God?

For the hour cometh and now is, when the true worshippers shall worship the Father in spirit and in truth: for such doth the Father seek to be his worshippers.

Unison: **God is a Spirit: and they that worship him must worship him in spirit and in truth.**

Selection 45

The Blessings of Public Worship

How amiable are thy tabernacles, O Lord of hosts!

My soul longeth, yea, even fainteth for the courts of the Lord:

My heart and my flesh cry out for the living God.

Yea, the sparrow hath found her a house, and the swallow a nest for herself, where she may lay her young.

Even thine altars, O Lord of hosts, my King, and my God.

Blessed are they that dwell in thy house: they will be still praising thee.

Blessed is the man whose strength is in thee; in whose heart are the highways to Zion.

Who, passing through the valley of Weeping, make it a place of springs;

Yea, the early rain covereth it with blessings.

They go from strength to strength; every one of them appeareth before God in Zion.

O Lord of hosts, hear my prayer: give ear, O God of Jacob.

Behold, O God our shield, and look upon the face of thine anointed.

For a day in thy courts is better than a thousand.

I had rather be a door-keeper in the house of my God, than to dwell in the tents of wickedness.

For the Lord God is a sun and a shield:

The Lord will give grace and glory;

No good thing will he withhold from them that walk uprightly.

O Lord of hosts, blessed is the man that trusteth in thee.

Selection 46

Morning Worship

Give ear to my words, O Lord, consider my meditation.

Hearken unto the voice of my cry, my King, and my God: for unto thee will I pray.

My voice shalt thou hear in the morning, O Lord;

In the morning will I direct my prayer unto thee, and will look up.

Part 2

I will lift up mine eyes unto the hills:

From whence shall my help come?

My help cometh from the Lord, who made heaven and earth.

He will not suffer thy foot to be moved:

He that keepeth thee will not slumber.

Behold, he that keepeth Israel will neither slumber nor sleep.

The Lord is thy keeper; the Lord is thy shade upon thy right hand.

The sun shall not smite thee by day, nor the moon by night.

The Lord will preserve thee from all evil: he will preserve thy soul.

The Lord will preserve thy going out and thy coming in from this time forth, and for evermore.

Selection 47
Evening Worship

O God, thou art my God; early will I seek thee: my soul thirsteth for thee, my flesh longeth for thee in a dry and thirsty land, where no water is.

To see thy power and thy glory, so as I have seen thee in the sanctuary.

Because thy lovingkindness is better than life, my lips shall praise thee.

Thus will I bless thee while I live: I will lift up my hands in thy name.

My soul shall be satisfied as with marrow and fatness; and my mouth shall praise thee with joyful lips:

When I remember thee upon my bed, and meditate on thee in the night watches.

Because thou hast been my help, therefore in the shadow of thy wings will I rejoice.

My soul followeth hard after thee: thy right hand upholdeth me.

O give thanks unto the Lord, for he is good: for his mercy endureth forever.

Let the redeemed of the Lord say so, whom he hath redeemed from the hand of the enemy;

And gathered them out of the lands, from the east, and from the west, from the north, and from the south.

They wandered in the wilderness in a solitary way; they found no city to dwell in.

Hungry and thirsty, their soul fainted in them.

Then they cried unto the Lord in their trouble, and he delivered them out of their distresses.

He led them forth by the right way, that they might go to a city of habitation.

O that men would praise the Lord for his goodness, and for his wonderful works to the children of men!

Selection 48
God's Guidance

It is a good thing to give thanks unto the Lord, and to sing praises unto thy name, O Most High;

To show forth thy lovingkindness in the morning, and thy faithfulness every night.

Thou, Lord, hast made me glad through thy work; I will triumph in the works of thy hands.

O Lord, how great are thy works! and thy thoughts are very deep.

Thou, Lord, art most high for evermore.

The righteous shall flourish like the palm tree: he shall grow like a cedar in Lebanon.

Those that are planted in the house of the Lord shall flourish in the courts of our God.

The Lord is upright. He is my rock, and there is no unrighteousness in him.

Praise ye the Lord. Praise, O ye servants of the Lord, praise the name of the Lord.

Blessed be the name of the Lord from this time forth and for evermore.

From the rising of the sun unto the going down of the same the Lord's name is to be praised.

The Lord is high above all nations, and his glory above the heavens.

Who is like unto the Lord our God, who dwelleth on high, who humbleth himself to behold the things that are in heaven, and in the earth!

He raiseth up the poor out of the dust, that he may set him with princes, even with the princes of his people. Praise ye the Lord.

Selection 49

Courage and Faith

The Lord is my light and my salvation; whom shall I fear?

The Lord is the strength of my life; of whom shall I be afraid?

When the wicked, even mine enemies and my foes, came upon me to eat up my flesh, they stumbled and fell.

Though a host should encamp against me, my heart shall not fear:

Though war should rise against me, even then will I be confident.

One thing have I asked of the Lord, that will I seek after;

That I may dwell in the house of the Lord all the days of my life, to behold the beauty of the Lord, and to inquire in his temple.

For in the time of trouble he will hide me in his pavilion;

In the secret of his tabernacle will he hide me; he will set me up upon a rock.

And now shall mine head be lifted up above mine enemies round about me;

Therefore will I offer in his tabernacle sacrifices of joy;

I will sing, yea, I will sing praises unto the Lord.

Hear, O Lord, when I cry with my voice:

Have mercy also upon me, and answer me.

When thou saidst, Seek ye my face;

My heart said unto thee, Thy face, Lord, will I seek.

Hide not thy face from me; put not thy servant away in anger;

Thou hast been my help;

leave me not, neither forsake me, O God of my salvation.

When my father and my mother forsake me,

Then the Lord will take me up.

Teach me thy way, O Lord, and lead me in a plain path, because of mine enemies.

Deliver me not over unto the will of mine enemies, for false witnesses are risen up against me, and such as breathe out cruelty.

I had fainted, unless I had believed to see the goodness of the Lord in the land of the living.

Wait on the Lord:

Be of good courage, and he shall strengthen thine heart:

Wait, I say, on the Lord.

Selection 50

The Soul's Longing for God

As the hart panteth after the water brooks, so panteth my soul after thee, O God.

My soul thirsteth for God, for the living God: when shall I come and appear before God?

My tears have been my meat day and night, while they continually say unto me, Where is thy God?

When I remember these things, I pour out my soul in me: for I had gone with the multitude, I went with them to the house of God, with the voice of joy and praise, with a multitude that kept holyday.

Why art thou cast down, O my soul? and why art thou disquieted in me?

Hope thou in God: for I

shall yet praise him for the help of his countenance.

Deep calleth unto deep at the noise of thy waterspouts:

All thy waves and thy billows are gone over me.

Yet the Lord will command his lovingkindness in the daytime,

And in the night his song shall be with me, and my prayer unto the God of my life.

I will say unto God my rock, Why hast thou forgotten me? Why go I mourning because of the oppression of the enemy?

As with a sword in my bones, mine enemies reproach me; while they say daily unto me, Where is thy God?

Why art thou cast down, O my soul? and why art thou disquieted within me?

Hope thou in God: for I shall yet praise him, who is the help of my countenance, and my God.

Judge me, O God, and plead my cause against an ungodly nation:

O deliver me from the deceitful and unjust man.

For thou art the God of my strength: why dost thou cast me off?

Why go I mourning because of the oppression of the enemy?

O send out thy light and thy truth: let them lead me;

Let them bring me unto thy holy hill, and to thy tabernacles.

Then will I go unto the altar of God, unto God my exceeding joy;

Yea, upon the harp will I praise thee, O God, my God.

Why art thou cast down, O my soul? and why art thou disquieted within me?

Hope in God: for I shall yet praise him, who is the help of my countenance, and my God.

Selection 51
Gratitude to Christ

Blessed be the God and Father of our Lord Jesus Christ, who hath blessed us with every spiritual blessing in the heavenly places in Christ:

Even as he chose us in him before the foundation of the world,

That we should be holy and without blemish before him in love:

Having foreordained us unto adoption as sons through Jesus Christ unto himself,

According to the good pleasure

of his will, to the praise of the glory of his grace, which he freely bestowed on us in the Beloved:

In whom we have our redemption through his blood, the forgiveness of our trespasses, according to the riches of his grace.

God, being rich in mercy, for his great love wherewith he loved us,

Even when we were dead through our trespasses,

Made us alive together with Christ (by grace have ye been saved),

And raised us up with him, and made us to sit with him in the heavenly places, in Christ Jesus:

That in the ages to come he might show the exceeding riches of his grace in kindness toward us in Christ Jesus:

For by grace have ye been saved through faith; and that not of yourselves, it is the gift of God;

Not of works, that no man should glory. For we are his workmanship,

Created in Christ Jesus for good works, which God afore prepared that we should walk in them.

Now unto him that is able to do exceeding abundantly above all that we ask or think, according to the power that worketh in us,

Unto him be the glory in the Church and in Christ Jesus unto all generations for ever and ever. Amen.

Selection 52
The Good Man

Blessed is the man that walketh not in the counsel of the ungodly.

Nor standeth in the way of sinners, nor sitteth in the seat of the scornful.

But his delight is in the law of the Lord;

And in his law doth he meditate day and night.

And he shall be like a tree planted by the rivers of water,

That bringeth forth his fruit in his season;

His leaf also shall not wither, and whatsoever he doeth shall prosper.

The ungodly are not so, but are like the chaff which the wind driveth away.

Therefore the ungodly shall not stand in the judgment.

Nor sinners in the congregation of the righteous.

For the Lord knoweth the way of the righteous,

But the way of the ungodly shall perish.

Selection 53
The Upright Life

Lord, who shall abide in thy tabernacle?

Who shall dwell in thy holy hill?

He that walketh uprightly, and worketh righteousness,

And speaketh the truth in his heart.

He that backbiteth not with his tongue,

Nor doeth evil to his neighbor, nor taketh up a reproach against his neighbor.

In whose eyes a vile person is contemned;

But who honoreth them that fear the Lord.

He that sweareth to his own hurt, and changeth not.

He that putteth not out his money to usury,

Nor taketh reward against the innocent.

He that doeth these things shall never be moved.

Selection 54
The Blessed Life

Blessed are the poor in spirit:

For theirs is the Kingdom of heaven.

Blessed are they that mourn:

For they shall be comforted.

Blessed are the meek:

For they shall inherit the earth.

Blessed are they that hunger and thirst after righteousness:

For they shall be filled.

Blessed are the merciful:

For they shall obtain mercy.

Blessed are the pure in heart:

For they shall see God.

Blessed are the peacemakers:

For they shall be called sons of God.

Blessed are they that are persecuted for righteousness' sake:

For theirs is the kingdom of heaven.

Blessed are ye when men shall revile you, and persecute you, and say all manner of evil against you falsely, for my sake. Rejoice, and be exceeding glad:

For great is your reward in heaven: for so persecuted they the prophets that were before you.

Ye are the salt of the earth: but if the salt have lost its savor, wherewith shall it be salted?

It is henceforth good for nothing, but to be cast out,

and to be trodden under foot of men.

Ye are the light of the world.

A city that is set on a hill cannot be hid.

Neither do men light a candle, and put it under a bushel, but on a candlestick; and it giveth light unto all that are in the house.

Let your light so shine before men, that they may see your good works, and glorify your Father which is in heaven.

Selection 55

Love Never Faileth

Though I speak with the tongues of men and of angels,

But have not love, I am become as sounding brass, or a tinkling cymbal.

And though I have the gift of prophecy, and understand all mysteries, and all knowledge; and though I have all faith, so that I could remove mountains,

But have not love, I am nothing.

And though I bestow all my goods to feed the poor, and though I give my body to be burned,

But have not love, it profiteth me nothing.

Love suffereth long, and is kind; love envieth not;

Love vaunteth not itself, is not puffed up,

Doth not behave itself unseemly, seeketh not its own.

Is not easily provoked, thinketh no evil;

Rejoiceth not in iniquity, but rejoiceth in the truth;

Beareth all things, believeth all things, hopeth all things, endureth all things.

Love never faileth:

But whether there be prophecies, they shall fail;

Whether there be tongues, they shall cease;

Whether there be knowledge, it shall vanish away.

For we know in part, and we prophesy in part.

But when that which is perfect is come, then that which is in part shall be done away.

When I was a child, I spake as a child, I understood as a child, I thought as a child:

But when I became a man, I put away childish things.

For now we see through a glass, darkly; but then face to face:

Now I know in part; but then shall I know even as also I am known.

And now abideth faith, hope, love, these three;

But the greatest of these is love.

Selection 56

Love and Service

Beloved, let us love one another: for love is of God; and every one that loveth is born of God, and knoweth God.

He that loveth not knoweth not God; for God is love.

In this was manifested the love of God toward us, because that God hath sent his only begotten Son into the world, that we might live through him.

Herein is love, not that we loved God, but that he loved us, and sent his Son to be the propitiation for our sins.

Beloved, if God so loved us, we also ought to love one another.

No man hath seen God at any time. If we love one another, God dwelleth in us, and his love is perfected in us.

Hereby we know that we dwell

in him and he in us, because he hath given us of his Spirit.

And we have seen and do testify that the Father sent the Son to be the Saviour of the world.

Whosoever shall confess that Jesus is the Son of God, God dwelleth in him and he in God.

And we have known and believed the love that God hath to us.

God is love; and he that dwelleth in love dwelleth in God, and God in him.

Herein is our love made perfect, that we may have boldness in the day of judgment:

Because as he is, so are we in this world.

There is no fear in love; but perfect love casteth out fear: because fear hath torment. He that feareth is not made perfect in love.

We love him, because he first loved us.

If a man say, I love God, and hateth his brother, he is a liar; for he that loveth not his brother whom he hath seen, how can he love God whom he hath not seen?

Unison: And this commandment have we from him, that he who loveth God love his brother also.

Selection 57

The Intercession of the Holy Spirit

Brethren, ye have been called unto liberty; only use not liberty for an occasion to the flesh, but by love serve one another.

For all the law is fulfilled in one word, even in this: Thou shalt love thy neighbor as thyself.

This I say then, Walk in the Spirit, and ye shall not fulfil the lust of the flesh.

For the flesh lusteth against the Spirit, and the Spirit against the flesh, and these are contrary the one to the other; so that ye cannot do the things that ye would.

But if ye be led of the Spirit, ye are not under the law, for the fruit of the Spirit is love, joy, peace, longsuffering, gentleness, goodness, faith, meekness, temperance: and against such there is no law.

And they that are Christ's have crucified the flesh with the affections and lusts. If we live in the Spirit, let us also walk in the Spirit.

Likewise the Spirit also helpeth our infirmities: for we know not how to pray as we ought:

But the Spirit himself maketh intercession for us with groanings which cannot be uttered.

And he that searcheth the hearts knoweth what is the mind of the Spirit, because he maketh intercession for the saints according to the will of God.

And we know that all things work together for good to them that love God, even to them who are the called according to his purpose.

What shall we then say to these things? If God be for us, who can be against us?

He that spared not his own Son, but delivered him up for

us all, how shall he not with him also freely give us all things?

Who shall lay anything to the charge of God's elect?

It is God that justifieth.

Who is he that condemneth? It is Christ that died, yea rather, that is risen again, who is even at the right hand of God, who also maketh intercession for us.

Who shall separate us from the love of Christ?

Shall tribulation, or distress, or persecution, or famine, or nakedness, or peril, or sword?

As it is written, For thy sake we are killed all the day long;

We are accounted as sheep for the slaughter.

Nay, in all these things we are more than conquerors through him that loved us.

For I am persuaded, that neither death, nor life, nor angels, nor principalities, nor powers, nor things present, nor things to come,

Nor height, nor depth, nor any other creature, shall be able to separate us from the love of God, which is in Christ Jesus our Lord.

Selection 58

The Blessedness of Suffering for Righteousness' Sake

Be ye all of one mind, having compassion one of another, love as brethren, be pitiful, be courteous:

Not rendering evil for evil, or railing for railing: but contrariwise blessing;

Knowing that ye are thereunto called, that ye should inherit a blessing.

For he that will love life, and see good days, let him refrain his tongue from evil, and his lips that they speak no guile:

Let him turn away from evil, and do good: let him seek peace, and ensue it.

For the eyes of the Lord are over the righteous, and his ears are open unto their prayers:

But the face of the Lord is against them that do evil.

And who is he that will harm you, if ye be followers of that which is good?

But and if ye suffer for righteousness' sake, happy are ye: and be not afraid of their terror, neither be troubled.

But sanctify the Lord God in your hearts:

And be ready always to give an answer to every one that asketh you a reason of the hope that is in you with meekness and fear:

Having a good conscience; that, whereas they speak evil

of you, as of evildoers, they may be ashamed that falsely accuse your good conversation in Christ.

For it is better, if the will of God be so, that ye suffer for well doing, than for evil doing.

For Christ also hath once suffered for sins, the just for the unjust, that he might bring us to God.

Selection 59

The Living Sacrifice

I beseech you therefore, brethren, by the mercies of God, to present your bodies a living sacrifice, holy, acceptable unto God, which is your spiritual service.

And be not fashioned according to this world:

But be ye transformed by the renewing of your mind,

That ye may prove what is that good, and acceptable, and perfect will of God.

Let love be without hypocrisy.

Abhor that which is evil; cleave to that which is good.

Be ye kindly affectioned one to another with brotherly love; in honor preferring one another;

Not slothful in business; fervent in spirit; serving the Lord;

Rejoicing in hope; patient in tribulation; continuing instant in prayer;

Distributing to the necessity of saints given to hospitality.

Bless them that persecute you; bless and curse not.

Rejoice with them that rejoice; weep with them that weep.

Be of the same mind one toward another.

Mind not high things, but condescend to men of low estate.

Be not wise in your own conceits. Render to no man evil for evil.

Take thought for things

honorable in the sight of all men.

If it be possible, as much as lieth in you, live peaceably with all men.

Dearly beloved, avenge not yourselves, but give place unto the wrath of God:

For it is written, Vengeance is mine; I will repay, saith the Lord.

Therefore if thine enemy hunger, feed him; if he thirst, give him drink:

For in so doing thou shalt heap coals of fire on his head.

Be not overcome of evil, but overcome evil with good.

Selection 60

Fatherhood and Brotherhood in Christ

I will mention the lovingkindnesses of the Lord, and the praises of the Lord, according to all that the Lord hath bestowed on us,

And the great goodness toward the House of Israel, which he hath bestowed on them according to his mercies, and according to the multitude of his lovingkindnesses.

For he said, Surely they are my people, children that will not lie: so he was their Saviour.

In all their affliction he was afflicted, and the angel of his presence saved them:

In his love and in his pity he redeemed them; and he bare them, and carried them all the days of old.

For thou, O Lord, art our Father, our Redeemer; thy name is from everlasting.

Behold, what manner of love the Father hath bestowed upon us, that we should be called the sons of God;

Beloved, now are we the sons of God, and it doth not yet appear what we shall be:

But we know that when he shall appear, we shall be like him: for we shall see him as he is.

And every man that hath this hope in him purifieth himself, even as he is pure.

In this the children of God are manifest, and the children of the devil:

Whosoever doeth not righteousness is not of God, neither he that loveth not his brother.

For this is the message that ye have heard from the beginning, that we should love one another.

We know that we have

passed from death unto life, because we love the brethren.

He that loveth not his brother abideth in death. Whosoever hateth his brother is a murderer:

And ye know that no murderer hath eternal life abiding in him.

Hereby perceive we the love of God, because he laid down his life for us: and we ought to lay down our lives for the brethren.

But whoso hath this world's goods, and seeth his brother have need,

And shutteth up his compassion from him, how doth the love of God abide in him?

My little children, let us not love in word, neither in tongue; but in deed and in truth.

And this is his commandment,

That we should believe on the name of his Son, Jesus Christ, and love one another.

Selection 61

The Family

Blessed is every one that feareth the Lord, that walketh in his ways.

For thou shalt eat the labor of thine hands;

Happy shalt thou be, and it shall be well with thee.

Thy wife shall be as a fruitful vine by the sides of thine house:

Thy children like olive plants round about thy table.

Behold, thus shall the man be blessed that feareth the Lord.

The Lord shall bless thee out of Zion: and thou shalt see the good of Jerusalem all the days of thy life.

Yea, thou shalt see thy children's children. Peace be unto Israel.

Now these are the commandments, the statutes, and the judgments, which the Lord your God commanded to teach you,

That ye might do them in the land whither ye go to possess it:

That thou mightest fear the Lord thy God, to keep all his statutes and his commandments,

Which I command thee, thou, and thy son, and thy son's son, all the days of thy life; and that thy days may be prolonged.

Hear, therefore, O Israel, and observe to do it; that it may be well with thee, and that ye may increase mightily,

As the Lord God of thy fathers hath promised thee, in the land that floweth with milk and honey.

Hear, O Israel: the Lord our God is one Lord: and thou shalt love the Lord thy God with all thine heart,

And with all thy soul, and with all thy might.

And these words, which I command thee this day, shall be upon thine heart:

And thou shalt teach them diligently unto thy children, and shalt talk of them when thou sittest in thine house,

And when thou walkest by the way, and when thou liest down, and when thou risest up.

And thou shalt bind them for a sign upon thine hand,

And they shall be as frontlets between thine eyes.

And thou shalt write them upon the posts of thy house, and on thy gates.

Selection 62

Children and the Kingdom

In that hour came the disciples unto Jesus, saying, Who then is greatest in the kingdom of heaven?

And he called to him a little child, and set him in the midst of them, and said,

Verily I say unto you, Except ye be converted, and become as little children, ye shall not enter into the kingdom of heaven.

Whosoever therefore shall humble himself as this little child, the same is greatest in the kingdom of heaven.

Take heed that ye despise not one of these little ones;

For I say unto you, That in heaven their angels do always behold the face of my Father which is in heaven.

Then were there brought unto him little children that he should lay his hands on them and pray:

And the disciples rebuked them.

But Jesus said, Suffer the little children, and forbid them not, to come unto me: for of such is the kingdom of heaven.

And he laid his hands on them, and departed thence.

Selection 63

God and Nature, the Moral Law, and Man

The heavens declare the glory of God;

And the firmament showeth his handiwork.

Day unto day uttereth speech,

And night unto night showeth knowledge.

There is no speech nor language where their voice is not heard.

Their line is gone out through all the earth, and their words to the end of the world.

In them hath he set a tabernacle for the sun, which is as a bridegroom coming out of his chamber,

And rejoiceth as a strong man to run a race.

His going forth is from the end of the heaven, and his circuit unto the ends of it:

And there is nothing hid from the heat thereof.

Part 2

The law of the Lord is perfect, converting the soul:

The testimony of the Lord is sure, making wise the simple.

The statutes of the Lord are right, rejoicing the heart:

The commandment of the Lord is pure, enlightening the eyes.

The fear of the Lord is clean, enduring forever:

The judgments of the Lord are true and righteous altogether.

More to be desired are they than gold, yea, than much fine gold:

Sweeter also than honey and the honeycomb.

Moreover by them is thy servant warned:

And in keeping of them there is great reward.

Who can understand his errors?

Cleanse thou me from secret faults.

Keep back thy servant also from presumptuous sins; let them not have dominion over me:

Then shall I be upright, and I shall be innocent from the great transgression.

Unison: Let the words of my mouth, and the meditation of my heart, be acceptable in thy sight, O Lord, my strength and my redeemer.

610

Part 3

O Lord, our Lord, how excellent is thy name in all the earth!

Who hast set thy glory above the heavens.

Out of the mouths of babes and sucklings hast thou ordained strength because of thine enemies,

That thou mightest still the enemy and the avenger.

When I consider thy heavens, the work of thy fingers, the moon and the stars, which thou hast ordained;

What is man, that thou art mindful of him? and the son of man, that thou visitest him?

For thou hast made him a little lower than the angels, and hast crowned him with glory and honor.

Thou madest him to have dominion over the works of thy hands;

Thou hast put all things under his feet:

All sheep and oxen, yea, and the beasts of the field;

The birds of the air, and the fish of the sea, and whatsoever passeth through the paths of the seas.

Unison: **O Lord, our Lord, how excellent is thy name in all the earth!**

Selection 64

The Word of Scripture

For ever, O Lord, thy word is settled in heaven.

Thy faithfulness is unto all generations: thou hast established the earth, and it abideth.

They continue this day according to thine ordinances: for all are thy servants.

Unless thy law had been my delight, I should then have perished in my affliction.

I will never forget thy precepts: for with them thou hast quickened me.

I am thine, save me; for I have sought thy precepts.

The wicked have waited for me to destroy me: but I will consider thy testimonies.

I have seen an end of all perfection: but thy commandment is exceeding broad.

Part 2

O how I love thy law! It is my meditation all the day.

Thou through thy commandments hast made me wiser than mine enemies: for they are ever with me.

I have more understanding than all my teachers: for thy testimonies are my meditation.

I understand more than the ancients, because I keep thy precepts.

I have refrained my feet from every evil way, that I might keep thy word.

I have not departed from thy judgments: for thou hast taught me.

How sweet are thy words unto my taste! yea, sweeter than honey to my mouth!

Through thy precepts I get understanding: therefore I hate every false way.

Part 3

Thy word is a lamp unto my feet, and a light unto my path.

I have sworn, and have confirmed it, that I will keep thy righteous judgments.

I am afflicted very much: quicken me, O Lord, according to thy word.

Accept, I beseech thee, the freewill offerings of my mouth, O Lord, and teach me thy judgments.

My soul is continually in my hand: yet I do not forget thy law.

The wicked have laid a snare for me: yet I erred not from thy precepts.

Thy testimonies have I taken as a heritage for ever: for they are the rejoicing of my heart.

I have inclined mine heart to perform thy statutes alway, even unto the end.

Selection 65
The Eternal Word

Doth not wisdom cry? and understanding put forth her voice?

She crieth at the gates at the entry of the city, at the coming in at the doors.

Unto you, O men, I call; and my voice is to the sons of man.

Hear; for I will speak of excellent things; and the opening of my lips shall be right things.

The Lord possessed me in the beginning of his way, before his works of old.

I was set up from everlasting, from the beginning, or ever the earth was.

When there were no depths, I was brought forth; when there were no fountains abounding with water.

Before the mountains were settled, before the hills was I brought forth:

When he prepared the heavens, I was there: when he set a compass upon the face of the depth:

When he established the clouds above: when he strengthened the fountains of the deep:

When he gave to the sea his decree, that the waters should not pass his commandment: when he appointed the foundations of the earth:

Then I was by him, as one brought up with him: and I was daily his delight, rejoicing always before him;

Rejoicing in the habitable part of his earth; and my delights were with the sons of men.

Now, therefore, hearken unto me, O ye children: for blessed are they that keep my ways.

Hear instruction, and be wise, and refuse it not.

Blessed is the man that heareth me, watching daily at my gates, waiting at the posts of my doors.

For whoso findeth me findeth life, and shall obtain favor of the Lord.

But he that sinneth against me wrongeth his own soul: all they that hate me love death.

Selection 66

The Word Incarnate

In the beginning was the Word, and the Word was with God, and the Word was God. The same was in the beginning with God.

All things were made by him; and without him was not anything made that was made.

In him was life; and the life was the light of men.

And the light shineth in darkness; and the darkness comprehended it not.

There was a man sent from God whose name was John.

The same came for a witness, to bear witness of the Light, that all men through him might believe.

He was not that Light, but was sent to bear witness of that Light.

That was the true Light, which lighteth every man that cometh into the world.

He was in the world, and the world was made by him, and the world knew him not.

He came unto his own, and his own received him not.

But as many as received him, to them gave he power to become the sons of God, even to them that believe on his name:

Which were born, not of blood, nor of the will of the flesh, nor of the will of man, but of God.

And the Word was made flesh, and dwelt among us,

And we beheld his glory, the glory as of the only begotten of the Father, full of grace and truth.

Selection 67

The Word of God in Living Experience

Grace and peace be multiplied unto you through the knowledge of God, and of Jesus our Lord,

According as his divine power hath given unto us all things that pertain unto life and godliness,

Through the knowledge of him that hath called us to glory and virtue:

Whereby are given unto us exceeding great and precious promises:

That by these ye might be partakers of the divine nature, having escaped the corruption that is in the world through lust.

We have also a more sure word of prophecy; whereunto ye do well that ye take heed,

As unto a light that shineth in a dark place, until the day dawn, and the day star arise in your hearts:

Knowing this first, that no prophecy of the scripture is of any private interpretation.

For the prophecy came not in old time by the will of man:

But holy men of God spake as they were moved by the Holy Ghost.

All scripture is given by inspiration of God, and is profitable for doctrine, for reproof, for correction, for instruction in righteousness:

That the man of God may be perfect, thoroughly furnished unto all good works.

For whatsoever things were written aforetime were written for our learning,

That through patience and through comfort of the scriptures we might have hope.

Wherefore, as the Holy Ghost saith, Today if ye will hear his voice, harden not your hearts.

For the word of God is quick, and powerful, and sharper than any two-edged sword,

Piercing even to the dividing asunder of soul and spirit, and of the joints and marrow,

And is a discerner of the thoughts and intents of the heart.

Seeing ye have purified your souls in obeying the truth through the Spirit unto unfeigned love of the brethren,

See that ye love one another with a pure heart fervently:

Being born again, not of corruptible seed, but of incorruptible, by the word of God, which liveth and abideth for ever.

For all flesh is as grass, and all the glory of man as the flower of grass.

The grass withereth, and the flower thereof falleth away: but the word of the Lord endureth for ever.

And this is the word which by the gospel is preached unto you.

Selection 68

Religious Education

Hear, ye children, the instruction of a father, and attend to know understanding.

For I give you good doctrine, forsake ye not my law.

Get wisdom, get understanding: forget it not; neither decline from the words of my mouth.

Forsake her not, and she shall preserve thee: love her, and she shall keep thee.

Wisdom is the principal thing;

therefore get wisdom: and with all thy getting get understanding.

Exalt her, and she shall promote thee: she shall bring thee to honor, when thou dost embrace her.

She shall give to thine head an ornament of grace; a crown of glory shall she deliver to thee.

Hear, O my son, and receive my sayings; and the years of thy life shall be many.

I have taught thee in the way of wisdom; I have led thee in right paths.

When thou goest, thy steps shall not be straitened; and when thou runnest, thou shalt not stumble.

Take fast hold of instruction; let her not go: keep her; for she is thy life.

Enter not into the path of the wicked, and go not in the way of evil men.

For they eat the bread of wickedness, and drink the wine of violence.

But the path of the just is as the shining light, that shineth more and more unto the perfect day.

Selection 69

Personal Temperance

Know ye not that your body is the temple of the Holy Ghost which is in you, which ye have from God, and that ye are not your own?

For ye are bought with a price: therefore glorify God in your body, and in your spirit, which are God's.

I beseech you therefore, brethren, by the mercies of God, that ye present your bodies a living sacrifice, holy, acceptable unto God, which is your reasonable service. And be not conformed to this world:

But be ye transformed by the renewing of your mind, that ye may prove what is that good, and acceptable, and perfect will of God.

Look therefore carefully how ye walk, not as unwise, but as wise; redeeming the time, because the days are evil.

Wherefore be ye not foolish, but understand what the will of the Lord is.

And be not drunken with wine, wherein is riot,

But be filled with the Spirit.

Who hath woe? who hath sorrow? who hath contentions?

Who hath babbling? who hath wounds without cause? who hath redness of eyes?

They that tarry long at the wine; they that go out to seek mixed wine.

Look not thou upon the wine when it is red,

When it giveth its color in the cup, when it goeth down smoothly:

At the last it biteth like a serpent, and stingeth like an adder.

Be not among winebibbers; among riotous eaters of flesh:

For the drunkard and the glutton shall come to poverty: and drowsiness shall clothe a man with rags.

Wherefore let him that thinketh he standeth take heed lest he fall.

If any man defile the temple of God, him shall God destroy;

For the temple of God is holy, which temple ye are.

This I say then, Walk in the Spirit, and ye shall not fulfill the lust of the flesh.

Selection 70

The Quest of the Kingdom of God and His Righteousness

Lay not up for yourselves treasures upon earth, where moth and rust doth corrupt,

And where thieves break through and steal:

But lay up for yourselves treasures in heaven, where neither moth nor rust doth corrupt,

And where thieves do not break through nor steal:

For where your treasure is, there will your heart be also.

No man can serve two masters:

For either he will hate the one, and love the other; or else he will hold to the one, and despise the other.

Ye cannot serve God and mammon.

Therefore I say unto you, Take no thought for your life, what ye shall eat, or what ye shall drink;

Nor yet for your body, what ye shall put on. Is not the life more than meat, and the body than raiment?

Behold the fowls of the air: for they sow not, neither do they reap, nor gather into barns;

Yet your heavenly Father feedeth them.

Are ye not much better than they?

Which of you by taking thought can add one cubit unto his stature?

And why take ye thought for raiment? Consider the lilies of the field, how they grow;

They toil not, neither do they spin:

And yet I say unto you, That

even Solomon in all his glory was not arrayed like one of these.

Wherefore, if God so clothe the grass of the field, which today is, and tomorrow is cast into the oven,

Shall he not much more clothe you, O ye of little faith?

Therefore take no thought, saying, What shall we eat? or, What shall we drink? or, Wherewithal shall we be clothed?

For after all these things do the Gentiles seek: for your heavenly Father knoweth that ye have need of all these things.

But seek ye first the kingdom of God and his righteousness;

And all these things shall be added unto you.

Take, therefore, no thought for the morrow:

For the morrow shall take thought for the things of itself.

Sufficient unto the day is the evil thereof.

Selection 71

Social Righteousness

Hear, O heavens; and give ear, O earth: for the Lord hath spoken: To what purpose is the multitude of your sacrifices unto me?

When ye come to appear before me, who hath required this at your hand, to tread my courts?

Wash you, make you clean; put away the evil of your doings from before mine eyes; cease to do evil: learn to do well;

Seek judgment, relieve the oppressed, judge the fatherless, plead for the widow.

Is not this the fast that I have chosen? to loose the bands of wickedness, to undo the heavy burdens,

And to let the oppressed go free, and that ye break every yoke?

Is it not to deal thy bread to the hungry, and that thou bring the poor that are cast out to thy house?

When thou seest the naked, that thou cover him; and that thou hide not thyself from thine own flesh?

Then shall thy light break forth as the morning, and thine health shall spring forth speedily;

And thy righteousness shall go before thee; the glory of the Lord shall be thy rearward.

Then shalt thou call, and the Lord will answer;

Thou shalt cry, and he will say, Here I am.

If thou draw out thy soul to the hungry, and satisfy the afflicted soul;

Then shall thy light rise in obscurity, and thy darkness be as the noonday;

And the Lord shall guide thee continually, and satisfy thy soul in drought, and make fat thy bones;

And thou shalt be like a watered garden, and like a spring of water, whose waters fail not.

He hath showed thee, O man, what is good;

And what doth the Lord require of thee, but to do justly, and to love mercy, and to walk humbly with thy God?

Selection 72

A Nation Blessed of God

Rejoice in the Lord, O ye righteous: praise is comely for the upright.

Praise the Lord with harp: sing unto him with the psaltery and an instrument of ten strings.

Sing unto him a new song; play skilfully with a loud noise.

For the word of the Lord is right; and all his works are done in truth.

He loveth righteousness and justice: the earth is full of the goodness of the Lord.

By the word of the Lord were the heavens made, and all the host of them by the breath of his mouth.

He gathered the waters of the sea together as a heap: he layeth up the deeps in storehouses.

Let all the earth fear the Lord: let all the inhabitants of the world stand in awe of him.

For he spake, and it was done; he commanded, and it stood fast.

The Lord bringeth the counsel of the nations to nought: he maketh the thoughts of the peoples to be of none effect.

The counsel of the Lord standeth fast for ever, the thoughts of his heart to all generations.

Blessed is the nation whose God is the Lord; the people whom he hath chosen for his own inheritance.

The Lord looketh from heaven; he beholdeth all the sons of men.

From the place of his habitation he looketh forth upon all the inhabitants of the earth.

He fashioneth the hearts of them all; he considereth all their works.

There is no king saved by the multitude of an host: a mighty man is not delivered by much strength.

A horse is a vain thing for safety; neither shall he deliver any by his great strength.

Behold, the eye of the Lord is upon them that fear him, upon them that hope in his mercy;

To deliver their soul from death, and to keep them alive in famine.

Our soul hath waited for the Lord: he is our help and our shield.

For our heart shall rejoice in him, because we have trusted in his holy name.

Let thy mercy, O Lord, be upon us, according as we hope in thee.

Selection 73

The Gracious Power and Reign of God

Praise ye the Lord: for it is good to sing praises unto our God;

For it is pleasant; and praise is comely.

The Lord doth build up Jerusalem: he gathereth together the outcasts of Israel.

He healeth the broken in heart, and bindeth up their wounds.

He telleth the number of stars; he calleth them all by their names.

Great is the Lord, and of great power; his understanding is infinite.

The Lord lifteth up the meek: he casteth the wicked down to the ground.

Sing unto the Lord with thanksgiving; sing praise upon the harp unto our God:

Who covereth the heavens with clouds, who prepareth rain for the earth,

Who maketh grass to grow upon the mountains.

He giveth to the beast his food, and to the young ravens which cry.

The Lord taketh pleasure in them that fear him, in those that hope in his mercy.

Praise the Lord, O Jerusalem; praise thy God, O Zion.

For he hath strengthened the bars of thy gates; he hath blessed thy children within thee.

He maketh peace in thy borders, and filleth thee with the finest of the wheat.

He sendeth forth his commandment upon earth: his word runneth very swiftly.

He giveth snow like wool: he scattereth the hoarfrost like ashes.

He casteth forth his ice like morsels: who can stand before his cold?

He sendeth out his word, and melteth them: he causeth his wind to blow, and the waters flow.

He showeth his word unto Jacob, his statutes and his judgments unto Israel.

He hath not dealt so with any nation:

And as for his judgments, they have not known them. Praise ye the Lord.

Selection 74

The Vision and Hope of World Peace

Behold, a king shall reign in righteousness, and he shall bring forth justice to the nations.

He shall stand and feed his flock in the strength of the Lord, in the majesty of the name of the Lord his God.

And this man shall be our peace;

And he will teach us of his ways and we will walk in his paths;

And he shall judge among many people, and rebuke strong nations afar off;

And they shall beat their swords into ploughshares, and their spears into pruning hooks;

Nation shall not lift up sword against nation, neither shall they learn war any more.

But they shall sit every man under his vine and under his fig tree; and none shall make them afraid.

Then justice shall dwell in the wilderness, and righteousness shall abide in the fruitful field.

And the work of righteousness shall be peace;

And the effect of righteousness, quietness and confidence forever.

And my people shall abide in a peaceable habitation, and in safe dwellings, and in quiet resting-places.

And they shall build houses, and inhabit them; they shall plant vineyards, and eat the fruit of them.

For as the days of a tree shall be the days of my people,

And long shall my chosen enjoy the work of their hands.

They shall not labor in vain, nor bring forth for calamity;

They shall not hurt nor destroy in all my holy mountain, saith the Lord;

For the earth shall be full of the knowledge of the Lord, as the waters cover the sea.

O praise the Lord, all ye nations:

Praise him, all ye peoples.

For his merciful kindness is great toward us:

And the truth of the Lord endureth for ever. Praise ye the Lord.

Selection 75

Thanksgiving

Bless the Lord, O my soul: and all that is within me, bless his holy name.

Bless the Lord, O my soul, and forget not all his benefits:

Who forgiveth all thine iniquities; who healeth all thy diseases;

Who redeemeth thy life from destruction; who crowneth thee with lovingkindness and tender mercies;

Who satisfieth thy mouth with good things; so that thy youth is renewed like the eagle's.

The Lord executeth righteousness and judgment for all that are oppressed.

He made known his ways unto Moses, his acts unto the children of Israel.

The Lord is merciful and gracious, slow to anger, and plenteous in mercy.

He will not always chide: neither will he keep his anger for ever.

He hath not dealt with us after our sins; nor rewarded us according to our iniquities.

For as the heaven is high above the earth, so great is his mercy toward them that fear him.

As far as the east is from the west, so far hath he removed our transgressions from us.

Like as a father pitieth his children, so the Lord pitieth them that fear him.

For he knoweth our frame; he remembereth that we are dust.

As for man, his days are as grass: as a flower of the field, so he flourisheth.

For the wind passeth over it, and it is gone; and the place thereof shall know it no more.

But the mercy of the Lord is from everlasting to everlasting upon them that fear him, and his righteousness u n t o children's children;

To such as keep his covenant, and to those that remember his commandments to do them.

The Lord hath established his throne in the heavens; and his kingdom ruleth over all.

Bless the Lord, ye his angels, that excel in strength, that do his commandments, harkening unto the voice of his word.

Bless ye the Lord, all ye his hosts;

Ye ministers of his, that do his pleasure.

Bless the Lord, all his works in all places of his dominion:

Bless the Lord, O my soul.

Selection 76

A Call to Universal Praise

Praise ye the Lord. Praise ye the Lord from the heavens:

Praise him in the heights.

Praise ye him, all his angels:

Praise ye him, all his hosts.

Praise ye him, sun and moon:

Praise him, all ye stars of light.

Praise him, ye heavens of heavens,

And ye waters that be above the heavens.

Let them praise the name of the Lord:

For he commanded, and they were created.

He hath also established them for ever and ever:

He hath made a decree which shall not pass.

Praise the Lord from the earth, ye dragons, and all deeps:

Fire, and hail; snow, and vapor; stormy wind fulfilling his word:

Mountains, and all hills;

Fruitful trees, and all cedars:

Beasts, and all cattle;

Creeping things, and flying fowl:

Kings of the earth, and all people;

Princes, and all judges of the earth:

Both young men, and maidens;

Old men, and children:

Let them praise the name of the Lord: for his name alone is excellent;

His glory is above the earth and heaven.

He also exalteth the horn of his people,

The praise of all his saints;

Unison: Praise ye the Lord.

Selection 77

Praise of God's Goodness

I will extol thee, my God, O king; and I will bless thy name for ever and ever.

Every day will I bless thee; and I will praise thy name for ever and ever.

Great is the Lord, and greatly to be praised; and his greatness is unsearchable.

One generation shall praise thy works to another, and shall declare thy mighty acts.

I will speak of the glorious honor of thy majesty, and of thy wondrous works.

And men shall speak of the might of thy terrible acts; and I will declare thy greatness.

They shall utter the memory of thy great goodness, and shall sing of thy righteousness.

The Lord is gracious, and full of compassion; slow to anger, and of great mercy.

The Lord is good to all: and his tender mercies are over all his works.

And thy works shall praise thee, O Lord; and thy saints shall bless thee.

They shall speak of the glory of thy kingdom, and talk of thy power;

To make known to the sons of men his mighty acts, and the glorious majesty of his kingdom.

Thy kingdom is an everlasting kingdom, and thy dominion endureth throughout all generations.

The Lord upholdeth all that fall, and raiseth up all those that are bowed down.

The eyes of all wait upon thee; and thou givest them their food in due season.

Thou openest thine hand, and satisfiest the desire of every living thing.

The Lord is righteous in all his ways, and gracious in all his works.

The Lord is nigh unto all them that call upon him, to all that call upon him in truth.

He will fulfill the desire of them that fear him: he also will hear their cry, and will save them.

The Lord preserveth all them that love him: but all the wicked will he destroy.

My mouth shall speak the praise of the Lord:

And let all flesh bless his holy name for ever and ever.

Selection 78

Harvest Ingathering

Praise waiteth for thee, O God, in Zion: and unto thee shall the vow be performed:

O thou that hearest prayer, unto thee shall all flesh come.

Iniquities prevail against me: as for our transgressions, thou wilt purge them away.

Blessed is the man whom thou choosest, and causest to approach unto thee, that he may dwell in thy courts:

We shall be satisfied with the goodness of thy house, even of thy holy temple.

By terrible things in righteousness wilt thou answer us, O God of our salvation;

Who art the confidence of all the ends of the earth, and of them that are afar off upon the sea:

Who by his strength setteth fast the mountains, being girded with power:

Who stilleth the noise of the seas, the noise of their waves, and the tumult of the peoples.

They also that dwell in the uttermost parts are afraid at thy tokens: thou makest the outgoings of the morning and the evening to rejoice.

Thou visitest the earth, and waterest it: thou greatly enrichest it with the river of God, which is full of water:

Thou preparest them grain, when thou hast so provided for it.

Thou waterest the ridges thereof abundantly: thou settlest the furrows thereof.

Thou makest it soft with showers: thou blessest the springing thereof.

Thou crownest the year with thy goodness; and thy paths drop fatness.

They drop upon the pastures of the wilderness: and the hills rejoice on every side.

The pastures are clothed with flocks; the valleys also are covered over with grain;

They shout for joy, they also sing.

Selection 79
Church Anniversary

We have heard with our ears, O God, our fathers have told us,

What work thou didst in their days, in the times of old.

How thou didst drive out the heathen with thy hand, and plantedst them;

How thou didst afflict the people, and cast them out.

For they got not the land in possession by their own sword, neither did their own arm save them;

But thy right hand, and thine arm, and the light of thy countenance, because t h o u hadst a favor unto them.

In God we boast all the day long,

And praise thy name for ever.

For he established a testimony in Jacob, and appointed a law in Israel,

Which he commanded our fathers, that they should make them known to their children;

That the generation to come might know them, even the children which should be born;

Who should arise and declare them to their children;

That they might set their hope in God, and not forget the works of God,

But keep his commandments.

Our fathers trusted in thee:

They trusted, and thou didst deliver them.

They cried unto thee, and were delivered:

They trusted in thee, and were not put to shame.

When they were but a few men in number,

Yea, very few, and sojourners in it,

And they went from nation to nation, from one kingdom to another people;

He suffered no man to do them wrong;

Yea, he reproved kings for their sakes, saying, Touch not mine anointed ones,

And do my prophets no harm.

The Lord bringeth the counsel of the nations to nought;

He maketh the thoughts of the peoples to be of no effect.

The counsel of the Lord standeth for ever,

The thoughts of his heart to all generations.

Blessed is the nation whose God is the Lord;

And the people whom he hath chosen for his own inheritance.

All the ends of the earth shall remember and turn unto the Lord:

And all the kindreds of the nations shall worship before thee.

For the kingdom is the Lord's:

And he is the ruler over the nations.

Unison: Blessed be the Lord God of Israel from everlasting and to everlasting. Amen, and Amen.

Selection 80

Memorial or All Saints' Day—I

I beheld, and lo, a great multitude, which no man could number, of all nations, and kindreds, and peoples, and tongues, stood before the throne, and before the Lamb, clothed with white robes, and palms in their hands;

And they cried with a loud voice, saying, Salvation to our God who sitteth upon the throne, and unto the Lamb.

And all the angels stood round about the throne, and about the elders and the four beasts, and fell before the throne on their faces, and worshipped God.

Saying, Amen: Blessing, and glory, and w i s d o m , and thanksgiving, and honor, and power, and might, be unto our God for ever and ever. Amen.

And one of the elders said unto me, Who are these which are arrayed in white robes? and whence came they?

These are they which came out of great tribulation, and have washed their robes, and made them white in the blood of the Lamb.

Therefore are they before the throne of God, and serve him day and night in his temple:

And he that sitteth on the throne shall dwell among them.

They shall hunger no more, neither thirst any more; neither shall the sun light on them, nor any heat.

For the Lamb which is in the midst of the throne shall feed them, and shall lead them unto living fountains of waters: and God shall wipe away all tears from their eyes.

Selection 81
Memorial or All Saints' Day—II

The souls of the righteous are in the hand of God.

And there shall no torment touch them.

In the sight of the unwise they seem to be dead;

And their departure was taken for a misfortune, and their going from us annihilation;

But they are in peace. For though they shall have experienced punishment according to the judgment of men,

Yet is their hope full of immortality.

And having been a little chastened, they shall be greatly rewarded;

For God proved them, and found them worthy of himself.

As gold in a furnace he tried them, and received them as a burnt offering.

And in the time of their visitation they shall blaze forth, and run to and fro like sparks among the stubble.

They shall judge nations, and have dominion over peoples, and their king shall be the Lord for ever.

They that put their trust in him shall understand the truth; and such as be faithful in love shall abide with him;

For grace and mercy shall be to his saints, and he will have care for his elect.

But the ungodly shall be punished according to their own imagination, who have despised the righteous and forsaken the Lord.

Selection 82
God the Refuge of His People

God is our refuge and strength, a very present help in trouble.

Therefore will we not fear, though the earth be removed, and though the mountains be carried into the midst of the sea;

Though the waters thereof roar and be troubled,

Though the mountains shake with the swelling thereof.

There is a river, the streams whereof make glad the city of God,

The holy place of the tabernacles of the Most High.

God is in the midst of her; she shall not be moved:

God shall help her, and that right early.

The nations raged, the kingdoms were moved: he uttered his voice, the earth melted.

The Lord of hosts is with us; the God of Jacob is our refuge.

Come, behold the works of the Lord,

What desolations he hath made in the earth.

He maketh wars to cease unto the end of the earth;

He breaketh the bow, and cutteth the spear in sunder; he burneth the chariots in the fire.

Be still, and know that I am God: I will be exalted among the nations, I will be exalted in the earth.

The Lord of hosts is with us; the God of Jacob is our refuge.

Responsive Readings

For Occasional Services Other Than the Festivals
of the Church Year

Selections

Armistice Day and Peace Sunday 4, 7, 74, 82

Bible Sunday 64, 65, 66, 67

Children's Services 62

Church Anniversaries 40, 43, 45, 48, 79, 82

Civic and Patriotic Services 2, 5, 20, 36, 71, 72, 82

Education Day 52, 53, 54, 55, 56, 63, 68

Festival of the Christian Home 60, 61, 62

Labor Sunday 20, 60, 71

Memorial Day and All Saints' Day 80, 81

Missions and the Kingdom of God
        4, 5, 6, 8, 13, 14, 15, 17, 18, 29, 36, 38, 60, 70, 73, 74

New Year 3, 9, 10, 26, 48, 49, 73, 82

Stewardship 55, 56, 59, 60, 71

Thanksgiving and Harvest Home 37, 48, 73, 74, 75, 76, 77, 78

World Temperance 69

ᴿesponsive ᴿeadings

Scripture References and Selection Numbers

THE HYMNAL

Indexes

Topical Index of Responsive Readings

THE HYMNAL

V. Eastertide

SEMESTER OF THE CHURCH: TRINITY SUNDAY TO ADVENT

VII. Trinity Season

Topical Index of Responsive Prayers — Litanies

Topical Index of Hymns

THE HYMNAL

640

INDEXES

641

THE HYMNAL

642

INDEXES

643

INDEXES

INDEXES

647

THE HYMNAL

648

INDEXES

THE HYMNAL

Metrical Index of Tunes

THE HYMNAL

654

Alphabetical Index of Tunes

(*Indicates Descant)

THE HYMNAL

INDEXES

657

Index of Composers, Arrangers and Sources

INDEXES

Index of Authors, Translators and Sources

Index of Responses and Canticles

Index of Descants

Index of First Lines of Hymns

INDEXES

671

THE HYMNAL

INDEXES

TEXAS/PASCOS '92: RELATIVISTIC ASTROPHYSICS AND PARTICLE COSMOLOGY